THE CHARLTON STANDARD CATALOGUE OF

BESWICK ANIMALS

THIRD EDITION

DIANA CALLOW
JOHN CALLOW

MARILYN SWEET
PETER SWEET

PUBLISHER
W. K. CROSS

The Charlton Press

TORONTO, ONTARIO ❖ BIRMINGHAM, MICHIGAN

Canadian Cataloguing In Publication Data

The National Library of Canada has catalogued this
publication as follows:

Main entry under title:

The Charlton standard catalogue of Beswick animals
2nd ed. (1996)
Continues: Charlton price guide to Beswick animals, ISSN 1202-9831
ISSN 1203-8318
ISBN 0-88968-185-6 (3rd ed.)

1. Porcelain animals– Catalogs. 2. Royal Doulton figurines– Catalogs. 3. Beswick
(Firm) – Catalogs. I. Charlton Press. II. Title: Beswick animals.

NK4660.C48   738.8'2'0294   C96-900264-5

EDITORIAL

Editor	Jean Dale
Assistant Editor	Nicola Leedham
Assistant Editor	Maria Angelica Villalba
Graphic Technician	Davina Rowan

ACKNOWLEDGMENTS

The Charlton Press wishes to thank those who have helped and assisted with the third edition of *The Charlton Standard Catalogue of Beswick Animals*.

SPECIAL THANKS

Our thanks go to Royal Doulton (U.K.) Limited who helped with additional technical information and photography.

CONTRIBUTORS TO THE FOURTH EDITION

The Publisher would like to thank the following individuals or companies who graciously supplied pricing, direct mail lists, photographs or allowed us access to their collections for photographic purposes. We offer sincere thanks to:

Mr. and Mrs. F. J. Bradfield, Norwich, U.K.; **William Cross Antiques and Collectibles**, Vancouver, B.C.; **Peter and Pam McBride**, Kent, U.K.; **Bill Peck**, Seattle, WA.; **Diane Pelleier**, Calgary, Alberta; **Laura Rock-Smith**, Sayville, N.Y.; **Joe Schenberg**, St. Louis, Mo.; **Judy Tollefson**, Argyle, Texas; **Eileen Vinther**, Denmark; **Kathleen A. Zenk**, Dunstable, Mass.

A SPECIAL NOTE TO COLLECTORS

We welcome and appreciate any comments or suggestions in regard to *The Charlton Standard Catalogue of Beswick Animals*. If you would like to participate in pricing or supply previously unavailable data or information, please contact Jean Dale at (416) 488-1418, or e-mail us at chpress@charltonpress.com.

**Printed in Canada
in the Province of Manitoba**

The Charlton Press

**Editorial Office
2040 Yonge Street, Suite 208
Toronto, Canada. M4S 1Z9
Telephone (416) 488-1418 Fax: (416) 488-4656
Telephone (800) 442-6042 Fax: (800) 442-1542
www.charltonpress.com**

HOW TO USE THIS CATALOGUE

THE PURPOSE

The third edition of this price guide covers the complete range of animals produced at the John Beswick Studios.

As with other catalogues in Charlton's Royal Doulton / Beswick reference library, this publication has been designed to serve two specifc purposes. First, to furnish the collector with accurate and detailed listings that provide the essential information needed to build a rewarding collection. Second, to provide collectors and dealers with an indication of current market prices for the complete line of Beswick animal figures.

VARIETY CLASSIFICATIONS

In developing the series of Royal Doulton / Beswick catalogues we found it necessary to divide the model changes into three classifications based on the degree of complexity.

STYLES: A change in style occurs when a major element of the design is altered or modified as a result of a deliberate mould change. While no Beswick model has been dramatically altered resulting in a style change, but one might use the model 3062A and B to illustrate a dramatic change, a free standing labrador dog and then the same dog on a ceramic plinth.

VERSIONS: Versions are modifications in a minor style element, such as the Siamese Cat, model 1559. In the first version the head of the cat shows puffed out cheeks, with the body being fleshy and having a short neck. The second version shows the cat with a sleek tapering face, a long neck and a lean body. Another example of a version change is model 1014 the Welsh Cob (rearing) where the first versions has the tail of the horse attached the the ceramic base whilst in the second version the tail of the horse hangs loose.

VARIATIONS: A change in colour is a variation; for example almost any of the horses or cats with the lists of colourways and finishes are variations.

THE LISTINGS

The main body of the book, chapters one to eight, which contain the majority of the animal figures is first listed alphabetically by chapter, i.e. birds, butterflys, cats, dogs, farm animals, etc., and then within each of these chapters the listings are in Beswick model number order. The remaining chapters are devoted to specialty items such as resin sculptures, whisky flasks and commissioned models. Each chapter has a short introduction and index by model number located on the chapter title page.

A WORD ON PRICING

The purpose of this catalogue is to give readers the most accurate, up-to-date retail prices for Beswick animal figures in the United States, Canada and the United Kingdom.

To accomplish this, The Charlton Press continues to access an international pricing panel of experts who submit prices based on both dealer and collector retail-price activity, as well as current auction results in the U.S., Canada, and the U.K. These market prices are carefully averaged to reflect accurate valuations for figures in each of these markets.

The prices published herein are for figures in mint condition. Collectors are cautioned that a repaired or restored piece may be worth as little as 25 percent of the value of the same figure in mint condition.

Current figures are priced according to the manufacturer's suggested retail price in each of the market regions. Please be aware that price or promotional sales discounting is always possible and can result in lower prices than those listed.

One exception, however, occurs in the case of current figures or recent limited editions issued in only one of the three markets. Since such items were priced by Doulton only in the country in which they were to be sold, prices for the other markets are not shown.

A further word on pricing. As mentioned previously, this is a catalogue giving prices for figures in the currency of a particular market (U.S. dollars for the American market and sterling for the U.K. market). The bulk of the prices given herein are not determined by currency exchange calculations, but by actual market activity in the market concerned.

In some case the number of models produced is so small that market activity does not exist. There is no price activity on which to base a price. An example of this is the "Spirit of Whitfield" with only four existing models. The price in this instance is purely between the buyer and the seller. We have therefore listed the last known auction price for this model. If this model was to be offered for sale at a future date the price may be higher or lower than the auction price listed depending on the demand for the model at that time. For models with little or no market data due to the limited number of figures produced, we have reverted to the following rarity table:

Rare	26 - 50 figures known
Very rare	11 - 25 figures known
Extremely rare	5 - 10 figures known
Auction results	1 - 4 figures known

When prices are italicized in the pricing tables, for example, the Galloway Bull (Model No. 1746A), this indicates that the price is only an indication. The prices are too high and too volatile to establish a solid market price. Once again, the final price determination must be made between buyer and seller.

TABLE OF CONTENTS

FURTHER READING

Storybook Figures

Collecting Cartoon Classics and other Character Figures, by Louise Irvine
Royal Doulton Bunnykins Figures, by Louise Irvine
Bunnykins Collectors Book, by Louise Irvine
Beatrix Potter Figures and Giftware, edited by Louise Irvine
The Beswick Price Guide, by Harvey May

Animals, Figures and Character Jugs

Royal Doulton Figures, by Desmond Eyles, Louise Irvine and Valerie Baynton
The Charlton Standard Catalogue of Beswick Animals, by Diane & John Callow and Marilyn and Peter Sweet
The Charlton Standard Catalogue of Royal Doulton Animals, by Jean Dale
The Charlton Standard Catalogue of Royal Doulton Beswick Figurines, by Jean Dale
The Charlton Standard Catalogue of Royal Doulton Beswick Jugs, by Jean Dale
Collecting Character and Toby Jugs, by Jocelyn Lukins
Collecting Doulton Animals, by Jocelyn Lukins
Doulton Flambé Animals, by Jocelyn Lukins
The Character Jug Collectors Handbook, by Kevin Pearson
The Doulton Figure Collectors Handbook, by Kevin Pearson

General

The Charlton Standard Catalogue of Beswick Pottery, by Diane and John Callow
The Charlton Standard Catalogue of Bunnykins, by Jean Dale
Discovering Royal Doulton, by Michael Doulton
The Doulton Story, by Paul Atterbury and Louise Irvine
Royal Doulton Series Wares, by Louise Irvine (Vols. 1-5)
Limited Edition Loving Cups and Jugs, by Louise Irvine and Richard Dennis
Doulton for the Collector, by Jocelyn Lukins
Doulton Kingsware Flasks, by Jocelyn Lukins
Doulton Burslem Advertising Wares, by Jocelyn Lukins
Doulton Lambeth Advertising Wares, by Jocelyn Lukins
The Doulton Lambeth Wares, by Desmond Eyles
The Doulton Burslem Wares, by Desmond Eyles
Hannah Barlow, by Peter Rose
George Tinworth, by Peter Rose
Sir Henry Doulton Biography, by Edmund Gosse
Phillips Collectors Guide, by Catherine Braithwaite
Royal Doulton, by Jennifer Queree
John Beswick: A World of Imagination. Catalogue reprint (1950-1996)

Magazines and Newsletters

Collect it! (Contact subscription department at: P.O. Box 3658, Bracknell, Berkshire RG12 7XZ.
    Telephone: (1344) 868 280 or e-mail: collectit@dialpipex.com)
Collecting Doulton Magazine, published by Francis Joseph, edited by Doug Pinchin

INTRODUCTION

An article entitled "Equestrian Figures for Collectors —Growth of the House of Beswick," in the *Pottery Gazette and Glass Trade Review* of September 1961, ended with this paragraph: "Among the potters of the present day yet to reach the one hundred-year mark, and whose products are already highly prized, none is more likely to be of future interest to collectors and antique dealers than the House of Beswick." How prophetic this has proved to be. In 1985 the Beswick Collector's Circle was formed as interest in the products of the Beswick factory was aroused. The circle has flourished as more and more people worldwide have joined the search to add to their collections and to seek information in order to enjoy their finds to the full. This book represents the most comprehensive attempt to date to form as complete a guide as possible to the Beswick animal collection.

In 1994 the John Beswick factory celebrated its centenary—a hundred years of producing an unbelievably wide variety of pottery items, from mundane household earthenware right through to the intricate ornamental ware and pure ornaments of all shapes and sizes.

Initially the factory produced plain and decorated ware. An advertisement from about 1900 lists "jugs, tea ware, dinner ware, toilet ware, flower pots, pedestals, novelties, vases, figures, bread trays, cheese dishes, etc., etc." The figures included the traditional Old Staffordshire dogs, but hares and hounds, horses, generals, a cow and calf, milkmaids, gardeners and Puss in Boots are also mentioned. Unfortunately many of these pieces were not marked Beswick.

From the start the Beswick factory was very much a family-run firm. James Wright Beswick, the founder, and his sons, John and Gilbert, and John's son, John Ewart, were all very committed to the factory's success. In 1934 ,when John Ewart Beswick became chairman and managing director and his uncle, Gilbert Beswick, was sales manager, several new pieces were introduced to the range, and recorded in the "shape book."

This was the start of shape numbers being impressed into the base whenever possible and also the more widespread use of a Beswick backstamp.

Five years later Arthur Gredington took up his appointment as the first full-time modeller. His influence was enormous, for he had a great talent for modelling not only accurate and realistic animals of all kinds , but also ones of the comical variety, for example the very appealing "Grebie," number 1006. Consequently his name appears more than that of any other person in this book, and it is a tribute to his skill that many of his models are still in production in 1996 as *Doulton Animals*.

James Hayward also made an outstanding contribution to the high quality associated with the Beswick name. As decorating manager from 1934 and art director from 1957, he was responsible for designing almost three thousand different decorations and patterns. He also designed new shapes, such as the 720 "Panda Cub," and was an outstanding glaze chemist. His experience with glazes was fundamental in the development of the matt glaze used initially on the top of the range *Connoisseur Series*.

Mould making

When a complex model, such as an animal, is being manufactured, the mould it will be produced from is of vital importance. In this department Albert Hallam had exceptional skill. He joined Beswick in 1926 at age 14 as an apprentice mouldmaker and went on to become head of the mouldmaking department and also a modeller. The series of butterflies are Albert Hallam's creations, as are a number of horses, dogs and cats, which were modelled after Arthur Gredington's retirement. These include at least one model that is very sought after today, number 2282 "Norwegian Fjord Horse."

Arthur Gredington in his studio

There are several other modellers whose work is featured in this book. Very little is known about some of them as they tended to be employed on a freelance basis, for example, Miss Catford, who modelled character-type animals like the 663 "Elephant" holding a five-ton weight and Mr. Garbet, who contributed cats, dogs and a sheep. Although small in number, significant contributions were also made by Alan Maslankowski, whose 2578 "Shire Horse" is quite magnificent, Colin Melbourne, who besides the unique "C.M." Series also modelled most of the Peter Scott ducks, Graham Orwell whose models included the 1374 "Galloping Horse" and 1391 "Mounted Indian," and Pal Zalman whose one equine model, the 1549 "Head tucked Horse," is still in production.

By the late 1960s, Ewart and Gilbert Beswick were nearing retirement, and as there was not another generation to follow them into the family business, the decision was made in 1969 to sell to Royal Doulton. Beswick animals continued to be produced, and although much rationalization took place, such as reducing the number of colourways of the horses and withdrawing many pieces, the ranges were also expanded by the regular introduction of new pieces.

Graham Tongue at work

Then in August 1989, the decision was implemented to make the vast majority of the remaining animals produced at the Beswick factory into *Doulton Animals*, and the pieces were all issued with DA numbers. At the same time, grey and palomino matts were withdrawn from the horses' colourways, and only a few continued to be available in grey and palomino glosses.

Currently the modelling team at Beswick is headed by design manager Graham Tongue and includes the young team of Warren Platt, Amanda Hughes-Lubeck and Martyn Alcock. Graham Tongue has worked at Beswick since 1966 and became head modeller in 1973, when Albert Hallam retired. He has concentrated on the modelling of animals, and his modelling skill is apparent in almost all the sections here.

Graham Tongue has the distinction of modelling the piece which holds the world-record price for a piece of Beswick, appropriately an equine model entitled the "Spirit of Whitfield." In 1987 he was commissioned by the Chatterley Mining Museum to model Kruger, the last pit pony used at the Staffordshire mine. The resulting model, based on the 2541 "Welsh Mountain Pony," was considerably adapted with incredible attention to detail. The result was superb. Only four models were made, one each for the Beswick and Chatterley Whitfield museums, one presented to HRH Princess Anne when she visited the museum, and one was auctioned in aid of the Princess's favourite charity. In April 1994 the mining museum was closed and everything was auctioned. The "Spirit of Whitfield" sold for £2,750, a far cry from one hundred years ago when Beswick was advertising pieces for 6 1/2d.

Although very few animals now carry the Beswick backstamp, this book illustrates the animal kingdom as seen through the eyes of the Beswick designers since the early 1930s. Cats and kittens with appealing eyes, birds and butterflies to fly across walls, a well-stocked zoo with animals from all over the world, everyday farm animals, animals which make you laugh, champion dogs, sleek horses and fish leaping from their pools are all lasting reminders of the Beswick story. The story will continue as more information emerges and the elusive models are discovered.

LABELS AND BACKSTAMPS

WHERE TO BUY

Discontinued Doulton and Beswick collectables can be found in Antique shops, Markets, Auctions, Shows and Fairs. Specialist dealers in Royal Doulton and Beswick collectables attend many of the events listed below. For Auction happenings it is necessary to subscribe to that Houses 20th Century or specialist Doulton Auction catalogues.

UNITED KINGDOM

Auction Houses

BBR AUCTIONS
Elsecar Heritage Centre
Nr. Barnsely, South Yorkshire, S74 8HJ
England
(01226) 745156
Attn: Alan Blakeman

BONHAMS
Montpelier Street, Knightsbridge
London, SW71HH
England
(0171) 584 9161

CHRISTIE'S SOUTH KENSINGTON
85 Old Brompton Road, London, SW7 3LD
England
(0171) 581 7611
www.christies.com
Attn: Michael Jeffery

DANIEL & HULME
66 Derby Street, Leek, Staffordshire, ST135AJ
England
(0153) 838 3339
www.danielhulme.co.uk
Attn: S.J. Hulme

LOUIS TAYLOR
Britannia House
10 Town Road, Hanley, ST1 2QG
England
(01782) 21411
Attn: Clive Hillier

PHILLIPS
101 New Bond Street, London, W1Y 0AS
England
(0171) 629 6602
www.phillips-auctions.com
Attn: Mark Oliver

SOTHEBY'S SUSSEX
Summers Place
Billingshurst, Sussex, RH14 9AF
England
(01403) 783933

THOMPSON RODDICK & LAURIE
60 Whitesands, Dumfries, DG1 2RS
Scotland
(01387) 255366
Attn: Sybelle Medcalf

PETER WILSON
Victoria Gallery, Market Street
Nantwich, Chesire, CW55DG
England
(01270) 623878

Antique Fairs

DOULTON AND BESWICK COLLECTORS FAIR
National Motorcycle Museum
Meriden, Birmingham
Usually March and August.
For information on times and dates:
DOULTON AND BESWICK DEALERS ASSOCIATION
(0181) 303 3316

DOULTON AND BESWICK COLLECTORS FAIR
The Queensway Hall Civic Centre, Dunstable, Bedforshire
Usually in October. For information on times and location:
UK FAIRS LTD.
10 Wilford Bridge Spur, Melton, Woodbridge,
Suffolk, 1P12 1RJ
(01394) 386663

DOULTON GROUP COLLECTORS FAIR
Trentham Gardens, Stoke-on-Trent
Usually the last week in May, or the first week in June.
For information on times and dates:
SINCLAIRS
1st Mary's Court, Tickhill, Doncaster, DN11 9QU
(01302) 745287

INTERNATIONAL ANTIQUE & COLLECTORS FAIR
Newark, Nottinghamshire
Usually six fairs annually. For information on times and dates:
INTERNATIONAL ANTIQUE & COLLECTORS FAIR LTD.
P.O. Box 100, Newark, Nottinghamshire, NG2 1DJ
(01636) 702326

WEST LONDON WADE BESWICK & DOULTON FAIR
Brunel University, Kingston Lane, Uxbridge, Middlesex
Usually three fairs a year. For information on times and location:
B & D FAIRS
P.O. Box 273, Uxbridge, Middlesex, UB9 4LP
(01895) 834694 or 834357

YESTERDAYS DOULTON FAIR
Usually in November.
For information on times and location:

London Markets

ALFIE'S ANTIQUE MARKET
13-25 Church Street, London
Tuesday - Saturday

CAMDEN PASSAGE MARKET
London
Wednesday and Saturday

NEW CALEDONIA MARKET
Bermondsey Square, London
Friday Morning

PORTOBELLO ROAD MARKET
London
Saturday

UNITED STATES

Auction Houses

CHRISTIE'S EAST
219 East 67th Street
New York, NY 10021
(212) 606-0400
www.christies.com
Attn: Timothy Luke

SOTHEBY'S ARCADE AUCTIONS
1334 York Avenue
New York, NU 10021
(212) 606-7000
www.sothebys.com
Attn: Andrew Cheney

Collectable Shows

ATLANTIQUE CITY
New Atlantic City Convention Centre
Atlantic City, NJ
Usually March and October.
For information on times and dates:
BRIMFIELD ASSOCIATES
P.O. Box 1800
Ocean City, NJ 08226
(609) 926-1800
www.atlantiquecity.com

FLORIDA DOULTON CONVENTION & SALE
Sheraton Inn
2440 West Cypress Creek Road
Ft. Lauderdale, FL., 33309
Usually mid-January
For information on times and dates:

PASCOE & COMPANY or	CHARLES DOMBECK
101 Almeria Avenue	9552 N.W. 9th Court
Coral Gables, FL	Plantation, FL
33134	33324
(305) 445-3229	(254) 452-9174

O'HARE NATIONAL ANTIQUES SHOW & SALE
Rosemont Convention Centre,
Chicago, IL
Usually April, August and November.
For information on times and dates:
MANOR HOUSE SHOWS INC.
P.O. Box 7320
Fort Lauderdale, FL 33338
(954) 563-6747

ROYAL DOULTON CONVENTION & SALE
John S. Knight Convention Centre
77 E. Mill Street, Akron, OH 44308
Usually August.
For information on times and dates:
COLONIAL HOUSE PRODUCTIONS
182 Front Street
Berea, OH, 44017
(800) 344-9299

CANADA

Auction Houses

MAYNARDS
415 West 2nd Avenue
Vancouver, BC
V5Y 1E3
(604) 876-1311

RITCHIES
288 King Street East
Toronto, ON
M5A 1KA
(416) 364-1864
Attn: Caroline Kaiser

Collectable Shows

CANADIAN ART & COLLECTIBLE SHOW & SALE
Kitchener Memorial Auditorium
Kitchener, ON
Usually early May.
For information on times and location:
George or Jackie Benninger
P.O. Box 130
Durham, ON
N0G 1R0
(519) 369-6950

CANADIAN DOULTON & COLLECTABLE FAIR
Toronto, ON
Usually early September.
For information on times and location:
George or Jackie Benninger
P.O. Box 130
Durham, ON
N0G 1R0
(519) 369-6950

Toronto Markets

HARBOURFRONT ANTIQUE MARKET
390 Queens Quay West
Toronto, ON
Tuesday - Saturday

SHOWCASE ANTIQUE MALL
610 Queen Street West
Toronto, ON
Monday - Sunday

ROYAL DOULTON INTERNATIONAL COLLECTORS CLUB

Founded in 1980 The Royal Doulton International Collectors Club provides an information service on all aspects of the company's products, past and present. A Club magazine, *Gallery*, is published four times per year with news on new products and current events that will assist the collector. Upon joining the club, each new member will receive a free gift and invitations to special events and exclusive offers..

A new visitor centre was opened in the summer of 1996 incorporating a display and design area especially for the Royal Doulton figure collection.

The Visitor Centre is located at:
Nile Street, Burslem, Stoke-on-Trent, ST6 2AJ, England.
For opening times and factory tour information please telephone (01782) 292292.

To join the club, please contact your local stockist, or contact the club directly at the address and numbers located below:

ROYAL DOULTON PLC
Minton House, London Road
Stoke-on-Trent, ST4 7QD, England

Telephone:
In the UK: (01782) 292292
In the USA and Canada: 1-800-747-3045 (toll free)
In Austrailia: 011 800-142-624 (toll free)
Fax: (01782) 292127
www.royal-doulton.com
e-mail: icc@royal-doulton.com

DOULTON CHAPTERS

Chapters of The Royal Doulton International Collectors Club have formed across North America and are worthy of consideration for collectors in these areas.

NEW ENGLAND CHAPTER
Anne Babchyck, President
Charles Briggs, Secretary
239 Cedar Street
Dedham, MA 02026
(781) 329-0214

NORTHERN CALIFORNIAN CHAPTER
P.O. Box 3665
Walnut Creek, CA 94598

OHIO CHAPTER
Dick Maschmeier
5556 Whitehaven Avenue
North Olmstead, OH
44070

MID-AMERICA CHAPTER
P.O. Box 483
McHenry, IL 60050

EDMONTON CHAPTER
Mildred's Collectibles
6814 104 Street
Edmonton, AB

Chapter One

BIRDS

The models of our "feathered friends" are a delight for any bird enthusiast, and there are plenty here to choose from.

They come in all sizes, from very small birds, such as the little wren, to the impressive and large pheasant from the Connoisseur Series. Some are expensive, some are not, and quite a few are still in production. The figures cover a wide range from the comic Fun Models to wall plaques to the precise realism of the Peter Scott Wildfowl collection. When displayed in groups, the colours of their plumage create an impressive display.

Among the birds in this group are species that you could see any day of the week in your garden and also more exotic or rare varieties, such as the bald eagle, penguin and kookaburra.

INDEX BY MODEL NUMBER

Model No. 317
DUCK - On pottery base

Designer:	Miss Greaves
Height:	8 ¼", 21.0 cm
Colours:	See below
Issued:	c.1936-1954
Series:	Fun Models

Description	U.K. £	U.S. $	Can. $
1. Blue - gloss	150.00	275.00	350.00
2. Blue/green - matt	125.00	250.00	325.00
3. Green - gloss	125.00	250.00	325.00
4. Natural - satin	150.00	275.00	350.00
5. White - gloss	110.00	225.00	300.00

Model No. 370
DUCKS - Candleholder

Designer:	James Hayward	
Height:	3 ½", 8.9 cm	
Colours:	1.	Various - satin matt
	2.	White - matt
Issued:	1935-by 1954	

Description	U.K. £	U.S. $	Can. $
1. Various - satin matt	45.00	90.00	125.00
2. White - matt	25.00	50.00	75.00

Model No. 450
PENGUIN

Designer:	Mr. Owen	
Height:	Large - 8", 20.3 cm	
	Small - 3 ½", 8.9 cm	
Colours:	1.	Black and white - gloss
	2.	Blue - gloss
Issued:	1936-by 1954	

Description	U.K. £	U.S. $	Can. $
1. Large - black	150.00	300.00	400.00
1. Small - black	95.00	175.00	250.00
2. Large - blue	175.00	300.00	400.00
2. Small - blue	125.00	175.00	250.00

Model No. 497
PELICAN - Match holder and ash-bowl

Designer:	Mr. Watkin	
Height:	4", 10.1 cm	
Colours:	1.	Various - satin matt
	2.	Blue - gloss
	3.	White - matt
Issued:	1937- by 1954	

Description	U.K. £	U.S. $	Can. $
1. Various - satin matt	65.00	150.00	200.00
2. Blue - gloss	75.00	175.00	225.00
3. White - matt	60.00	150.00	200.00

Model No. 617
DUCK - Ashtray

Designer:	Mr. Watkin
Height:	3", 7.6 cm
Colours:	1. Various - satin matt
	2. Blue - gloss
	3. White - matt
Issued:	1938-by 1954

Description	U.K. £	U.S. $	Can. $
1. Various	85.00	150.00	200.00
2. Blue	100.00	175.00	225.00
3. White	65.00	110.00	150.00

Model No. 618
PUFFIN

Designer:	Mr. Owen
Height:	9", 22.9 cm
Colours:	Blue - gloss
Issued:	1938-by 1954

Description	U.K. £	U.S. $	Can. $
Blue - gloss	200.00	300.00	425.00

Model No. 749
MALLARD DUCK - Rising

Designer:	Arthur Gredington
Height:	6 ½", 16.5 cm
Colours:	Browns, teal green and white - gloss
Issued:	1939-by 1965

Description	U.K. £	U.S. $	Can. $
Gloss	150.00	250.00	375.00

Model No. 750
MALLARD DUCK - Settling

Designer:	Arthur Gredington
Height:	6 ½", 16.5 cm
Colours:	Browns, teal green and white - gloss
Issued:	1939-by 1965

Description	U.K. £	U.S. $	Can. $
Gloss	150.00	250.00	375.00

Model No. 754
PHEASANT - Ashtray

Designer: Mr. Watkin
Height: 3 ½", 8.9 cm
Colours: Teal green and brown - gloss
Issued: 1939-1970

Description	U.K. £	U.S. $	Can. $
Gloss	30.00	50.00	50.00

Note: Model no. 767A was used for this ashtray.

Model No. 755
DUCK - Ashtray

Designer: Mr. Watkin
Height: 4", 10.1 cm
Colours: Teal green, brown and white - gloss
Issued: 1939-1969

Description	U.K. £	U.S. $	Can. $
Gloss	30.00	50.00	50.00

Note: Model no. 756/3 was used for this ashtray.

Model No. 756
MALLARD DUCK - Standing

Designer: Mr. Watkin
Height: 756/1 - 7", 17.8 cm
             756/2 - 5 ¾", 14.6 cm
             756/2A - 4 ½", 11.9 cm
             756/3 - 3 ½", 8.9 cm
Colours: 1.   Brown, teal green and white - gloss
             2.   Blue - gloss
Issued: 1939-1973

Description	U.K. £	U.S. $	Can. $
756/1 Brown	65.00	125.00	150.00
756/1 Blue	125.00	175.00	275.00
756/2 Brown	45.00	75.00	100.00
756/2 Blue	95.00	150.00	200.00
756/2 A Brown	35.00	60.00	75.00
756/2 A Blue	85.00	125.00	175.00
756/3 Brown	25.00	40.00	60.00
756/3 Blue	75.00	110.00	150.00

Note: Model no. 756/3 has grass around feet.
        Model no. 902 makes a set of five pieces.

Model No. 760
DUCK WITH LADYBIRD ON BEAK

Designer: Mr. Watkin
Height: 3 ¾", 9.5 cm
Colours: White with yellow beak,
              ladybird on beak - gloss
Issued: 1939-1971
Series: Fun Models

Description	U.K. £	U.S. $	Can. $
Gloss	50.00	95.00	150.00

Model No. 762
DUCK ON SKIS

Designer: Mr. Watkin
Height: 3 ¼", 8.3 cm
Colours: White with orange beak - gloss
Issued: 1939-1969
Series: Fun Models

Description	U.K. £	U.S. $	Can. $
Gloss	50.00	95.00	150.00

Model No. 765
DUCK FAMILY

Designer: Arthur Gredington
Height: 2 ¾" x 7", 7.0 x 17.8 cm
Colours: White with yellow beaks - gloss
Issued: 1939-1971

Description	U.K. £	U.S. $	Can. $
Gloss	45.00	100.00	150.00

Model No. 767A
PHEASANT
First Version - Curved tail

Designer: Mr. Watkin
Height: 3", 7.6 cm
Colours: Red brown, teal green - gloss
Issued: 1939-1971

Description	U.K. £	U.S. $	Can. $
Gloss	25.00	35.00	45.00

Note: This model was used on 754 (pheasant ashtray).

Model No. 767B
PHEASANT
Second Version - Straight tail

Designer:	Mr. Watkin
Height:	3", 7.6 cm
Colours:	Red, brown and teal green - gloss or matt
Issued:	1. Gloss - 1971-1995
	2. Matt - 1983-1989

Description	U.K. £	U.S. $	Can. $
1. Gloss	15.00	25.00	40.00
2. Matt	20.00	40.00	60.00

Model No. 768
SEAGULL ON ROCK

Designer:	Arthur Gredington
Height:	8 ½", 21.6 cm
Colours:	Cream and dark brown, green and yellow base - gloss
Issued:	1939-by 1954

Description	U.K. £	U.S. $	Can. $
Gloss	275.00	550.00	675.00

Model No. 769
DUCK - Night light holder

Designer:	Mr. Watkin
Height:	6", 20.3 cm
Colours:	Yellow and white duck, orange beak - gloss
Issued:	1939-by 1954

Description	U.K. £	U.S. $	Can. $
Gloss		Rare	

Model No. 800
PENGUIN - Chick

Designer:	Arthur Gredington
Height:	2", 5.0 cm
Colours:	Black and white with yellow markings - gloss
Issued:	1940-1973
Set:	801, 802, 803

Description	U.K. £	U.S. $	Can. $
Gloss	15.00	25.00	40.00

Model No. 801
PENGUIN - Chick

Designer:	Arthur Gredington
Height:	2", 5.0 cm
Colours:	Black and white with yellow markings - gloss
Issued:	1940-1973
Set:	800, 802, 803

Description	U.K. £	U.S. $	Can. $
Gloss	15.00	25.00	40.00

Model No. 802
PENGUIN - With umbrella

Designer:	Arthur Gredington
Height:	4 ¼", 10.8 cm
Colours:	1. Black and white, red umbrella - gloss
	2. Black and white, green umbrella - gloss
Issued:	1940-1973
Set:	800, 801, 803

Description	U.K. £	U.S. $	Can. $
1. Red umbrella	30.00	50.00	75.00
2. Green umbrella	65.00	110.00	150.00

Note: Model 802 was altered in 1956.

Photograph not
available at press time

Model No. 803
PENGUIN - With walking stick

Designer:	Arthur Gredington
Height:	3 ¾", 9.5 cm
Colours:	Black and white with yellow markings, black walking stick - gloss
Issued:	1940-1973
Set:	800, 801, 802

Description	U.K. £	U.S. $	Can. $
Gloss	30.00	40.00	50.00

Note: Model 802 was altered in 1956.

Model No. 817/1
MALLARD DUCK - Squatting

Designer:	Mr. Watkin
Height:	7 ½", 19.1 cm
Colours:	Brown, teal green and white - gloss
Issued:	1940-1954
Set:	817/2

Description:	U.K. £	U.S. $	Can. $
Gloss	175.00	250.00	300.00

Model No. 817/2
MALLARD DUCK - Squatting

Designer:	Mr. Watkin	
Height:	6 ¾", 17.2 cm	
Colours:	Brown, teal green and white - gloss	
Issued:	1940-1970	
Set:	817/1	

Description	U.K. £	U.S. $	Can. $
Gloss	135.00	225.00	300.00

Model No. 820
GEESE (Pair)

Designer:	Arthur Gredington
Height:	4", 10.1 cm
Colours:	White with orange feet and beaks - gloss
Issued:	1940-1971
Series:	Fun Models
Set:	821, 822

Description	U.K. £	U.S. $	Can. $
Gloss	35.00	60.00	85.00

Model No. 821
GOSLING - Facing left

Designer:	Arthur Gredington
Height:	2 ¼", 5.7 cm
Colours:	White with orange beak - gloss
Issued:	1940-1971
Series:	Fun Models
Set:	820, 822

Description	U.K. £	U.S. $	Can. $
Gloss	20.00	35.00	50.00

Model No. 822
GOSLING - Facing right

Designer:	Arthur Gredington
Height:	1 ¾", 4.3 cm
Colours:	White with orange beak - gloss
Issued:	1940-1971
Series:	Fun Models
Set:	820, 821

Description	U.K. £	U.S. $	Can. $
Gloss	20.00	35.00	50.00

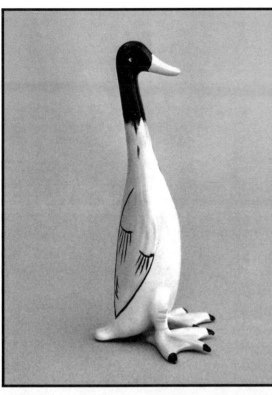

Model No. 827
HARDY'S DUCK - Standing

Designer:	Mr. Watkin
Height:	Large - 7 ½", 19.1 cm
	Medium - 6", 15.0 cm
	Small - 5", 12.7 cm
Colours:	1. White; brown and yellow - gloss
	2. White; solid decorated wing - gloss
	3. White; solid decorated neck, wing - gloss
	4. White; yellow bill, feet - gloss
Issued:	1940-by 1954

Description	U.K. £	U.S. $	Can. $
1. Large	125.00	250.00	300.00
2. Large	125.00	250.00	300.00
3. Large	125.00	250.00	300.00
4. Large	125.00	250.00	300.00
1. Medium	100.00	200.00	250.00
2. Medium	100.00	200.00	250.00
3. Medium	100.00	200.00	250.00
4. Medium	100.00	200.00	250.00
1. Small	90.00	175.00	225.00
2. Small	90.00	175.00	225.00
3. Small	90.00	175.00	225.00
4. Small	90.00	175.00	225.00

Model No. 849
PHEASANT ON BASE - Flying upwards

Designer:	Arthur Gredington
Height:	6", 15.0 cm
Colours:	Browns, teal green and yellow - gloss
Issued:	1940-1971

Description	U.K. £	U.S. $	Can. $
Gloss	125.00	225.00	325.00

Model No. 850
PHEASANT ON BASE - Settling

Designer:	Arthur Gredington
Height:	5 ¾", 14.6 cm
Colours:	Browns, teal green and yellow - gloss
Issued:	1940-1971

Description	U.K. £	U.S. $	Can. $
Gloss	125.00	225.00	325.00

Photograph not
available at press time

Model No. 862
FANTAIL PIGEON

Designer: Miss Joachin
Height: Unknown
Colours: Unknown
Issued: 1940-Unknown

Description	U.K. £	U.S. $	Can. $
Extremely Rare			

Note: Possibly not produced.

Model No. 902
MALLARD DUCK - Standing

Designer: Arthur Gredington
Height: 10", 25.4 cm
Colours: 1.   Brown and teal green - gloss
            2.   Brown, teal green or white - gloss
Issued: 1940-1970

Description	U.K. £	U.S. $	Can. $
1. Brown	125.00	200.00	275.00
2. Brown/white	125.00	200.00	275.00

Note: Makes a set of five with 756/1, 756/2, 756/2A, 756/3.

Model No. 919A
DUCK - Large

Designer: Mr. Watkin
Height: 3 ¾", 9.5 cm
Colours: 1.   Brown, teal green, white and pink
                 - gloss
            2.   White with yellow beak and feet - gloss
Issued: 1941-1971

Description	U.K. £	U.S. $	Can. $
1. Brown	35.00	45.00	65.00
2. White	35.00	45.00	65.00

Model No. 919B
DUCK - Medium

Designer: Mr. Watkin
Height: 2 ½", 6.4 cm
Colours: 1.   Brown, teal green, white and pink - gloss
            2.   White with yellow beak and feet - gloss
Issued: 1941-1971

Description	U.K. £	U.S. $	Can. $
1. Brown	25.00	35.00	45.00
2. White	25.00	35.00	45.00

Model No. 919C
DUCK - Small

Designer:	Mr. Watkin
Height:	2", 5.0 cm
Colours:	1. Brown, teal green, white and pink - gloss
	2. White with yellow beak and feet - gloss
Issued:	1941-1971

Description	U.K. £	U.S. $	Can. $
1. Brown	20.00	35.00	45.00
2. White	20.00	35.00	45.00

Model No. 925
AMERICAN BLUE JAYS

Designer:	Arthur Gredington
Height:	5", 12.7 cm
Colours:	Blue and white - gloss
Issued:	1941-by 1965

Description	U.K. £	U.S. $	Can. $
Gloss	100.00	175.00	275.00

Model No. 926
BALTIMORE ORIOLES

Designer:	Arthur Gredington
Height:	5", 12.7 cm
Colours:	1. Golden and dark brown with blue markings - gloss
	2. Chestnut brown, green claws - gloss
Issued:	1941-by 1965

Description	U.K. £	U.S. $	Can. $
1. Golden	100.00	175.00	275.00
2. Chestnut	100.00	175.00	300.00

Model No. 927
CARDINAL

Designer:	Arthur Gredington
Height:	5 ¾", 14.6 cm
Colours:	Dark red - gloss
Issued:	1941-by 1959

Description	U.K. £	U.S. $	Can. $
Gloss	85.00	175.00	225.00

Model No. 928
TANAGER

Designer:	Arthur Gredington
Height:	5 ¾", 14.6 cm
Colours:	1. Red - gloss
	2. Yellow, green and orange - gloss
	3. Various - gloss
Issued:	1941-1959

Description	U.K. £	U.S. $	Can. $
1. Red	85.00	125.00	175.00
2. Yellow/green	85.00	125.00	175.00
3. Various	85.00	125.00	175.00

Model No. 929
CHICKADEE

Designer:	Arthur Gredington
Height:	5 ¾", 14.6 cm
Colours:	Dark and light blue, white and
	yellow - gloss or lustre
Issued:	1941-1968

Description	U.K. £	U.S. $	Can. $
1. Gloss	50.00	85.00	125.00
2. Lustre	75.00	125.00	175.00

Model No. 930
PARAKEET

Designer:	Arthur Gredington
Height:	6", 15.0 cm
Colours:	Green and yellow - gloss
Issued:	1941-1975

Description	U.K. £	U.S. $	Can. $
Gloss	65.00	150.00	200.00

Model No. 980A
ROBIN
First Version - Base is green mound

Designer:	Arthur Gredington
Height:	3", 7.6 cm
Colours:	Brown and red - gloss
Issued:	1942-1973

Description	U.K. £	U.S. $	Can. $
Gloss	35.00	55.00	75.00

Model No. 980B
ROBIN
Second Version - Base is a branch and leaf

Designer:	Arthur Gredington
Remodelled:	Albert Hallam
Height:	3″, 7.6 cm
Colours:	Brown and red - gloss or matt
Issued:	1. Gloss - 1973 to the present
	2. Matt - 1983-1992

Description	U.K. £	U.S. $	Can. $
1. Gloss	13.50	N/A	N/A
2. Matt	15.00	35.00	50.00

Model No. 991A
CHAFFINCH
First Version - Base is a green mound

Designer:	Arthur Gredington
Height:	2 ¾″, 7.0 cm
Colours:	Pink, brown and black - gloss
Issued:	1943-1973

Description	U.K. £	U.S. $	Can. $
Gloss	35.00	55.00	75.00

Model No. 991B
CHAFFINCH
Second Version - Base is a branch

Designer:	Arthur Gredington
Remodelled:	Albert Hallam
Height:	2 ¾″, 7.0 cm
Colours:	Pink, brown, black - gloss or matt
Issued:	1. Gloss - 1973 to the present
	2. Matt - 1983-1992

Description	U.K. £	U.S. $	Can. $
1. Gloss	13.50	N/A	N/A
2. Matt	15.00	35.00	50.00

Model No. 992A
BLUE TIT
First Version - Base is a green mound

Designer:	Arthur Gredington
Height:	2 ½″, 6.4 cm
Colours:	White, blue and green - gloss
Issued:	1943 - 1973

Description	U.K. £	U.S. $	Can. $
Gloss	35.00	55.00	75.00

Model No. 992B
BLUE TIT
Second Version - Base is branch and leaves

Designer:	Arthur Gredington
Remodelled:	Unknown
Height:	2 ¼", 5.7 cm
Colours:	White, blue and green - gloss or matt
Issued:	1. Gloss - 1973 to the present
	2. Matt - 1983-1992

Description	U.K. £	U.S. $	Can. $
1. Gloss	13.50	N/A	N/A
2. Matt	15.00	35.00	50.00

Model No. 993A
WREN
First Version - Base is a green mound

Designer:	Arthur Gredington
Height:	2 ¼", 5.7 cm
Colours:	Light brown, pink breast - gloss
Issued:	1943-1973

Description	U.K. £	U.S. $	Can. $
Gloss	35.00	50.00	80.00

Model No. 993B
WREN
Second Version - Base is a green leaf

Designer:	Arthur Gredington
Remodelled:	Graham Tongue
Height:	2 ¼", 5.7 cm
Colours:	Dark and light brown - gloss or matt
Issued:	1. Gloss - 1973 to the present
	2. Matt - 1983-1992

Description	U.K. £	U.S. $	Can. $
1. Gloss	13.50	N/A	N/A
2. Matt	15.00	35.00	50.00

Model No. 994
SHELLDRAKE - Beak closed

Designer:	Arthur Gredington
Height:	6", 15.0 cm
Colours:	White, brown and green - gloss
Issued:	1943-1965

Description	U.K. £	U.S. $	Can. $
Gloss	150.00	250.00	375.00

Model No. 995
SHELLDRAKE - Beak open

Designer:	Arthur Gredington
Height:	6 ¼", 15.9 cm
Colours:	White, brown and green - gloss
Issued:	1943-1965

Description	U.K. £	U.S. $	Can. $
Gloss	150.00	275.00	350.00

Model No. 1001
COCKEREL

Designer:	Arthur Gredington
Height:	5 ¾", 14.6 cm
Colours:	Green, red and yellow - gloss
Issued:	1944-by 1959
Series:	Stylistic Models

Description	U.K. £	U.S. $	Can. $
Gloss	225.00	400.00	500.00

Model No. 1004
ROOSTER

Designer:	Arthur Gredington
Height:	7", 17.8 cm
Colours:	White, green, red, blue and black - gloss
Issued:	1944-by 1959
Series:	Stylistic Model

Description	U.K. £	U.S. $	Can. $
Gloss	200.00	375.00	500.00

Model No. 1006
GREBIE

Designer:	Arthur Gredington
Height:	5 ¼", 13.3 cm
Colours:	Green and browns - gloss
Issued:	1945-by 1954
Series:	Stylistic Model

Description	U.K. £	U.S. $	Can. $
Gloss	275.00	450.00	600.00

Model No 1015
COURTING PENGUINS

Designer:	Arthur Gredington
Height:	5 ½", 14.0 cm
Colours:	1. Black and white with yellow markings - gloss
	2. Blue - gloss
Issued:	1945-1965

Description	U.K. £	U.S. $	Can. $
1. Black/white	190.00	325.00	475.00
2. Blue	225.00	400.00	550.00

Model No. 1018
BALD EAGLE

Designer:	Arthur Gredington
Height:	7 ¼", 18.4 cm
Colours:	1. Brown and white - gloss or matt
	2. Bronze with black - satin
Issued:	1a. Gloss - 1945-1995
	1b. Matt - 1983-1989
	2. Britannia Collection - 1989-1992

Description	U.K. £	U.S. $	Can. $
1a. Gloss	75.00	150.00	225.00
1b. Matt	85.00	150.00	225.00
2. Satin	65.00	125.00	200.00

Model No. 1022
TURTLE DOVES

Designer:	Arthur Gredington
Height:	7 ½", 19.1 cm
Colours:	Browns, pale blue and pink, light brown and green base - gloss
Issued:	1945-1970

Description	U.K. £	U.S. $	Can. $
Gloss	200.00	375.00	550.00

Model No. 1041A
GREY WAGTAIL
First Version - Head down, light green base

Designer:	Arthur Gredington
Height:	2 ½", 6.4 cm
Colours:	Yellow, grey and black - gloss
Issued:	1945-1973

Description	U.K. £	U.S. $	Can. $
Gloss	35.00	55.00	75.00

Model No. 1041B
GREY WAGTAIL
Second Version - Head up, dark blue and green base

Designer:	Arthur Gredington
Remodelled:	Albert Hallam
Height:	2 ½", 6.4 cm
Colours:	Yellow, grey and black - gloss or matt
Issued:	1. Gloss - 1973 to the present
	2. Matt - 1983-1989

Description	U.K. £	U.S. $	Can. $
1. Gloss	13.50	N/A	N/A
2. Matt	15.00	35.00	50.00

Model No. 1042A
BULLFINCH
First Version - Yellow base and flowers

Designer:	Arthur Gredington
Height:	2 ½", 6.4 cm
Colours:	Red breast, dark brown feathers, yellow flowers and base - gloss
Issued:	1945-1973

Description	U.K. £	U.S. $	Can. $
Gloss	35.00	55.00	75.00

Model No. 1042B
BULLFINCH
Second Version - Base is a twig

Designer:	Arthur Gredington
Remodelled:	Graham Tongue
Height:	2 ½", 6.4 cm
Colours:	Red, dark brown - gloss or matt
Issued:	1. Gloss - 1973 to the present
	2. Matt - 1983-1989

Description	U.K. £	U.S. $	Can. $
1. Gloss	13.50	N/A	N/A
2. Matt	15.00	35.00	50.00

Model No. 1046A
BARN OWL
First Version - Split tail feathers

Designer:	Arthur Gredington
Height:	7 ¼", 18.4 cm
Colours:	Golden brown and white - gloss
Issued:	1946-Unknown

Description	U.K. £	U.S. $	Can. $
Gloss	125.00	220.00	275.00

Model No. 1046B
BARN OWL
Second Version - Closed tail feathers

Designer:	Arthur Gredington
Height:	7 ¼″, 18.4 cm
Colours:	Golden brown and white - gloss or matt
Issued:	1. Gloss - Unknown-1997
	2. Matt - 1983-1989

Description	U.K. £	U.S. $	Can. $
1. Gloss	35.00	60.00	85.00
2. Matt	40.00	70.00	100.00

Model No. 1052
BARNACLE GOOSE

Designer:	Arthur Gredington
Height:	6 ½″, 16.5 cm
Colours:	Dark grey-blue and white - gloss
Issued:	1943-1968

Description	U.K. £	U.S. $	Can. $
Gloss	400.00	700.00	1,000.00

Model No. 1099
COCK AND HEN - Salt and Pepper

Designer:	Unknown
Height:	2″, 5.0 cm
Colours:	Teal green, brown, yellow and red - gloss
Issued:	1947-1959

Description	U.K. £	U.S. $	Can. $
Pair	40.00	65.00	90.00

Model No. 1159
KOOKABURRA

Designer:	Arthur Gredington
Height:	5 ¾″, 14.6 cm
Colours:	Brown, blue and fawn - gloss
Issued:	1949-1976

Description	U.K. £	U.S. $	Can. $
Gloss	115.00	190.00	250.00

Model No. 1178
GOULDIAN FINCH - Wings out

Designer:	Arthur Gredington
Height:	4", 10.1 cm
Colours:	Purple, green and yellow - gloss
Issued:	1949-by 1959

Description	U.K. £	U.S. $	Can. $
Gloss	135.00	250.00	350.00

Model No. 1179
GOULDIAN FINCH - Wings in

Designer:	Arthur Gredington
Height:	4 ½", 11.9 cm
Colours:	Purple, green and yellow - gloss
Issued:	1949-by 1959

Description	U.K. £	U.S. $	Can. $
Gloss	135.00	250.00	350.00

Model No. 1180
COCKATOO - Small

Designer:	Arthur Gredington
Height:	8 ½", 21.6 cm
Colours:	1. Pink and grey - gloss
	2. Turquoise and yellow - gloss
Issued:	1949-1975

Description	U.K. £	U.S. $	Can. $
1. Pink/grey	100.00	175.00	275.00
2. Turq./yellow	100.00	175.00	225.00

Note: Large version is model no. 1818.

Model No. 1212
DUCKS (Three) - Ashtray

Designer:	Arthur Gredington
Height:	2 ¾", 7.0 cm
Colours:	1. Blue - gloss
	2. Teal green, white and brown - gloss
Issued:	1. 1951-1965
	2. 1951-1970

Description	U.K. £	U.S. $	Can. $
1. Blue	40.00	55.00	75.00
2. Teal green	35.00	55.00	75.00

Model No. 1216A
BUDGERIGAR - Facing left
First Version - Flowers in high relief on base

Designer:	Arthur Gredington
Height:	7", 17.8 cm
Colours:	1. Blue with dark brown markings - gloss
	2. Green with yellow markings - gloss
Issued:	1951-1967

Description	U.K. £	U.S. $	Can. $
1. Blue	185.00	350.00	550.00
2. Green	200.00	375.00	600.00

Model No. 1216B
BUDGERIGAR - Facing left
Second Version - No flowers on base

Designer:	Arthur Gredington
Height:	7", 17.8 cm
Colours:	Blue, green or yellow - gloss
Issued:	1. Blue - 1967-1975
	2. Green - 1967-1972
	3. Yellow - 1970-1972

Description	U.K. £	U.S. $	Can. $
1. Blue	125.00	225.00	400.00
2. Green	150.00	240.00	450.00
3. Yellow	175.00	325.00	500.00

Model No. 1217A
BUDGERIGAR - Facing right
First Version - Flowers in high relief on base

Designer:	Arthur Gredington
Height:	7", 17.8 cm
Colours:	1. Blue - gloss
	2. Green - gloss
Issued:	1951-1967

Description	U.K. £	U.S. $	Can. $
1. Blue	185.00	350.00	550.00
2. Green	200.00	375.00	600.00

Model No. 1217B
BUDGERIGAR - Facing right
Second Version - No flowers on base

Designer:	Arthur Gredington
Height:	7", 17.8 cm
Colours:	1. Blue - gloss
	2. Green - gloss
Issued:	1967-1970

Description	U.K. £	U.S. $	Can. $
1. Blue	140.00	250.00	450.00
2. Green	160.00	275.00	450.00

Model No. 1218A
GREEN WOODPECKER
First Version - Flowers in high relief on base

Designer: Arthur Gredington
Height: 9", 22.9 cm
Colours: Green, red and white - gloss
Issued: 1951-1967

Description	U.K. £	U.S. $	Can. $
Gloss	200.00	375.00	525.00

Model No. 1218B
GREEN WOODPECKER
Second Version - No flowers on base

Designer: Arthur Gredington
Height: 9", 22.9 cm
Colours: Green, red and white - gloss or matt
Issued: 1. Gloss - 1967-1989
             2. Matt - 1983-1988

Description	U.K. £	U.S. $	Can. $
1. Gloss	100.00	175.00	250.00
2. Matt	100.00	175.00	250.00

Model No. 1219A
JAY
First Version - Flowers in high relief on base

Designer:	Arthur Gredington
Height:	6", 15.0 cm
Colours:	Pink , blue and white - gloss
Issued:	1951-1967

Description	U.K. £	U.S. $	Can. $
Gloss	265.00	450.00	575.00

Model No. 1219B
JAY
Second Version - No flowers on base

Designer:	Arthur Gredington
Height:	6", 15.0 cm
Colours:	Pink, blue and white - gloss
Issued:	1967-1971

Description	U.K. £	U.S. $	Can. $
Gloss	200.00	350.00	500.00

Model No. 1225A
PHEASANT
First Version - Flowers in high relief on base

Designer:	Arthur Gredington
Height:	7 ¾", 19.7 cm
Colours:	Red-brown, teal green, green base - gloss
Issued:	1951-1967

Description	U.K. £	U.S. $	Can. $
Gloss	200.00	375.00	475.00

Model No. 1225B
PHEASANT
Second Version - No flowers on base

Designer:	Arthur Gredington
Height:	7 ¾", 19.7 cm
Colours:	Red-brown, teal green, green base - gloss
Issued:	1967-1977

Description	U.K. £	U.S. $	Can. $
Gloss	150.00	275.00	375.00

Model No. 1226A
PHEASANT
First Version - Flowers in high relief on base

Designer:	Arthur Gredington
Height:	6", 15.0 cm
Colours:	Red-brown, teal green, green base - gloss
Issued:	1951-1967

Description	U.K. £	U.S. $	Can. $
Gloss	175.00	300.00	400.00

Model No. 1226B
PHEASANT
Second Version - No flowers on base

Designer:	Arthur Gredington
Height:	6", 15.0 cm
Colours:	Red-brown, teal green, green base - gloss
Issued:	1967-1977

Description	U.K. £	U.S. $	Can. $
Gloss	140.00	250.00	350.00

Model No. 1383A
PIGEON
First Version - Three stripes on wings

Designer:	Mr. Orwell
Height:	5 ½", 14.0 cm
Colours:	1. Blue - gloss
	2. Red - gloss
Issued:	1955-1972

Description	U.K. £	U.S. $	Can. $
1. Blue - gloss	95.00	175.00	250.00
2. Red - gloss	95.00	175.00	225.00

Model No. 1383B
PIGEON
Second Version - Two stripes on wings

Designer:	Mr. Orwell
Height:	5 ½", 14.0 cm
Colours:	Blue or red - gloss or matt
Issued:	1. Gloss - 1955-1989
	2. Matt - 1983-1988

Description	U.K. £	U.S. $	Can. $
1a. Blue - gloss	110.00	200.00	275.00
1b. Blue - matt	100.00	175.00	275.00
2a. Red - gloss	115.00	200.00	225.00
2b. Red - matt	100.00	175.00	225.00

Model No. 1518

MALLARD DUCK

Designer: Arthur Gredington
Length: See below
Colours: Teal green, brown, white, yellow beak - gloss
Issued: See below
Series: Peter Scott Wildfowl

Description	Issued	Length	U.K. £	Price U.S. $	Can. $
Large	1958-1971	6 ½", 16.5 cm	125.00	200.00	275.00
Medium	1958-1971	5 ½", 14.0 cm	95.00	175.00	225.00
Small - First Version	1958-1962	4 ½", 11.9 cm	100.00	175.00	225.00
Small - Second Version	1962-1971	3 ¾", 11.9 cm	75.00	125.00	165.00

Model No. 1519

MANDARIN DUCK

Designer:	Arthur Gredington
Length:	See below
Colours:	Tan-brown and blue with red beak - gloss
Issued:	1958-1971
Series:	Peter Scott Wildfowl

Description	Length	U.K. £	Price U.S. $	Can. $
Large	4 ½", 11.9 cm	125.00	200.00	275.00
Medium	3 ¾", 9.5 cm	95.00	175.00	225.00
Small	3", 7.6 cm	75.00	125.00	165.00

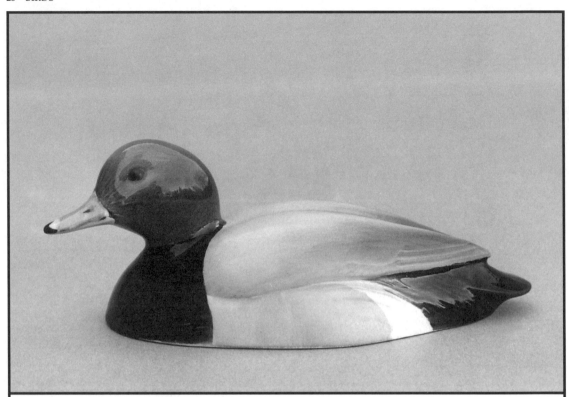

Model No. 1520

POCHARD DUCK

Designer: Arthur Gredington
Length: See below
Colours: Brown, grey and black - gloss
Issued: 1958-1971
Series: Peter Scott Wildfowl

Description	Length	U.K. £	Price U.S. $	Can. $
Large	5 ½", 14.0 cm	110.00	175.00	250.00
Medium	4 ½", 11.9 cm	75.00	125.00	175.00
Small	3 ½", 8.9 cm	65.00	110.00	150.00

Model No. 1521
KING EIDER DUCK

Designer:	Colin Melbourne
Length:	4", 10.1 cm
Colours:	Dark grey with tan, brown, green and white - gloss
Issued:	1958-1971
Series:	Peter Scott Wildfowl

Description	U.K. £	U.S. $	Can. $
Gloss	75.00	125.00	175.00

Model No. 1522
SMEW DUCK

Designer:	Colin Melbourne
Length:	3", 7.6 cm
Colours:	Grey, black and white - gloss
Issued:	1958-1971
Series:	Peter Scott Wildfowl

Description	U.K. £	U.S. $	Can. $
Gloss	85.00	150.00	200.00

Model No. 1523
TUFTED DUCK

Designer:	Colin Melbourne
Length:	2 ¾", 7.0 cm
Colours:	Black and white - gloss
Issued:	1958-1971
Series:	Peter Scott Wildfowl

Description	U.K. £	U.S. $	Can. $
Gloss	85.00	150.00	200.00

Model No. 1524
GOLDENEYE DUCK

Designer:	Colin Melbourne
Length:	3 ½", 8.9 cm
Colours:	Black, white and green - gloss
Issued:	1958-1971
Series:	Peter Scott Wildfowl

Description	U.K. £	U.S. $	Can. $
Gloss	95.00	175.00	225.00

Model No. 1525
GOOSANDER

Designer: Colin Melbourne
Length: 4 ½", 11.9 cm
Colours: Pink, black and white, orange
              beak - gloss
Issued: 1958-1971
Series: Peter Scott Wildfowl

Description	U.K. £	U.S. $	Can. $
Gloss	85.00	150.00	200.00

Model No. 1526
WIDGEON DUCK

Designer: Colin Melbourne
Length: 3 ½", 8.9 cm
Colours: Pink, brown yellow, black and
              white - gloss
Issued: 1958-1971
Series: Peter Scott Wildfowl

Description	U.K. £	U.S. $	Can. $
Gloss	95.00	175.00	225.00

Model No. 1527
SHELDUCK

Designer: Colin Melbourne
Length: 4", 10.1 cm
Colours: Dark grey, tan, white, green and
              brown - gloss
Issued: 1958-1971
Series: Peter Scott Wildfowl

Description	U.K. £	U.S. $	Can. $
Gloss	85.00	150.00	200.00

Model No. 1528
SHOVELER

Designer: Colin Melbourne
Length: 3 ½", 8.9 cm
Colours: Tan, blue, white and dark brown - gloss
Issued: 1958-1971
Series: Peter Scott Wildfowl

Description	U.K. £	U.S. $	Can. $
Gloss	85.00	150.00	200.00

Model No. 1529
TEAL DUCK

Designer:	Colin Melbourne
Length:	2 ¾", 7.0 cm
Colours:	Tan, yellow, black, white with blue beak - gloss
Issued:	1958-1971
Series:	Peter Scott Wildfowl

Description	U.K. £	U.S. $	Can. $
Gloss	85.00	150.00	200.00

Model No. 1614
FANTAIL PIGEON

Designer:	Arthur Gredington
Height:	5", 12.7 cm
Colours:	White - gloss
Issued:	1959-1969

Description	U.K. £	U.S. $	Can. $
Gloss	250.00	450.00	600.00

Model No. 1684
SWAN - Head up

Designer:	Arthur Gredington
Height:	3", 7.6 cm
Colours:	White - gloss
Issued:	1960-1973
Set:	1685, 1686, 1687

Description	U.K. £	U.S. $	Can. $
Gloss	60.00	100.00	135.00

Model No. 1685
SWAN - Head down

Designer:	Arthur Gredington
Height:	2", 5.0 cm
Colours:	White - gloss
Issued:	1960-1973
Set:	1684, 1686, 1687

Description	U.K £	U.S. $	Can. $
Gloss	60.00	100.00	135.00

Model No. 1686
CYGNET - Facing left

Designer:	Arthur Gredington
Height:	1", 2.5 cm
Colours:	Grey - gloss
Issued:	1960-1971
Set:	1684, 1685, 1687

Description	U.K. £	U.S. $	Can. $
Gloss	40.00	60.00	85.00

Model No. 1687
CYGNET - Facing right

Designer:	Arthur Gredington
Height:	1", 2.5 cm
Colours:	Grey - gloss
Issued:	1960-1971
Set:	1684, 1685, 1686

Description	U.K. £	U.S. $	Can. $
Gloss	40.00	60.00	85.00

Model No. 1774
PHEASANT - On pottery base

Designer:	Albert Hallam
Height:	4 ¾", 12.1 cm
Colours:	Red-brown, teal green and beige - gloss
Issued:	1961-1975

Description	U.K. £	U.S. $	Can. $
Gloss	85.00	150.00	225.00

Model No. 1818
COCKATOO - Large

Designer:	Albert Hallam
Height:	11 ½", 29.2 cm
Colours:	1. Pink and grey - gloss
	2. Turquoise and yellow - gloss
Issued:	1962-1973

Description	U.K. £	U.S. $	Can. $
1. Pink/grey	165.00	275.00	375.00
2. Turq./yellow	175.00	300.00	425.00

Model No. 1892
LEGHORN COCKEREL

Designer: Arthur Gredington
Height: 9", 22.9 cm
Colours: Teal green, red, orange and yellow - gloss
Issued: 1963-1983

Description	U.K. £	U.S. $	Can. $
Gloss	190.00	325.00	475.00

Model No. 1899
SUSSEX COCKEREL

Designer: Arthur Gredington
Height: 7", 17.8 cm
Colours: Black, white and pink - gloss
Issued: 1963-1971

Description	U.K. £	U.S. $	Can. $
Gloss	300.00	500.00	675.00

Model No. 1957
TURKEY

Designer: Albert Hallam
Height: 7 ¼", 18.4 cm
Colours: 1.   Bronze - gloss
             2.   White - gloss
Issued: 1964-1969

Description	U.K. £	U.S. $	Can. $
1. Bronze	200.00	375.00	575.00
2. White	350.00	575.00	700.00

Model No. 2026
OWL

Designer: Albert Hallam
Height: 4 ½", 11.9 cm
Colours: Golden brown and white - gloss
Issued: 1965 to the present

Description	U.K. £	U.S. $	Can. $
Gloss	15.00	N/A	N/A

Model No. 2059
GAMECOCK

Designer: Arthur Gredington
Height: 9 ½", 24.0 cm
Colours: Brown, teal green, cream and red - gloss
Issued: 1966-1975

Description	U.K. £	U.S. $	Can. $
Gloss	275.00	425.00	650.00

Model No. 2062
GOLDEN EAGLE

Designer: Graham Tongue
Height: 9 ½", 24.0 cm
Colours: Dark brown - gloss, matt, or satin matt
Issued: 1. 1966-1974 - Gloss
       2. 1970-1972 - Matt
       3. 1973-1989 - Satin matt
Series: 3. Connoisseur

Description	U.K. £	U.S. $	Can. $
1. Gloss	175.00	275.00	375.00
2. Matt	150.00	275.00	375.00
3. Satin matt	125.00	275.00	375.00

Model No. 2063
GROUSE (Pair)

Designer: Albert Hallam
Height: 5 ½", 14.0 cm
Colours: Red-brown - gloss
Issued: 1966-1975

Description	U.K. £	U.S. $	Can. $
Gloss	275.00	450.00	600.00

Model No. 2064
PARTRIDGE (Pair)

Designer: Albert Hallam
Height: 5 ½", 14.0 cm
Colours: Brown and blue - gloss
Issued: 1966-1975

Description	U.K. £	U.S. $	Can. $
Gloss	250.00	425.00	600.00

Photograph not
available at press time

Model No. 2067
TURKEY

Designer: Albert Hallam
Height: 2 ½", 6.4 cm
Colours: 1. White and red - gloss
2. Bronze - gloss
Issued: 1966-1969

Description	U.K. £	U.S. $	Can. $
1. White	100.00	175.00	250.00
2. Bronze	100.00	175.00	225.00

Model No. 2071
OWL (Contemporary)

Designer: Graham Tongue
Height: 5", 12.7 cm
Colours: Unknown
Issued: 1966-Unknown
Series: Contemporary Models

Description	U.K. £	U.S. $	Can. $
	Extremely Rare		

Model No. 2078
PHEASANTS (Pair)

Designer: Arthur Gredington
Height: 6 ¾", 17.2 cm
Colours: Red-brown and teal green with
yellow markings - gloss
Issued: 1966-1975

Description	U.K. £	U.S. $	Can. $
Gloss	300.00	550.00	750.00

Model No. 2105A
GREENFINCH
First Version - With flower on base

Designer: Graham Tongue
Height: 3", 7.6 cm
Colours: Green and yellow - gloss
Issued: 1967-1973

Description	U.K. £	U.S. $	Can. $
Gloss	35.00	55.00	75.00

Model No. 2105B
GREENFINCH
Second Version - Wthout flower on base

Designer: Graham Tongue
Remodelled: Albert Hallam
Height: 3", 7.6 cm
Colours: Natural - gloss or matt
Issued: 1. Gloss - 1973 to the present
              2. Matt - 1983-1992

Description	U.K. £	U.S. $	Can. $
1. Gloss	13.50	N/A	N/A
2. Matt	15.00	35.00	50.00

Model No. 2106A
WHITETHROAT
First Version - Mouth open, base is a green mound

Designer: Graham Tongue
Height: 3", 7.6 cm
Colours: Dark grey, white and pink - gloss
Issued: 1967-1973

Description	U.K. £	U.S. $	Can. $
Gloss	35.00	55.00	75.00

Model No. 2106B
WHITETHROAT
Second Version - Mouth closed, base is a leaf

Designer: Graham Tongue
Remodelled: Albert Hallam
Height: 3", 7.6 cm
Colours: Natural - gloss or matt
Issued: 1. Gloss - 1973-1996
              2. Matt - 1983-1992

Description	U.K. £	U.S. $	Can. $
1. Gloss	13.00	25.00	30.00
2. Matt	17.00	35.00	50.00

Model No. 2183
BALTIMORE ORIOLE

Designer: Albert Hallam
Height: 3 ½", 8.9 cm
Colours: Black and red - gloss or matt
Issued: 1. Gloss - 1968-1973
           2. Matt - 1970-1972

Description	U.K. £	U.S. $	Can. $
1. Gloss	100.00	175.00	250.00
2. Matt	100.00	175.00	225.00

Model No. 2184
CEDAR WAXWING

Designer: Graham Tongue
Height: 4 ½", 11.9 cm
Colours: Brown, black and yellow - gloss or matt
Issued: 1. Gloss - 1968-1973
2. Matt - 1970-1972

Description	U.K. £	U.S. $	Can. $
1. Gloss	110.00	175.00	275.00
2. Matt	110.00	175.00	225.00

Model No. 2187
AMERICAN ROBIN

Designer: Graham Tongue
Height: 4", 10.1 cm
Colours: Dark grey and red - gloss or matt
Issued: 1. Gloss - 1968-1973
2. Matt - 1970-1972

Description	U.K. £	U.S. $	Can. $
1. Gloss	125.00	225.00	275.00
2. Matt	85.00	175.00	225.00

Model No. 2188
BLUE JAY

Designer: Albert Hallam
Height: 4 ½", 11.9 cm
Colours: Blue and white - gloss or matt
Issued: 1. Gloss - 1968-1973
2. Matt - 1970-1972

Description	U.K. £	U.S. $	Can. $
1. Gloss	150.00	225.00	300.00
2. Matt	110.00	190.00	300.00

Model No. 2189
BLACK CAPPED CHICADEE

Designer: Graham Tongue
Height: 4 ½", 11.9 cm
Colours: Yellow, white, grey, green and black - gloss or matt
Issued: 1. Gloss - 1968-1973
2. Matt - 1970-1972

Description	U.K. £	U.S. $	Can. $
1. Gloss	125.00	225.00	275.00
2. Matt	110.00	175.00	250.00

Model No. 2190
EVENING GROSBEAK

Designer:	Albert Hallam
Height:	4″, 10.1 cm
Colours:	Black and yellow - gloss or matt
Issued:	1. Gloss - 1968-1973
	2. Matt - 1970-1972

Description	U.K. £	U.S. $	Can. $
1. Gloss	135.00	225.00	300.00
2. Matt	110.00	200.00	275.00

Model No. 2191
QUAIL

Designer:	Albert Hallam
Height:	5″, 12.7 cm
Colours:	Browns, black and white - gloss or matt
Issued:	1. Gloss - 1968-1971
	2. Matt - 1970-1972

Description	U.K. £	U.S. $	Can. $
1. Gloss	150.00	275.00	375.00
2. Matt	100.00	175.00	275.00

Model No. 2200
CHICKEN - Running

Designer:	Graham Tongue
Height:	1 ¼″, 3.2 cm
Colours:	Yellow - gloss
Issued:	1968-1973
Set:	2201, 2202

Description	U.K. £	U.S. $	Can. $
Gloss	60.00	100.00	125.00

Model No. 2201
CHICKEN - Pecking

Designer:	Graham Tongue
Height:	1″, 2.5 cm
Colours:	Yellow - gloss
Issued:	1968-1973
Set:	2200, 2202

Description	U.K. £	U.S. $	Can. $
Gloss	60.00	100.00	125.00

Model No. 2202
CHICKEN - Sitting

Designer:	Graham Tongue
Height:	1 ½", 3.8 cm
Colours:	Yellow - gloss
Issued:	1968-1973
Set:	2200, 2201

Description	U.K. £	U.S. $	Can. $
Gloss	60.00	100.00	125.00

Photograph not
available at press time

Model No. 2238
OWL

Designer:	Harry Sales
Height:	6 ¾", 17.2 cm
Colours:	Unknown
Issued:	1968-1971
Series:	Moda Range

Description	U.K. £	U.S. $	Can. $
	200.00	325.00	425.00

Photograph not
available at press time

Model No. 2239
BIRD

Designer:	Harry Sales
Height:	5", 12.7 cm
Colours:	Unknown
Issued:	1968-1971
Series:	Moda Range

Description	U.K. £	U.S. $	Can. $
	200.00	325.00	425.00

Model No. 2240
COCKEREL

Designer:	Harry Sales
Height:	6", 15.0 cm
Colours:	1. Blue - gloss
	2. Brown - matt
Issued:	1968-1971
Series:	Moda Range

Description	U.K. £	U.S. $	Can. $
1. Blue	150.00	250.00	325.00
2. Brown	110.00	175.00	275.00

Model No. 2273
GOLDFINCH

Designer:	Graham Tongue
Height:	3″, 7.6 cm
Colours:	Brown, white, red and yellow - gloss or matt
Issued:	1. Gloss - 1969-1995
	2. Matt - 1983-1992

Description	U.K. £	U.S. $	Can. $
1. Gloss	13.00	25.00	30.00
2. Matt	17.00	35.00	50.00

Model No. 2274
STONECHAT

Designer:	Albert Hallam
Height:	3″, 7.6 cm
Colours:	Dark brown and white, red breast - gloss or matt
Issued:	1. Gloss - 1969-1997
	2. Matt - 1983-1992

Description	U.K. £	U.S. $	Can. $
1. Gloss	15.00	25.00	30.00
2. Matt	17.00	35.00	50.00

Model No. 2305
MAGPIE

Designer:	Albert Hallam
Height:	5″, 12.7 cm
Colours:	Black and white - gloss
Issued:	1970-1982

Description	U.K. £	U.S. $	Can. $
Gloss	75.00	150.00	225.00

Model No. 2307
EAGLE ON ROCK

Designer:	Graham Tongue
Height:	3 ¾″, 9.5 cm
Colours:	Browns - gloss
Issued:	1970-1975

Description	U.K. £	U.S. $	Can. $
Gloss	150.00	250.00	350.00

Model No. 2308
SONGTHRUSH

Designer:	Albert Hallam
Height:	5 ¾", 14.6 cm
Colours:	Brown with yellow speckled breast - gloss and matt
Issued:	1. Gloss - 1970-1989
	2. Matt - 1983-1989

Description	U.K. £	U.S. $	Can. $
1. Gloss	65.00	125.00	200.00
2. Matt	50.00	110.00	175.00

Model No. 2315
CUCKOO

Designer:	Albert Hallam
Height:	5", 12.7 cm
Colours:	Blue - gloss
Issued:	1970-1982

Description	U.K. £	U.S. $	Can. $
Gloss	80.00	150.00	225.00

Model No. 2316
KESTREL

Designer:	Graham Tongue
Height:	6 ¾", 17.2 cm
Colours:	Browns, white and blue - gloss or matt
Issued:	1. Gloss - 1970-1989
	2. Matt - 1983-1989

Description	U.K. £	U.S. $	Can. $
1. Gloss	75.00	135.00	200.00
2. Matt	60.00	120.00	200.00

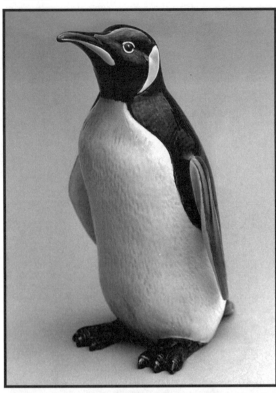

Model No. 2357
PENGUIN

Designer: Albert Hallam
Height: 12", 30.5 cm
Colours: Black and white - gloss
Issued: 1971-1976
Series: Fireside Model

Description	U.K. £	U.S. $	Can. $
Gloss	350.00	600.00	850.00

Model No. 2359
HERON - Stylistic

Designer: Albert Hallam
Height: 10 ½", 26.7 cm
Colours: Black - satin
Issued: 1971-Unknown

Description	U.K. £	U.S. $	Can. $
Satin	75.00	125.00	200.00

Model No. 2371
KINGFISHER

Designer: Albert Hallam
Height: 5", 12.7 cm
Colours: Blue and brown - gloss or matt
Issued: 1. Gloss - 1971 to the present
              2. Matt - 1983-1989

Description	U.K. £	U.S. $	Can. $
1. Gloss	35.00	N/A	N/A
2. Matt	45.00	75.00	100.00

Photograph not
available at press time

Model No. 2398
PENGUIN CHICK - Standing

Designer:	Graham Tongue		
Height:	7", 17.8 cm		
Colours:	Blue, black and white - gloss		
Issued:	1971-1976		

Description	U.K. £	U.S. $	Can. $
Gloss	225.00	350.00	475.00

Model No. 2399
PENGUIN CHICK

Designer:	Albert Hallam		
Height:	6 ¾", 17.2 cm		
Colours:	Black and white - gloss		
Issued:	1972-Unknown		

Description	U.K. £	U.S. $	Can. $
Gloss	Extremely Rare		

Note: Probably not put into production.

Model No. 2413
NUTHATCH

Designer:	Graham Tongue	
Height:	3", 7.6 cm	
Colours:	Dark blue and white - gloss or matt	
Issued:	1. Gloss - 1972-1995	
	2. Matt - 1983-1989	

Description	U.K. £	U.S. $	Can. $
1. Gloss	15.00	30.00	45.00
2. Matt	15.00	30.00	45.00

Model No. 2415
GOLDCREST

Designer:	Graham Tongue	
Height:	3", 7.6 cm	
Colours:	Green, yellow and grey - gloss or matt	
Issued:	1. Gloss - 1972 to the present	
	2. Matt - 1983-1989	

Description	U.K. £	U.S. $	Can. $
1. Gloss	13.50	N/A	N/A
2. Matt	35.00	60.00	75.00

Model No. 2416A
LAPWING
First Version - Tail feathers split

Designer: Albert Hallam
Height: 5 ½", 14.0 cm
Colours: Black, dark green and white - gloss
Issued: 1972-Unknown

Description	U.K. £	U.S. $	Can. $
Gloss	130.00	225.00	300.00

Model No. 2416B
LAPWING
Second Version - Tail feathers together

Designer: Albert Hallam
Height: 5 ½", 14.0 cm
Colours: Black, dark green and white - gloss
Issued: Unknown-1982

Description	U.K. £	U.S. $	Can. $
Gloss	90.00	175.00	250.00

Model No. 2417
JAY

Designer: Graham Tongue
Height: 5", 12.7 cm
Colours: Brown, white and blue - gloss
Issued: 1972-1982

Description	U.K. £	U.S. $	Can. $
Gloss	75.00	150.00	225.00

Model No. 2420
LESSER SPOTTED WOODPECKER

Designer: Graham Tongue
Height: 5 ½", 14.0 cm
Colours: Red, white and black - gloss
Issued: 1972-1982

Description	U.K. £	U.S. $	Can. $
Gloss	90.00	175.00	275.00

Model No. 2434
PENGUIN CHICK - Sliding

Designer:	Graham Tongue	
Height:	3 ¾" x 8", 9.5 x 20.3 cm	
Colours:	Blue, black and white - gloss	
Issued:	1972-1976	

Description	U.K. £	U.S. $	Can. $
Gloss	400.00	600.00	750.00

Model No. 3272
TAWNY OWL

Designer:	Mr. Sutton
Height:	3 ¼", 8.3 cm
Colours:	Brown and white - gloss
Issued:	1990 to the present

Description	U.K. £	U.S. $	Can. $
Gloss	13.50	N/A	N/A

Model No. 2760
PHEASANT

Designer:	Graham Tongue	
Height:	10 ½", 26.7 cm	
Colours:	1.	Tan and brown - satin matt
	2.	Bronze with black shading - satin
Issued:	1.	Satin matt - 1982-1989
	2.	Matt - 1989-1992
Series:	1.	Connoisseur
	2.	Britannia Collection

Description	U.K. £	U.S. $	Can. $
1. Connoisseur	150.00	300.00	425.00
2. Britannia	200.00	325.00	450.00

Note: Transferred to Royal Doulton backstamp (DA 38 Open Ground) 08/89. Satin matt version.

Model No. 3273
BARN OWL

Designer: Martyn Alcock
Height: 3 ¼", 8.3 cm
Colours: Light brown and white - gloss
Issued: 1990 to the present

Description	U.K. £	U.S. $	Can. $
Gloss	13.50	N/A	N/A

Model No. 3274
GREAT TIT

Designer: Martyn Alcock
Height: 3", 7.6 cm
Colours: Black, yellow, white and grey - gloss
Issued: 1990-1995

Description	U.K. £	U.S. $	Can. $
Gloss	15.00	30.00	40.00

Model No. 3275
KINGFISHER

Designer: Mr. Sutton
Height: 2 ¾", 7.0 cm
Colours: Blue head and wings, orange breast - gloss
Issued: 1990 to the present

Description	U.K. £	U.S. $	Can. $
Gloss	13.50	N/A	N/A

BIRD WALL PLAQUES

Model No. 596

MALLARD

Designer: Mr. Watkin
Length: See below
Issued: See below
Colours: 1. Brown, teal green and white - gloss
2. White with yellow beaks - matt

Model No.	Finish	Issued	Length	U.K. £	Price U.S. $	Can. $
596/0	Gloss	1938-1971	11 ¾", 29.8 cm	70.00	110.00	130.00
596/0	Matt	1938-1971	11 ¾", 29.8 cm	65.00	110.00	130.00
596/1	Gloss	1938-1973	10", 25.4 cm	60.00	100.00	100.00
596/1	Matt	1938-1973	10", 25.4 cm	55.00	100.00	100.00
596/2	Gloss	1938-1973	8 ¾", 22.2 cm	50.00	85.00	85.00
596/2	Matt	1938-1973	8 ¾", 22.2 cm	45.00	85.00	85.00
596/3	Gloss	1938-1973	7", 17.8 cm	40.00	65.00	70.00
596/3	Matt	1938-1973	7", 17.8 cm	35.00	65.00	70.00
596/4	Gloss	1938-1971	5 ¾", 14.6 cm	30.00	50.00	60.00
596/4	Matt	1938-1971	5 ¾", 14.6 cm	25.00	50.00	60.00

Note: These also exist with a small "pocket" between the wings.

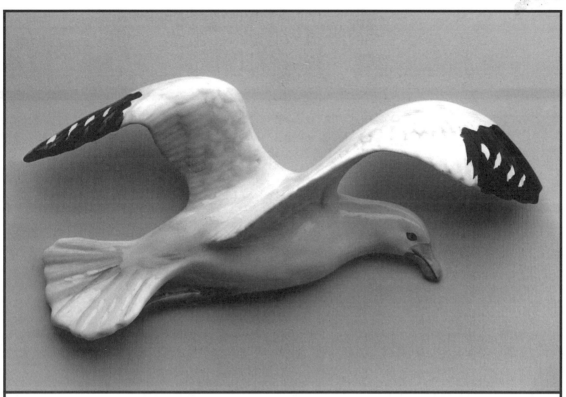

Model No. 658

SEAGULL
Style One - Wings up, apart

Designer: Mr. Watkin
Length: See below
Colours: 1. White, black and yellow - gloss
          2. White and yellow - matt
          3. White - matt
Issued: 1938-1967

Model No.	Finish	Length	U.K. £	U.S. $	Can. $
				Price	
658/1	Gloss	14", 35.5 cm	75.00	100.00	125.00
658/1	Matt	14", 35.5 cm	65.00	100.00	125.00
658/1	Matt	14", 35.5 cm	60.00	100.00	125.00
658/2	Gloss	11 ¾", 29.8 cm	65.00	90.00	110.00
658/2	Matt	11 ¾", 29.8 cm	55.00	90.00	110.00
658/2	Matt	11 ¾", 29.8 cm	50.00	90.00	110.00
658/3	Gloss	10", 25.4 cm	55.00	75.00	90.00
658/3	Matt	10", 25.4 cm	45.00	75.00	90.00
658/3	Matt	10", 25.4 cm	40.00	75.00	90.00
658/4	Gloss	8", 20.3 cm	45.00	60.00	80.00
658/4	Matt	8", 20.3 cm	35.00	60.00	80.00
658/4	Matt	8", 20.3 cm	30.00	60.00	80.00

Model No. 661

PHEASANT

Designer: Mr. Watkin
Length: See below
Colours: 1. Teal green, browns and white - gloss
2. White - matt
Issued: 1938-1971

Model No.	Finish	Length	U.K. £	Price U.S. $	Can. $
661/1	Gloss	12", 30.5 cm	75.00	100.00	125.00
661/1	Matt	12", 30.5 cm	65.00	100.00	125.00
661/2	Gloss	10 ¼", 26.0 cm	65.00	85.00	100.00
661/2	Matt	10 ¼", 26.0 cm	55.00	85.00	100.00
661/3	Gloss	8 ½", 21.6 cm	55.00	75.00	90.00
661/3	Matt	8 ½", 21.6 cm	45.00	75.00	90.00

Model No. 705
BLUE TIT - Flying to the right

Designer: Mr. Watkin
Height: 4 ½", 11.9 cm
Size: Large
Colours: Blue and browns - gloss
Issued: 1939-1967
Set: 706, 707

Description	U.K. £	U.S. $	Can. $
Gloss	75.00	150.00	200.00

Model No. 706
BLUE TIT - Flying to the left

Designer: Mr. Watkin
Height: 4 ½", 11.9 cm
Size: Medium
Colours: Blue and browns - gloss
Issued: 1939-1967
Set: 705, 707

Description	U.K. £	U.S. $	Can. $
Gloss	75.00	150.00	200.00

Model No. 707
BLUE TIT - Wings up, flying to the left

Designer: Mr. Watkin
Height: 4 ½", 11.9 cm
Size: Small
Colours: Blue and browns - gloss
Issued: 1939-1967
Set: 705, 706

Description	U.K. £	U.S. $	Can. $
Gloss	75.00	150.00	200.00

Model No. 729

KINGFISHER - Flying to the right

Designer: Arthur Gredington
Height: See below
Colours: 1. Green and yellow - gloss
            2. Blue - gloss
Issued: 1939-1971

Model No.	Colour	Height	U.K. £	Price U.S. $	Can. $
729/1 Large	Green	7 ½", 19.1 cm	65.00	150.00	250.00
729/1 Large	Blue	7 ½", 19.1 cm	125.00	250.00	350.00
729/2 Medium	Green	6", 15.0 cm	55.00	125.00	225.00
729/2 Medium	Blue	6", 15.0 cm	125.00	225.00	325.00
729/3 Small	Green	5", 12.7 cm	45.00	100.00	200.00
729/3 Small	Blue	5", 12.7 cm	110.00	200.00	300.00

Note: Model no. 729/2 can be paired with no. 743 to make a facing pair.

Model No. 731
FLAMINGO

Designer:	Mr. Watkin
Length:	15", 38.1 cm
Colours:	1. Pearl orange and black - gloss
	2. White, yellow and black wing tips - satin
Issued:	1939-1954

Description	U.K. £	U.S. $	Can. $
1. Gloss	250.00	550.00	750.00
2. Satin	250.00	550.00	750.00

Model No. 743
KINGFISHER

Designer:	Arthur Gredington
Height:	6", 15.0 cm
Colours:	Greens and yellow - gloss
Issued:	1939-1954

Description	U.K. £	U.S. $	Can. $
Gloss	125.00	250.00	350.00

Note: Model no. 743 can be paired with no. 729/2 to make a facing pair.

Model No. 757

SWALLOW

Designer:	Arthur Gredington
Height:	See below
Colours:	Blues - gloss
Issued:	1939-1973

				Price	
Model No.	Size	Height	U.K. £	U.S. $	Can. $
757/1	Large	7 ½", 19.1 cm	85.00	135.00	185.00
757/2	Medium	6 ¼", 15.9 cm	75.00	120.00	160.00
757/3	Small	5", 12.7 cm	65.00	110.00	135.00

Model No. 922
SEAGULL
Style Two - Wings up, together

Designer:	Arthur Gredington
Height:	Large - 12", 30.5 cm
	Medium - 10 ½", 26.7 cm
	Small - 9 ½", 24.0 cm
Colours:	White, grey and black - gloss or matt
Issued:	1941-1971

Description	U.K. £	U.S. $	Can. $
Large - gloss	80.00	135.00	175.00
Large - matt	70.00	135.00	175.00
Medium - gloss	70.00	115.00	160.00
Medium - matt	60.00	115.00	160.00
Small - gloss	60.00	100.00	150.00
Small - matt	50.00	100.00	150.00

Model No. 1023
HUMMING BIRD

Designer:	Arthur Gredington
Height:	Large - 5 ¾", 14.6 cm
	Medium - 5", 12.7 cm
	Small - 4 ¾", 12.1 cm
Colours:	Browns, grey and red - gloss
Issued:	1944-1967

Description	U.K. £	U.S. $	Can. $
Large - gloss	100.00	175.00	275.00
Medium - gloss	90.00	150.00	250.00
Small - gloss	80.00	200.00	225.00

Model No. 1188

PINK LEGGED PARTRIDGE

Designer: Arthur Gredington
Length: See below
Colours: Browns, white and grey - gloss
Issued: 1950-1967

Model No.	Size	Length	U.K. £	Price U.S. $	Can. $
1188/1	Large	10 ½", 26.7 cm	110.00	200.00	300.00
1188/2	Medium	9", 22.9 cm	95.00	175.00	275.00
1188/3	Small	7 ½", 19.1 cm	80.00	150.00	250.00

Model No. 1344

GREEN WOODPECKER

Designer: Mr. Orwell
Length: See below
Colours: Greens and brown, red head - gloss
Issued: 1954-1968

Model No.	Size	Length	U.K. £	Price U.S. $	Can. $
1344/1	Large	7 ½", 19.1 cm	125.00	225.00	300.00
1344/2	Medium	6", 15.0 cm	110.00	200.00	275.00
1344/3	Small	5", 12.7 cm	90.00	175.00	250.00

Model No. 1530

TEAL

Designer: Arthur Gredington
Length: See below
Colours: Brown, grey and green - gloss
Issued: 1958-1968

Model No.	Size	Length	U.K. £	Price U.S. $	Can. $
1530/1	Large	8 ¼", 21.0 cm	165.00	275.00	375.00
1530/2	Medium	7 ¼", 18.4 cm	140.00	225.00	325.00
1530/3	Small	6 ¼", 15.9 cm	115.00	200.00	275.00

Chapter Two

BUTTERFLY PLAQUES

Butterflies are an unusual choice for the medium of pottery, and these few wall plaques tend to be rare. It is also unusual to find them in perfect condition, as often the antennae have suffered from the passage of time. These butterfly wall plaques were modelled in large, medium and small sizes. The Beswick attention to detail is very apparent here.

At the present time, the information on these models is virtually nonexistent, and there have been no catalogues found in which they are illustrated. Fortunately, each model is impressed on the back with the name of the butterfly and the shape number. If this were not the case, then identification would be a problem.

INDEX BY MODEL NUMBER

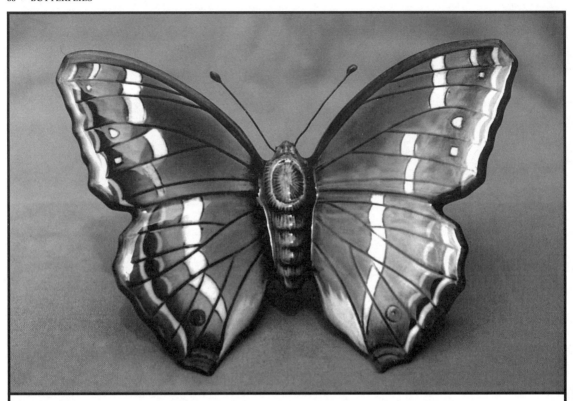

Model No. 1487

PURPLE EMPEROR BUTTERFLY

Designer: Albert Hallam
Height: 6 ¼″ x 4″, 15.9 x 10.1 cm
Size: Large

Colours	Issued	U.K. £	Price U.S. $	Can. $
Blue and white - gloss	1957-by 1963	275.00	450.00	625.00

Model No. 1488
RED ADMIRAL BUTTERFLY

Designer: Albert Hallam
Dimensions: 6 ¼" x 4", 15.9 x 10.1 cm
Size: Large
Colours: Browns, blue and white - gloss
Issued: 1957-by 1963

Description	U.K. £	U.S. $	Can. $
Gloss	275.00	450.00	625.00

Model No. 1489
PEACOCK BUTTERFLY

Designer: Albert Hallam
Dimensions: 6 ¼" x 4", 15.9 x 10.1 cm
Size: Large
Colours: Browns, black and yellow - gloss
Issued: 1957-by 1963

Description	U.K. £	U.S. $	Can. $
Gloss	275.00	450.00	625.00

Model No. 1490
CLOUDED YELLOW BUTTERFLY

Designer: Albert Hallam
Dimensions: 5 ¼" x 3 ½", 13.3 x 8.9 cm
Size: Medium
Colours: Yellow, black and red - gloss
Issued: 1957-by 1963

Description	U.K. £	U.S. $	Can. $
Gloss	250.00	425.00	575.00

Model No. 1491
TORTOISESHELL BUTTERFLY

Designer: Albert Hallam
Dimensions: 5 ¼" x 3 ½", 13.3 x 8.9 cm
Size: Medium
Colours: Yellow, blue and black - gloss
Issued: 1957-by 1963

Description	U.K. £	U.S. $	Can. $
Gloss	250.00	425.00	575.00

Model No. 1492
SWALLOW-TAIL BUTTERFLY

Designer:	Albert Hallam
Dimensions:	5 ¼″ x 3 ½″, 13.3 x 8.9 cm
Size:	Medium
Colours:	Brown, green and blue wings - gloss
Issued:	1957-by 1963

Description	U.K. £	U.S. $	Can. $
Gloss	250.00	425.00	575.00

Model No. 1493
SMALL COPPER BUTTERFLY

Designer:	Albert Hallam
Dimensions:	3 ¾″ x 2 ¼″, 9.5 x 5.7 cm
Size:	Small
Colours:	Browns - gloss
Issued:	1957-by 1963

Description	U.K. £	U.S. $	Can. $
Gloss	225.00	375.00	525.00

Model No. 1494
PURPLE HAIRSTREAK BUTTERFLY

Designer:	Albert Hallam
Dimensions:	3 ¾″ x 2 ¼″, 9.5 x 5.7 cm
Size:	Small
Colours:	Browns and grey - gloss
Issued:	1957-by 1963

Description	U.K. £	U.S. $	Can. $
Gloss	225.00	375.00	525.00

Model No. 1495
SMALL HEATH BUTTERFLY

Designer:	Albert Hallam
Dimensions:	3 ¾″ x 2 ¼″, 9.5 x 5.7 cm
Size:	Small
Colours:	Browns - gloss
Issued:	1957-by 1963

Description	U.K. £	U.S. $	Can. $
Gloss	225.00	375.00	525.00

Chapter Three

CATS

Cat lovers will appreciate the variety of felines offered here. As well as realistic models, there are cats playing instruments and playing ball, zodiac cats and cats just clowning around.

These figures were also produced in a large selection of colours and finishes:

Colourways	Dates of Issue
Black gloss	Model No. 1897 only
Black matt	1984 - 1988
British Blue (lead grey gloss)	1964 - 1966
Chocolate point gloss	1953 - 1963
Copper lustre	1971 only
Ginger matt	1984 - 1988
Ginger (dark) gloss	1945 - 1970
Ginger (pale) gloss	1959 - 1963
Ginger striped gloss	1965 - 1989
Ginger Swiss roll gloss	1964 - 1966
Grey matt	1984 - 1988
Grey (shaded) gloss	1965 - 1989
Grey (smokey blue) gloss	1945 - 1970
Grey striped gloss	1962 - 1973
Grey Swiss roll gloss	1964 - 1966
Royal blue gloss	Only one example known
Seal point gloss	1963 - 1989
Seal point matt	1984 - 1988
White (large eyes) gloss	1963 - 1989
White (small eyes) gloss	1945 - 1963
White matt	1984 - 1988
White Zodiac cat	1958 - 1970

Colours listed under individual cats are those on which they could be found. The Swiss roll decoration has two Swiss roll patterns, one on the shoulder and one on the hip.

INDEX BY MODEL NUMBER

Model 1031 White gloss (large eyes) left, (small eyes) right

Model No. 1026
CAT CONDUCTOR

Designer:	Arthur Gredington
Height:	2", 5.0 cm
Colours:	Grey striped - gloss
Issued:	1945-1973
Series:	Cat Orchestra
Set:	1027, 1028, 1029

Description	U.K. £	U.S. $	Can. $
Gloss	60.00	100.00	125.00

Model No. 1027
CAT WITH CELLO

Designer:	Arthur Gredington
Height:	2", 5.0 cm
Colours:	Grey striped - gloss
Issued:	1945-1973
Series:	Cat Orchestra
Set:	1026, 1028, 1029

Description	U.K. £	U.S. $	Can. $
Gloss	60.00	100.00	125.00

Model No. 1028
CAT WITH FIDDLE

Designer:	Arthur Gredington
Height:	2", 5.0 cm
Colours:	Grey striped - gloss
Issued:	1945-1973
Series:	Cat Orchestra
Set:	1026, 1027, 1029

Description	U.K. £	U.S. $	Can. $
Gloss	70.00	110.00	140.00

Model No. 1029
CAT WITH SAXOPHONE

Designer:	Arthur Gredington
Height:	2", 5.0 cm
Colours:	Grey striped - gloss
Issued:	1945-1973
Series:	Cat Orchestra
Set:	1026, 1027, 1028

Description	U.K. £	U.S. $	Can. $
Gloss	60.00	100.00	125.00

Model No. 1030
CAT - Seated, head looks up

Designer: Arthur Gredington
Height: 6 ¼", 15.9 cm

Colourway	Finish	Intro.	Disc.	U.K. £	Price U.S. $	Can. $
British Blue (lead grey)	Gloss	1964	1966	225.00	425.00	575.00
Ginger (dark)	Gloss	1945	1970	95.00	160.00	210.00
Ginger (pale)	Gloss	1959	1963	85.00	150.00	195.00
Ginger striped	Gloss	1965	1973	110.00	185.00	250.00
Ginger Swiss roll	Gloss	1964	1966	200.00	400.00	600.00
Grey (shaded)	Gloss	1971	1973	85.00	150.00	195.00
Grey (smokey blue)	Gloss	1945	1970	65.00	110.00	150.00
Grey striped	Gloss	1962	1973	110.00	185.00	250.00
Grey Swiss roll	Gloss	1964	1966	225.00	475.00	650.00
Royal blue	Gloss	*Unknown			Unique	
White (small eyes)	Gloss	1945	1963	80.00	135.00	185.00
White (large eyes)	Gloss	1963	1973	75.00	120.00	160.00

Note: * Only one example known.

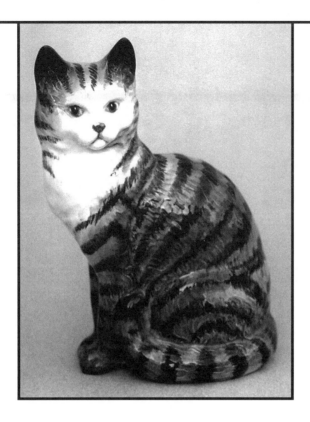

Model No. 1031
CAT - Seated, head looks forward

Designer: Arthur Gredington
Height: 4 ½", 11.9 cm

Colourway	Finish	Intro.	Disc.	U.K. £	Price U.S. $	Can. $
British Blue (lead grey)	Gloss	1964	1966	220.00	375.00	500.00
Ginger (dark)	Gloss	1945	1970	80.00	140.00	185.00
Ginger (pale)	Gloss	1959	1963	70.00	120.00	160.00
Ginger striped	Gloss	1965	1973	90.00	160.00	200.00
Ginger Swiss roll	Gloss	1964	1966	200.00	375.00	500.00
Grey (shaded)	Gloss	1971	1973	75.00	125.00	175.00
Grey (smokey blue)	Gloss	1945	1970	60.00	100.00	135.00
Grey striped	Gloss	1962	1973	95.00	160.00	200.00
Grey Swiss roll	Gloss	1964	1966	220.00	400.00	550.00
White (small eyes)	Gloss	1945	1963	70.00	120.00	160.00
White (large eyes)	Gloss	1963	1973	60.00	100.00	135.00

Model No. 1296
SIAMESE KITTENS - Curled together

Designer: Miss Granoska
Length: 2 ¾", 7.0 cm

			Price	
Colours	**Issued**	**U.K. £**	**U.S. $**	**Can. $**
Chocolate point - gloss	1953-1963	55.00	95.00	125.00
Seal point - gloss	1964-1989	45.00	85.00	95.00
Seal point - matt	1984-1989	55.00	95.00	125.00
Copper lustre - gloss	1971 (export only)	75.00	130.00	175.00
One white/one pale grey - gloss	*Unknown		Unique	

Note: 1. The Seal point model with a gloss finish was transferred to R.D. backstamp (DA122) 08/89.
         2. * Only one example known.

Model No. 1316
PERSIAN KITTENS - Seated

Designer: Miss Granoska
Height: 3 ½″, 8.9 cm

Colourway	Finish	Intro.	Disc.	U.K. £	Price U.S. $	Can. $
British Blue (lead grey)	Gloss	1964	1966	150.00	275.00	375.00
Ginger (dark)	Gloss	1953	1970	55.00	95.00	125.00
Ginger (pale)	Gloss	1959	1963	45.00	75.00	100.00
Ginger striped	Gloss	1971	1973	70.00	120.00	160.00
Ginger Swiss roll	Gloss	1964	1966	140.00	275.00	375.00
Grey (shaded)	Gloss	1965	1973	45.00	75.00	100.00
Grey striped	Gloss	1962	1973	70.00	120.00	160.00
Grey Swiss roll	Gloss	1964	1966	160.00	300.00	400.00
White (large eyes)	Gloss	1963	1973	45.00	75.00	100.00

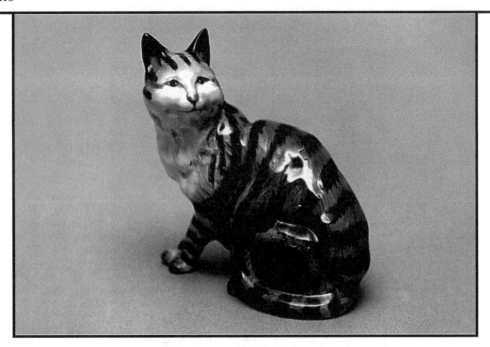

Model No. 1435
CAT - Seated

Designer: Colin Melbourne
Height: 5 ¼", 13.3 cm
Colours: Grey striped - gloss
Issued: 1956-1963

Colourway	Finish	Intro.	Disc.	U.K. £	Price U.S. $	Can. $
Grey striped	Gloss	1956	1963	200.00	350.00	450.00

Model No. 1436
KITTEN - Seated

Designer: Colin Melbourne
Height: 3 ¼", 8.3 cm

Colourway	Finish	Intro.	Disc.	U.K. £	Price U.S. $	Can. $
Black	Matt	1984	1989	30.00	50.00	65.00
British Blue (lead grey)	Gloss	1964	1966	95.00	175.00	300.00
Ginger	Matt	1984	1989	25.00	40.00	55.00
Ginger (dark)	Gloss	1956	1970	30.00	50.00	65.00
Ginger (pale)	Gloss	1959	1963	20.00	35.00	45.00
Ginger striped	Gloss	1965	1989	40.00	65.00	90.00
Ginger Swiss roll	Gloss	1964	1966	95.00	175.00	300.00
Grey	Matt	1984	1989	35.00	60.00	80.00
Grey (shaded)	Gloss	1965	1989	25.00	40.00	55.00
Grey striped	Gloss	1962	1973	30.00	50.00	65.00
Grey Swiss roll	Gloss	1964	1966	100.00	200.00	350.00
White (small eyes)	Gloss	1956	1963	40.00	65.00	90.00
White (large eyes)	Gloss	1963	1989	30.00	50.00	65.00
White	Matt	1984	1989	40.00	65.00	90.00

Note: Transferred to the R.D. backstamp (DA123) 08/89 in ginger, grey, white - gloss.

Model No. 1437
CAT - Seated, looking up

Designer: Colin Melbourne
Height: 3 ¼", 8.3 cm
Colours: Grey striped - gloss
Issued: 1956-1963

Description	U.K. £	Price U.S. $	Can. $
Grey striped	200.00	350.00	425.00

Model No. 1438
CAT - Standing, looking back

Designer: Colin Melbourne
Height: 3 ¾", 9.5 cm
Colours: Grey striped - gloss
Issued: 1956-1963

Description	U.K. £	Price U.S. $	Can. $
Grey striped	200.00	375.00	475.00

Photograph not
available at press time

Model No. 1541
CAT - Seated

Designer: Mr. Garbet
Height: Unknown
Colours: Unknown
Issued: 1958-1961

Description	U.K. £	U.S. $	Can. $
Extremely Rare			

Photograph not
available at press time

Model No. 1542
CAT - Lying, left front paw up

Designer: Mr. Garbet
Height: Unknown
Colours: Unknown
Issued: 1958-1961

Description	U.K. £	U.S. $	Can. $
Extremely Rare			

Model No. 1543
CAT - Seated, left front paw up

Designer: Mr. Garbet
Height: Unknown
Colours: Dark pewter- Satin gloss
Issued: 1958-1961

Description	U.K. £	U.S. $	Can. $
Satin gloss		Extremely Rare	

Model No. 1558A
SIAMESE CAT - Lying, facing left
First Version -
Puffed out cheeks, short neck, fleshy body

Designer: Pal Zalmen
Length: 7 ¼", 18.4 cm
Colours: Chocolate point - gloss
Issued: 1958-c.1963

Description	U.K. £	U.S. $	Can. $
Gloss	85.00	150.00	200.00

Model No. 1558B
SIAMESE CAT - Lying, facing left
Second Version -
Sleek, tapering face, long neck and body

Designer: Pal Zalmen
Remodelled: Albert Hallam
Length: 7 ¼", 18.4 cm
Colours: 1. Seal point - gloss or matt
              2. Copper lustre - gloss
Issued: 1a. Gloss - c.1963-1989
              1b. Matt - 1984-1989
              2.   1971 (export only)

Description	U.K. £	U.S. $	Can. $
1a. Gloss	40.00	70.00	95.00
1b. Matt	50.00	85.00	115.00
2. Copper lustre	100.00	175.00	125.00

Note: Transferred to R.D. backstamp (DA124) 08/89,
         in seal point - gloss.

Model No. 1559A
SIAMESE CAT - Lying, facing right
Version One -
Puffed out cheeks, short neck, fleshy body

Designer: Pal Zalmen
Length: 7 ¼", 18.4 cm
Colours: Chocolate point - gloss
Issued: 1958-c.1963

Description	U.K. £	U.S. $	Can. $
Gloss	85.00	150.00	200.00

Model No. 1559B
SIAMESE CAT - Lying, facing right
Version Two -
Sleek, tapering face, long neck and body

Designer: Pal Zalmen
Remodelled: Albert Hallam
Length: 7 ¼", 18.4 cm
Colours: 1. Seal Point - gloss or matt
         2. Copper lustre - gloss
Issued: 1a. Gloss - c.1963-1989
         1b. Matt - 1984-1989
         2. Gloss - 1971 (export only)

Description	U.K. £	U.S. $	Can. $
1a. Gloss	40.00	70.00	95.00
1b. Matt	50.00	85.00	115.00
2. Copper lustre	100.00	175.00	225.00

Note: Transferred to R.D. backstamp (DA125) 08/89, seal point - gloss.

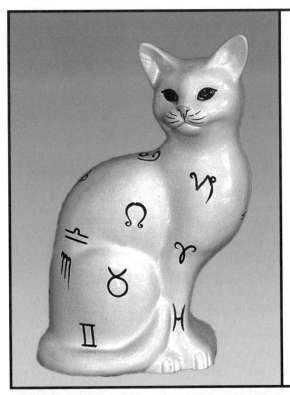

Model No. 1560
ZODIAC CAT - Seated, facing right

Designer: Pal Zalmen
Length: 11", 27.9 cm
Colours: 1.   Black - gloss
             2.   White with zodiac symbols - gloss
Issued: 1958-1967
Set: Stylized model forming a pair with 1561

Description	U.K. £	U.S. $	Can. $
1. Black	275.00	475.00	600.00
2. White	225.00	425.00	550.00

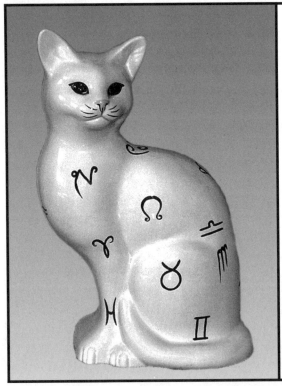

Model No. 1561
ZODIAC CAT - Seated, facing left

Designer: Pal Zalmen
Length: 11", 27.9 cm
Colours: 1.   Black - gloss
             2.   White with zodiac symbols - gloss
Issued: 1958-1967
Set: Stylized model forming a pair with 1560

Description	U.K. £	U.S. $	Can. $
1. Black	275.00	475.00	600.00
2. White	225.00	425.00	550.00

Model No. 1677
SIAMESE CAT - Climbing

Designer: Albert Hallam
Length: 6 ½", 16.5 cm
Colours: Seal point - gloss
Issued: 1960-1997

Description	U.K. £	U.S. $	Can. $
Gloss	15.00	30.00	40.00

Model No. 1803
CAT - Seated, looking up

Designer: Albert Hallam
Height: 1 ¼", 3.2 cm
Colours: Ginger striped - gloss
Issued: 1962-1971
Series: Bedtime Chorus

Description	U.K. £	U.S. $	Can. $
Gloss	55.00	125.00	175.00

Photograph not
available at press time

Model No. 1857
SIAMESE CAT - Climbing

Designer: Albert Hallam
Length: 5 ½", 14.0 cm
Colours: Seal point - gloss
Issued: 1962-Unknown

Description	U.K. £	U.S. $	Can. $
	Extremely Rare		

Note: Similar in shape to model no. 1677.

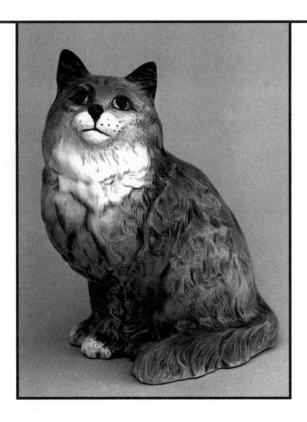

Model No. 1867
PERSIAN CAT - Seated, looking up

Designer: Albert Hallam
Height: 8 ½", 21.6 cm

Colourway	Finish	Intro.	Disc.	U.K. £	Price U.S. $	Can. $
Black	Matt	1984	1989	60.00	100.00	135.00
British Blue (lead grey)	Gloss	1964	1966	225.00	425.00	600.00
Ginger	Matt	1984	1989	70.00	115.00	160.00
Ginger (dark)	Gloss	1963	1970	70.00	115.00	160.00
Ginger striped	Gloss	1965	1989	150.00	250.00	335.00
Ginger Swiss roll	Gloss	1964	1966	175.00	400.00	575.00
Grey (shaded)	Gloss	1963	1989	55.00	90.00	125.00
Grey	Matt	1984	1989	70.00	115.00	160.00
Grey striped	Gloss	1963	1973	160.00	275.00	350.00
Grey Swiss roll	Gloss	1964	1966	225.00	425.00	600.00
White (large eyes)	Gloss	1963	1989	55.00	95.00	125.00
White	Matt	1984	1989	60.00	100.00	135.00

Note: Transferred to R.D. backstamp (DA126) 08/89, in ginger, grey and white gloss.

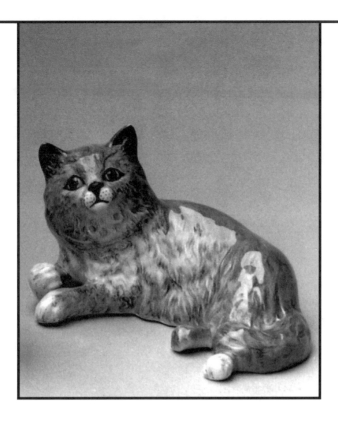

Model No. 1876
PERSIAN CAT - Lying

Designer: Albert Hallam
Height: 3 ½" x 6 ½", 8.0 x 6.5 cm

Colourway	Finish	Intro.	Disc.	U.K. £	Price U.S. $	Can. $
British Blue (lead grey)	Gloss	1964	1966	250.00	500.00	650.00
Ginger (dark)	Gloss	1963	1970	150.00	250.00	325.00
Ginger striped	Gloss	1965	1971	160.00	275.00	350.00
Ginger Swiss roll	Gloss	1964	1966	225.00	450.00	600.00
Grey (shaded)	Gloss	1963	1971	110.00	190.00	250.00
Grey striped	Gloss	1963	1971	160.00	275.00	350.00
Grey Swiss roll	Gloss	1964	1966	275.00	550.00	750.00
White (large eyes)	Gloss	1963	1971	110.00	190.00	250.00

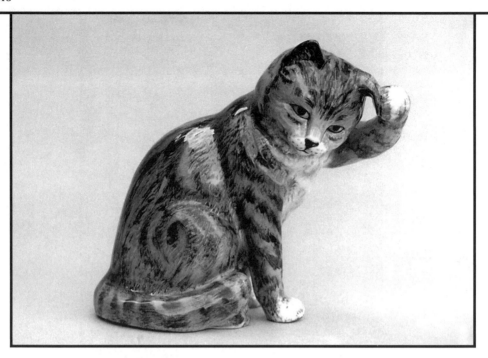

Model No. 1877
CAT - Seated, scratching ear

Designer: Albert Hallam
Height: 6 ½", 16.5 cm

Colourway	Finish	Intro.	Disc.	U.K. £	Price U.S. $	Can. $
British Blue (lead grey)	Gloss	1964	1966	350.00	600.00	800.00
Ginger (dark)	Gloss	1963	1970	160.00	275.00	350.00
Ginger striped	Gloss	1965	1971	230.00	375.00	500.00
Ginger Swiss roll	Gloss	1964	1966	325.00	600.00	800.00
Grey (shaded)	Gloss	1963	1971	150.00	250.00	330.00
Grey striped	Gloss	1963	1971	275.00	450.00	600.00
Grey Swiss roll	Gloss	1964	1966	375.00	650.00	850.00
White (large eyes)	Gloss	1963	1971	150.00	220.00	300.00

Model No. 1880
PERSIAN CAT - Seated, looking up

Designer: Albert Hallam
Height: 5 ¼", 13.3 cm

Colourway	Finish	Intro.	Disc.	U.K. £	Price U.S. $	Can. $
British Blue (lead grey)	Gloss	1964	1966	200.00	375.00	500.00
Ginger (dark)	Gloss	1963	1970	150.00	250.00	330.00
Ginger striped	Gloss	1965	1971	165.00	275.00	375.00
Ginger Swiss roll	Gloss	1964	1966	200.00	400.00	550.00
Grey (shaded)	Gloss	1963	1971	135.00	225.00	300.00
Grey striped	Gloss	1963	1971	165.00	275.00	375.00
Grey Swiss roll	Gloss	1964	1966	215.00	450.00	600.00
White (large eyes)	Gloss	1963	1971	115.00	200.00	260.00

Model No. 1882
SIAMESE CAT - Seated, head forward

Designer: Albert Hallam
Height: 9 ½″, 24.0 cm
Series: Fireside Model

Colourway	Finish	Intro.	Disc.	U.K. £	Price U.S. $	Can. $
Black	Gloss	1986	1989	75.00	135.00	200.00
Black	Matt	1986	1989	85.00	160.00	225.00
Copper lustre	Gloss	1971	1971	175.00	300.00	400.00
Seal point	Gloss	1963	1989	80.00	135.00	185.00
Seal point	Matt	1984	1989	90.00	160.00	200.00

Note: 1. Transferred to R.D. backstamp (DA127) 08/89, seal point - gloss.
2. Copper lustre issued for export only.

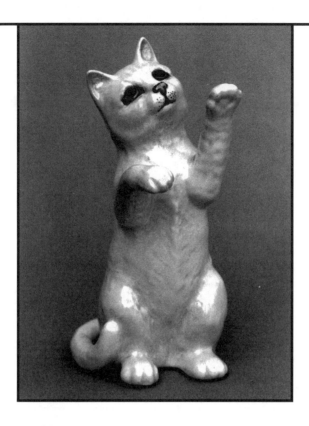

Model No. 1883
PERSIAN CAT - On hind legs

Designer: Albert Hallam
Height: 6", 15.0 cm

Colourway	Finish	Intro.	Disc.	U.K. £	Price U.S. $	Can. $
British Blue (lead grey)	Gloss	1964	1966	250.00	475.00	650.00
Ginger (dark)	Gloss	1963	1970	150.00	250.00	350.00
Ginger striped	Gloss	1965	1971	165.00	275.00	400.00
Ginger Swiss roll	Gloss	1964	1966	225.00	400.00	600.00
Grey (shaded)	Gloss	1963	1971	135.00	225.00	300.00
Grey striped	Gloss	1963	1971	165.00	275.00	400.00
Grey Swiss roll	Gloss	1964	1966	250.00	475.00	650.00
White (large eyes)	Gloss	1963	1971	120.00	200.00	275.00

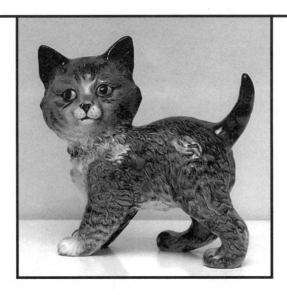

Model No. 1885
PERSIAN KITTEN - Standing

Designer: Albert Hallam
Height: 4 ¾″, 12.1 cm

Colourway	Finish	Intro.	Disc.	U.K. £	Price U.S. $	Can. $
British Blue (lead grey)	Gloss	1964	1966	225.00	375.00	500.00
Ginger (dark)	Gloss	1963	1970	100.00	175.00	225.00
Ginger striped	Gloss	1965	1973	120.00	200.00	275.00
Ginger Swiss roll	Gloss	1964	1966	175.00	325.00	450.00
Grey (shaded)	Gloss	1963	1973	100.00	175.00	225.00
Grey striped	Gloss	1963	1973	135.00	225.00	300.00
Grey Swiss roll	Gloss	1964	1966	225.00	375.00	500.00
White (large eyes)	Gloss	1963	1973	90.00	150.00	200.00

Model 1880
Persian Cat
Ginger (dark)

Model 1030
Cat
Grey (smokey blue)

Model 1880
Persian Cat
British Blue (lead grey)

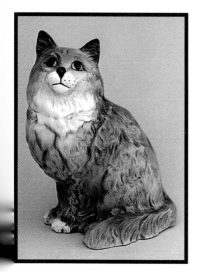

Model 1867
Persian Cat
Grey (shaded)

Model 1031
Cat
Grey striped

Model 1031
Cat
Ginger striped

Model 1437
Cat
Grey striped

Model 1296
Siamese Kittens
Chocolate point, Seal point

Model 1885
Persian Kitten
Grey Swiss roll

Model 1436
Kitten
Ginger (pale)

Model 1883
Persian Cat
White (large eyes)

Top Row: Models 1877 and 1876 Grey Swiss roll
Bottom Row: Model 1886 Grey Swiss roll

Top Row: Models 1882, 2139, 1897 Seal Point
Middle Row: Model 1296 Chocolate Point; 1887 Seal Point
Bottom Row: Model 1559 and 1558 Chocolate Point

Top Row: Models 1885 Ginger (pale)
1436, 1031 Ginger (pale) and ginger stripe
Bottom Row: Models 1883 Ginger Swiss roll
1316, 1886 Ginger (dark) 1886 Ginger Swiss roll
and Ginger striped

Top Row: Model 1030, Grey stripe, Grey (Smokey blue)
Centre Row: 1031 White (large eyes), (small eyes)
Bottom Row: Model 1031 Grey striped,
Ginger striped, Grey (smokey blue)

WHITE
Top Row: Models 1898, 1560, 1880
Middle Row: Models 1031, 1877, 1883, 1886
Bottom Row: Models 1559, 1436, 1885, 1876

BRITISH BLUE (lead grey)
Top Row: Models 1880, 1885
Bottom Row: Model 1883

GREY STRIPED
Top Row: Models 1438, 1435
Middle Row: Models 1437, 1316
Bottom Row: 1436, 1030, 1031, 1436

GREY STRIPED AND GREY SWISS ROLL
Top Row: Models 1898, 1885 Grey striped
Bottom Row: Model 1883 Grey striped
and Models 1867, 1876 Grey Swiss roll

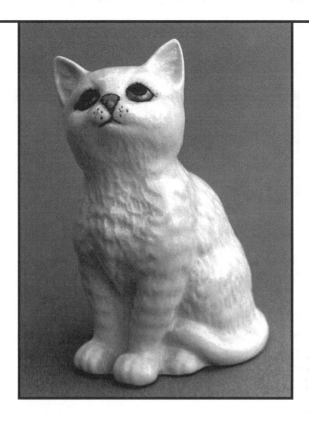

Model No 1886
PERSIAN CAT - Seated, looking up

Designer: Albert Hallam
Height: 4", 10.1 cm

Colourway	Finish	Intro.	Disc.	U.K. £	Price U.S. $	Can. $
Black	Matt	1984	1989	40.00	65.00	90.00
British Blue (lead grey)	Gloss	1964	1966	100.00	200.00	275.00
Ginger	Matt	1984	1989	35.00	60.00	75.00
Ginger (dark)	Gloss	1963	1970	35.00	60.00	75.00
Ginger striped	Gloss	1965	1989	55.00	95.00	125.00
Ginger Swiss roll	Gloss	1964	1966	85.00	175.00	250.00
Grey	Matt	1984	1989	50.00	80.00	110.00
Grey (shaded)	Gloss	1965	1989	35.00	60.00	75.00
Grey striped	Gloss	1962	1973	60.00	100.00	125.00
Grey Swiss roll	Gloss	1964	1966	100.00	200.00	275.00
White (large eyes)	Gloss	1963	1989	30.00	50.00	70.00
White	Matt	1984	1989	25.00	45.00	60.00

Note: Transferred to R.D. backstamp (DA128) 08/89 in ginger, grey and white - gloss.

Model No. 1887
SIAMESE CAT - Seated, head turned back

Designer: Albert Hallam
Height: 4", 10.1 cm

Colourway	Finish	Intro.	Disc.	U.K. £	Price U.S. $	Can. $
Copper lustre	Gloss	1971	1971	90.00	150.00	200.00
Seal point	Gloss	1971	1989	25.00	50.00	65.00
Seal point	Matt	1984	1989	30.00	60.00	75.00

Note: 1. Transferred to R.D. backstamp (DA129) 08/89, in seal point - gloss.
2. Copper lustre produced for export only.

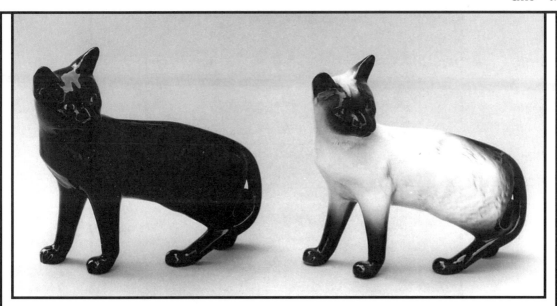

Model No. 1897
SIAMESE CAT - Standing

Designer: Albert Hallam
Height: 6 ½", 16.5 cm
Series: Fireside Model

Colourway	Finish	Intro.	Disc.	U.K. £	Price U.S. $	Can. $
Black	Gloss	1987	1989	60.00	100.00	130.00
Black	Matt	1987	1989	65.00	110.00	150.00
Copper lustre	Gloss	1971	1971	175.00	300.00	400.00
Seal point	Gloss	1963	1980	35.00	60.00	80.00
Seal point	Matt	1984	1989	45.00	75.00	100.00

Note: 1. In 1987 introduced as "Lucky Black Cat."
2. Transferred to R.D. backstamp 08/89, in seal point (DA 130) and black (DA131) - gloss.
3. Copper lustre produced for export only.

Model No. 1898
PERSIAN CAT - Standing, tail erect

Designer: Albert Hallam
Height: 5", 12.7 cm

Colourway	Finish	Intro.	Disc.	U.K. £	Price U.S. $	Can. $
Black	Matt	1984	1989	35.00	60.00	80.00
British Blue (lead grey)	Gloss	1964	1966	175.00	300.00	400.00
Ginger	Matt	1984	1989	65.00	110.00	150.00
Ginger striped	Gloss	1965	1989	60.00	100.00	130.00
Ginger Swiss roll	Gloss	1964	1966	175.00	300.00	400.00
Grey	Matt	1984	1989	40.00	65.00	90.00
Grey (shaded)	Gloss	1963	1989	35.00	60.00	80.00
Grey Swiss roll	Gloss	1964	1966	200.00	330.00	450.00
White (large eyes)	Gloss	1963	1989	40.00	65.00	90.00
White	Matt	1984	1989	45.00	75.00	100.00

Note: Transferred to R.D. backstamp (DA132) 08/89, in ginger, grey and white - gloss.

Model No. 2100
CAT WITH MOUSE

Designer:	Albert Hallam	
Height:	3", 7.6 cm	
Colours:	Brown cat, white mouse - gloss	
Issued:	1967-1973	
Series:	Fun Models	

Description	U.K. £	U.S. $	Can. $
Gloss	95.00	170.00	225.00

Model No. 2101
CAT - Laughing

Designer:	Albert Hallam
Height:	3", 7.6 cm
Colours:	Grey - gloss
Issued:	1967-1973
Series:	Fun Models

Description	U.K. £	U.S. $	Can. $
Gloss	95.00	150.00	200.00

Model No. 2139
SIAMESE CAT - Seated, head up

Designer:	Mr. Garbet	
Height:	13 ¾", 34.9 cm	
Colours:	1.	Seal point - gloss
	2.	Copper lustre
Issued:	1.	1967-1989
	2.	1971 (export only)
Series:	Fireside Models	

Description	U.K. £	U.S. $	Can. $
1. Gloss	75.00	150.00	200.00
2. Copper lustre	150.00	275.00	375.00

Note: Transferred to (DA83) 08/89, in seal point - gloss.

Model No. 2156/2157
CAT CRUET, SALT AND PEPPER

Designer:	Unknown
Height:	5 ½", 14.0 cm
Colours:	Black cat (pepper), white cat (salt) - gloss
Issued:	1967-1969

Description	U.K.£	U.S.$	Can.$
Black	40.00	75.00	100.00
White	40.00	75.00	100.00

Model No. 2233
CAT AND DOG WALL PLAQUE
Cat left, dog right

Designer:	Graham Tongue		
Height:	9" x 6 ¼", 23 x 15.9 cm (Concave)		
Colours:	Unknown - gloss		
Issued:	1968-Unknown		
Series:	Wall Plaques		

Description	U.K.£	U.S.$	Can.$
Gloss	75.00	150.00	225.00

Model No. 2236
CAT WALL PLAQUE

Designer:	Graham Tongue		
Height:	9" x 6 ¼", 23 x 15.9 cm (Concave)		
Colours:	Ginger cat with yellow eyes on dark pewter background - gloss		
Issued:	1968-Unknown		
Series:	Wall Plaques		

Description	U.K.£	U.S.$	Can.$
Gloss	75.00	125.00	175.00

Photograph not
available at press time

Photograph not
available at press time

Model No. 2301
CAT - Climbing

Designer:	Albert Hallam
Height:	4 ½", 11.9 cm
Colours:	Unknown
Issued:	1969-Unknown

Description	U.K. £	U.S. $	Can. $
	Extremely Rare		

Note: Similar to model no. 1677. Possibly not issued.

Model No. 2311
SIAMESE CAT

Designer:	Graham Tongue
Length:	1 ½", 3.8 cm
Colours:	Unknown
Issued:	1970-Unknown

Description	U.K. £	U.S. $	Can. $
	Extremely rare		

Note: Similar to model no. 2139. Possibly not issued.

Model No. 2480
CHESHIRE CAT

Designer:	Graham Tongue
Height:	1 ½", 3.8 cm
Colours:	Tabby - gloss
Issued:	1973-1982
Series:	Alice in Wonderland

Description	U.K. £	U.S. $	Can. $
Gloss	475.00	800.00	1,000.00

Note: For the rest of the pieces in the Alice in Wonderland series see *The Charlton Standard Catalogue of Royal Doulton Beswick Storybook Figurines*.

Model No. 2761
CAT ON CHIMNEY POT - Salt and pepper

Designer:	Unknown
Height:	4", 10.1 cm
Colours:	White and gold - gloss
Issued:	1982-1985
Series:	Fun Models

Description	U.K. £	U.S. $	Can. $
Gloss	90.00	150.00	175.00

Model No. 2805
CAT ON POST BOX - Money Box

Designer:	Unknown
Height:	6 ¼", 15.9 cm
Colours:	White cat on red post box - gloss
Issued:	1983-1986
Series:	Fun Models

Description	U.K. £	U.S. $	Can. $
Gloss	75.00	100.00	125.00

Model No. 2810
CAT EGG CUP

Designer:	Unknown
Height:	2 ½", 6.4 cm
Colours:	Ginger kitten with white egg cup - gloss
Issued:	1983-1986
Series:	Fun Models

Description	U.K. £	U.S. $	Can. $
Gloss	50.00	75.00	100.00

Model No. 3012
SPORTING CAT

Designer:	Warren Platt
Length:	4 ¼", 10.8 cm
Colours:	1.Cat dressed as a soccer player with striped jersey; black, blue, burgundy, red, yellow
	2.Cat dressed as a soccer player with plain jersey; black, blue, burgundy, red, yellow
Modelled:	1986
Issued:	1987-1987
Series:	Fun Models

		Price		
Colourways	Finish	U.K. £	U.S. $	Can. $
Black stripe	Gloss	60.00	100.00	125.00
Black	Gloss	60.00	100.00	125.00
Blue stripe	Gloss	60.00	100.00	125.00
Blue	Gloss	60.00	100.00	125.00
Burgundy stripe	Gloss	60.00	100.00	125.00
Burgundy	Gloss	60.00	100.00	125.00
Red stripe	Gloss	60.00	100.00	125.00
Red	Gloss	60.00	100.00	125.00
Yellow stripe	Gloss	60.00	100.00	125.00
Yellow	Gloss	60.00	100.00	125.00

Note: Introduced as a trial in August 1987, but not put into general production, although many sets were sold from the factory shop.

Chapter Four

DOGS

Beswick produced mantelpiece dogs of the old Staffordshire type from about 1898. In 1933, when the shape book was created — in which each model was illustrated by a sketch with details such as height, modeller and dates — these dogs, in various sizes, were the initial numbers. During the 1930s dogs of the novelty type were produced with several unrealistic-looking decorations, including blue and green gloss and mottled blue in a satin-type finish. In fact customers could order novelties in any decoration to match the domestic ware being made at the time. Then in 1941, Arthur Gredington, following his success with realistic models of horses, created the first of the champion dogs, the Dalmatian "Arnoldene," shape number 961. Seven other breeds were also produced in 1941, and four more the following year. These figures were all modelled in a show stance from champions of their particular breed, and almost all of them were modelled by Arthur Gredington.

Over the years most of the popular breeds joined the Beswick "kennel," and many were also produced in a smaller size. Action poses were added to the collection, such as the 1507 Spaniel running. This type of model was reintroduced with the Good Companions series in 1987, the same time several more medium-sized dogs were issued. These and the Good Companions, had a short production run with the Beswick backstamp (some for less than a year), as from August 1989 they were issued with Royal Doulton backstamps and given DA numbers. By 1994 all the Beswick medium-sized dogs had been withdrawn, leaving only the small dogs collection with Beswick backstamps.

Many of the dogs share with the horses the distinction of being in continual production for four or five decades. During this time there has been a deterioration in the moulds and decorating processes; therefore, the quality of the models is variable. It is well worth looking out for the older figures that exhibit more mould detail and toning and shading in colour.

The dogs collection also includes some of Beswick's largest models; the seated Fireside models range from the 2377 Yorkshire Terrier at 10 ¼" to the 13 ½" 2314 Labrador. At the other extreme is the tiny 1 ½" singing dog from the Bedtime Chorus set, a very elusive little fellow.

INDEX BY MODEL NUMBER

Model No.	Description	Page No.	Model No.	Description	Page No.
1 to 6	Old Staffordshire Dogs	96	1242	Dog - Barking	114
87	Dog Standing in Armchair - Bookend	97	1294	Poodle "Ebonit av Barbett"	114
88	Scottie -Ashtray	97	1299A	Corgi "Black Prince" - Large	114
171	Dog - Begging	97	1299B	Corgi - Large	114
286	Dog - Seated	98	1378	Old English Dogs	115
301	Sealyham Plaque - Bow on right	98	1386	Poodle	116
302	Sealyham - Standing	98	1460	Dachshund - Seated	117
307	Sealyham Plaque	98	1461	Dachshund - Begging	117
308	Puppy - Seated	99	1548	Labrador "Solomon of Wendover" - Large	118
324	Character Dog - Begging	99	1731	Bulldog "Bosun" - Small	119
361	Dachshund - Standing	100	1736	Corgi - Small	119
373	Sealyham Plaque	100	1738	Pup with Bone	119
453	Old English Sheepdog - Seated	100	1753	Bull Terrier - Small	119
454	Lollopy Dog - Seated Puppy	100	1754	Cocker Spaniel	120
624	Dog - Toothbrush Holder	101	1762A	Alsatian, First Version - Small	121
668	Dog Plaque	101	1762B	Alsatian, Second Version - Small	121
761	Dog with Toothache	101	1763	Dalmatian - Small	121
804	Dog with Ladybird on Nose	101	1786A	Whippet "Winged Foot Marksman of	121
805	Dog with Ladybird on Tail	102		Allways," First Version	
810	Bulldog with Sailor's Hat - Ashtray	102	1786B	Whippet "Winged Foot Marksman of	122
811	Dog Playing Accordion	102		Allways," Second Version	
812	Dog Asleep on Drum	102	1791	Collie "Lochinvar Of Ladypark" - Large	122
813	Dog with Ladybird on Nose	103	1792	Sheepdog - Large	122
831	Dog with Glasses Reading a Book	103	1814	Collie - Small	122
869	Five Puppy Ashtray	103	1824	Dog - Singing	123
907	Dog with Ladybird on Tail	103	1852	Boxer - Small	123
916	Three Puppy Ashtray	104	1854	Sheepdog - Small	123
917	Three Puppies	104	1855	Retriever	123
941	Foxhound, First Version	104	1871	Poodle	124
942	Foxhound, First Version	104	1872	Bulldog	124
943	Foxhound, First Version	105	1918	Ashtray with Dog	124
944	Foxhound, First Version	105	1932	Dachshund - Ashtray	124
961	Dalmatian "Arnoldene" - Large	105	1933A	Beagle "Wendover Billy" - Large	125
962	Airedale Terrier "Cast Iron Monarch"	105	1933B	Beagle "Wendover Billy" - on plinth	125
963	Wire-haired Terrier	106	1939	Beagle "Wendover Billy" - Small	125
	"Talavera Romulus"		1944	Yorkshire Terrier - Lying	125
964	Smooth-haired Terrier	106	1956	Labrador - Small	126
	"Endon Black Rod"		1982A	Staffordshire Bull Terrier,	127
965	Bulldog "Basford British Mascot" - Large	106		"Bandits Brintiga"	
966	Irish Setter "Sugar of Wendover"	106	1982B	Staffordshire Bull Terrier	127
967	Cocker Spaniel "Horseshoe Primula"	107	1990	Old English Sheepdog	127
968	Great Dane "Ruler of Oubourgh"	108	1997	Pug "Cutmil Cutie" - Large	128
969	Alsatian "Ulrica of Brittas" - Large	108	1998	Pug - Small	128
970	Bull Terrier "Romany Rhinestone"	108	2023	Jack Russell Terrier - Large	128
	- Large		2037	Scottie	128
971	Sealyham "Forestedge Foxglove"	108	2038	West Highland Terrier	129
972	Greyhound "Jovial Roger"	109	2045A	Basset Hound "Fochno Trinket"	129
973	English Setter "Bayldone Baronet"	109	2045B	Basset Hound "Fochno Trinket"	129
1002	Puppit Dog	109		on plinth	
1054	Spaniel Holding "My Plate"	110	2102	Yorkshire Terrier Laughing	129
1055A	Cairn Terrier, First Version	110	2107A	King Charles Spaniel "Blenheim"	130
	- With ball on left leg		2107B	King Charles Spaniel	130
1055B	Cairn Terrier, Second Version	110		"Josephine of Blagreaves"	
	- Without ball		2108	Poodle "Ivanola Gold Digger"	130
1057	Spaniel - Running	111	2109	Jack Russel Terrier - Small	130
1058	Dog with Collar "Scamp"	111	2112	Cairn Terrier	131
1059	Pekinese - Begging	111	2130	Dog Praying	131
1060	Red Setter - Lying	111	2221	St. Bernard "Corna Garth Stroller"	131
1061	Terrier - Lying	112	2232	Old English Sheepdog	131
1062	Terrier - Walking	112	2235	Bassethound - Wall Plaque	132
1088	Comical Dachshund	112	2262	Foxhound, Second Version	132
1202	Boxer "Blue Mountain Greta" - Large	112	2263	Foxhound, Second Version	132
1220	English Setter	113	2264	Foxhound, Second Version	133
1239	Dog with Ruff - Begging	113	2265	Foxhound, Second Version	133
1240	Dog - Seated	113	2268	Poodle - Wall Plaque	133
1241	Dog - Howling	113	2271	Dalmatian	133

Model Nos. 1 to 6 OLD STAFFORDSHIRE DOGS

Designer: Unknown
Colours: Unknown
Issued: 1933-1955
Series: Mantelpiece Dogs

Model No.	1	2	3	4	5	6
Height:	13 ¾", 34.9 cm	11 ½", 29.2 cm	10", 25.4 cm	9", 22.9 cm	7 ½", 19.1 cm	5 ½", 14.0 cm

Price	Model No. 1	Model No. 2	Model No. 3	Model No. 4	Model No. 5	Model No. 6
U.K. £	85.00	75.00	65.00	55.00	45.00	35.00
U.S. $	150.00	130.00	115.00	95.00	75.00	60.00
Can. $	200.00	175.00	150.00	125.00	100.00	80.00

Note: Prices above are for singles, they are available in pairs, left and right facing.

Model No. 87
DOG STANDING IN ARMCHAIR - Bookend

Designer: Unknown
Height: 7", 18.0 cm
Colours: See below
Issued: 1934-by 1966
Series: Fun Models

Description	U.K. £	U.S. $	Can. $
1. Various	85.00	150.00	225.00
2. Blue	100.00	200.00	300.00
3. White	85.00	150.00	225.00

Note: Prices are for single bookends.

Model No. 88
SCOTTIE - Ashtray

Designer: Unknown
Height: 3 ¼", 8.3 cm
Colours: 1. Various - satin matt
            2. Blue - gloss
            3. White - matt
Issued: 1934-1965

Description	U.K. £	U.S. $	Can. $
1. Various	25.00	50.00	75.00
2. Blue	25.00	50.00	75.00
3. White	30.00	50.00	75.00

Model No. 171
DOG - Begging

Designer: Unknown
Height: 4 ¾", 12.1 cm
Colours: White and tan - gloss
Issued: 1934-by 1954

Description	U.K. £	U.S. $	Can. $
Gloss	60.00	125.00	175.00

Model No. 286
DOG - Seated

Designer: Mr. Watkin
Height: 6 ¼", 15.9 cm
Colours: 1. White and tan - gloss
2. Blue - gloss
Issued: 1. 1934-1967
2. 1934-by 1954

Description	U.K. £	U.S. $	Can. $
1. White/tan	30.00	120.00	250.00
2. Blue	75.00	120.00	275.00

Model No. 301
SEALYHAM PLAQUE - Bow on right

Designer: Unknown
Height: 7 ½", 19.1 cm
Colours: Cream, blue bow - satin finish
Issued: 1936-1940
Series: Wall Plaques

Description	U.K. £	U.S. $	Can. $
Satin finish	80.00	295.00	375.00

Photograph not
available at press time

Model No. 302
SEALYHAM - Standing

Designer: Mr. Watkin
Height: 6", 15.0 cm
Colours: 1. White with dark ears - gloss
2. Blue - gloss
Issued: 1. 1936-1967
2. 1936-by 1964

Description	U.K. £	U.S. $	Can. $
1. White/dark ears	35.00	250.00	300.00
2. Blue	85.00	300.00	300.00

Model No. 307
SEALYHAM PLAQUE

Designer: Mr. Watkin
Height: 7", 17.8 cm
Colours: Cream - satin finish
Issued: 1935-1940
Series: Wall Plaques

Description	U.K. £	U.S. $	Can. $
Satin finish	80.00	295.00	375.00

Note: Similar to No. 301, but dog's left ear is up and the right ear is down.

Model No. 308
PUPPY - Seated

Designer:	Mr. Watkin	
Height:	6 ¼", 15.9 cm	
Colours:	1.	White with brown ears - gloss
	2.	Blue - gloss
Issued:	1.	1935-1967
	2.	1935-by 1954

Description	U.K. £	U.S. $	Can. $
1. White/brown	35.00	150.00	225.00
2. Blue	75.00	175.00	225.00

Note: Also issued as a money-box.

Model No. 324
Character Dog - Begging

Designer:	Miss Greaves	
Height:	7", 17.8 cm	
Colours:	1.	Cream - gloss
	2.	Blue - gloss
Issued:	1.	1936-by 1954
	2.	1936-by 1954
Series:	Fun Models	

Description	U.K. £	U.S. $	Can. $
1. Cream	85.00	150.00	250.00
2. Blue	120.00	200.00	300.00

Photograph not
available at press time

Model No. 361
DACHSHUND - Standing

Designer:	Mr. Watkin
Height:	5 ½", 14.0 cm
Colours:	1. Black/tan - gloss 2. Tan - gloss
	3. Blue - gloss
Issued:	1. 1936-1983 2. 1936-1983
	3. 1936-by 1954

Description	U.K. £	U.S. $	Can. $
1. Black/tan	35.00	120.00	150.00
2. Tan	35.00	120.00	150.00
3. Blue	90.00	170.00	220.00

Model No. 373
SEALYHAM PLAQUE

Designer:	Unknown
Height:	7", 17.8 cm
Colours:	White dog with blue bow - satin matt
Issued:	1936-1940
Series:	Wall Plaques

Description	U.K. £	U.S. $	Can. $
White dog	80.00	295.00	375.00

Model No. 453
OLD ENGLISH SHEEPDOG - Seated

Designer:	Unknown
Height:	8 ½", 21.6 cm
Colours:	1. Grey and white - gloss
	2. Blue - gloss
Issued:	1. 1936-1973
	2. 1936-by 1954

Description	U.K. £	U.S. $	Can. $
1. Grey/white	85.00	275.00	375.00
2. Blue	120.00	300.00	425.00

Model No. 454
LOLLOPY DOG - Seated Puppy

Designer:	Miss Greaves
Height:	4 ¼", 10.8 cm
Colours:	1. Various - satin matt
	2. Blue - gloss
	3. White - matt
Issued:	1. 1936-by 1954 2. 1936-1969
	3. 1936-1969

Description	U.K. £	U.S. $	Can. $
1. Various	25.00	70.00	60.00
2. Blue	20.00	70.00	50.00
3. White	25.00	70.00	60.00

Model No. 624
DOG- Toothbrush holder

Designer:	Miss Catford
Height:	4", 10.1 cm
Colours:	1. Various - satin matt
	2. Blue - gloss
	3. White - matt
Issued:	1938-by 1954

Description	U.K. £	U.S. $	Can. $
1. Various	150.00	300.00	350.00
2. Blue	150.00	300.00	350.00
3. White	150.00	300.00	350.00

Model No. 668
DOG PLAQUE

Designer:	Mr. Symcox
Height:	11", 27.9 cm
Colours:	Deep red brown - gloss
Issued:	1938-1960
Series:	Wall Plaques

Description	U.K. £	U.S. $	Can. $
Gloss	150.00	295.00	375.00

Model No. 761
DOG WITH TOOTHACHE

Designer:	Mr. Watkin
Height:	4 ¼", 10.8 cm
Colours:	1. White dog with red kerchief - gloss
	2. White dog with green kerchief - gloss
Issued:	1939-1971
Series:	Fun Models

Description	U.K. £	U.S. $	Can. $
1. Red kerchief	65.00	100.00	200.00
2. Green kerchief	85.00	125.00	250.00

Model No. 804
DOG WITH LADYBIRD ON NOSE

Designer:	Mr. Watkin
Height:	4", 10.1 cm
Colours:	White with red ladybird - gloss
Issued:	1940-1969
Series:	Fun Models

Description	U.K. £	U.S. $	Can. $
Gloss	45.00	100.00	135.00

Model No. 805
DOG WITH LADYBIRD ON TAIL

Designer:	Mr. Watkin
Height:	1. Large - 3 ¾", 9.5 cm
	2. Small - 2 ½", 6.4 cm
Colours:	White dog with red ladybird - gloss
Issued:	1940-1969
Series:	Fun Models

Description	U.K. £	U.S. $	Can. $
1. Large	35.00	70.00	80.00
2. Small	25.00	50.00	50.00

Model No. 810
BULLDOG WITH SAILOR'S HAT - Ashtray

Designer:	Arthur Gredington
Height:	4", 10.1 cm
Colours:	White dog, white sailor cap with blue band, biscuit coloured base - gloss
Issued:	1940-by 1954

Description	U.K. £	U.S. $	Can. $
Gloss	150.00	275.00	400.00

Model No. 811
DOG PLAYING ACCORDION

Designer:	Mr. Watkin
Height:	4", 10.1 cm
Colours:	White dog with green and brown accordion - gloss
Issued:	1940-1970

Description	U.K. £	U.S. $	Can. $
Gloss	65.00	100.00	175.00

Model No. 812
DOG ASLEEP ON DRUM

Designer:	Mr. Watkin
Height:	3", 7.6 cm
Colours:	White dog, yellow, blue and red drum - gloss
Issued:	1940-1970
Series:	Fun Models

Description	U.K. £	U.S. $	Can. $
Gloss	65.00	115.00	175.00

Model No. 813
DOG WITH LADYBIRD ON NOSE

Designer:	Mr. Watkin		
Height:	4", 10.1 cm		
Colours:	White dog, red ladybird - gloss		
Issued:	1940-1970		
Series:	Fun Models		

Description	U.K. £	U.S. $	Can. $
Gloss	45.00	100.00	135.00

Model No. 831
DOG WITH GLASSES READING A BOOK

Designer:	Arthur Gredington		
Height:	6 ¼", 15.9 cm		
Colours:	White dog, yellow-red glasses, brown and white book - gloss		
Issued:	1940-1970		
Series:	Fun Models		

Description	U.K. £	U.S. $	Can. $
Gloss	85.00	150.00	225.00

Model No. 869
FIVE PUPPY ASHTRAY

Designer:	Mr. Watkin		
Height:	2", 5.0 cm		
Colours:	1. Brown puppies, green ashtray - gloss		
	2. Light tan puppies with black shading, green ashtray - gloss		
Issued:	1940-1967		

Description	U.K. £	U.S. $	Can. $
1. Brown	40.00	65.00	75.00
2. Light tan	40.00	65.00	75.00

Model No. 907
DOG WITH LADYBIRD ON TAIL

Designer:	Mr. Watkin		
Height:	3 ¾", 9.5 cm		
Colours:	White dog, red ladybird - gloss		
Issued:	1941-1971		
Series:	Fun Models		

Description	U.K. £	U.S. $	Can. $
Gloss	45.00	100.00	150.00

Model No. 916
THREE PUPPY ASHTRAY

Designer:	Mr. Watkin
Height:	2″, 5.0 cm
Colours:	1. Brown puppies, green ashtray - gloss
	2. Light brown puppies with black shading, green ashtray - gloss
Issued:	1941-1967

Description	U.K. £	U.S. $	Can. $
1. Brown	25.00	45.00	50.00
2. Light brown	25.00	45.00	50.00

Note: The three dogs are same as used in model no. 917.

Model No. 917
THREE PUPPIES

Designer:	Mr. Watkin
Height:	2″, 5.0 cm
Colours:	Brown puppies - gloss
Issued:	1941-1965

Description	U.K. £	U.S. $	Can. $
Gloss	20.00	45.00	65.00

Note: The three dogs are same as used in model no. 916.

Model No. 941
FOXHOUND
First Version - Thick legs and tail

Designer:	Mr. Watkin
Height:	2 ¾″, 7.0 cm
Colours:	White, tan and black - gloss
Issued:	1941-1969
Varieties:	2262

Description	U.K. £	U.S. $	Can. $
Gloss	30.00	50.00	85.00

Note: Remodelled in 1969 see also no. 2263.

Model No. 942 •
FOXHOUND
First Version - Thick legs and tail

Designer:	Mr. Watkin
Height:	2 ¾″, 7.0 cm
Colours:	White, tan and black - gloss
Issued:	1941-1969
Varieties:	2263

Description	U.K. £	U.S. $	Can. $
Gloss	30.00	50.00	85.00

Note: Remodelled in 1969 see also no. 2262.

Model No. 943
FOXHOUND
First Version - Thick legs and tail

Designer:	Mr. Watkin
Height:	2 ¾", 7.0 cm
Colours:	White, tan and black - gloss
Issued:	1941-1969
Varieties:	2265

Description	U.K. £	U.S. $	Can. $
Gloss	30.00	50.00	85.00

Note: Remodelled in 1969 see also no. 2265.

Model No. 944
FOXHOUND
First Version - Thick legs and tail

Designer:	Mr. Watkin
Height:	2 ¾", 7.0 cm
Colours:	White, tan and black - gloss
Issued:	1941-1969
Varieties:	2264

Description	U.K. £	U.S. $	Can. $
Gloss	30.00	50.00	85.00

Note: Remodelled in 1969 see also no. 2264.

Model No. 961
DALMATION "ARNOLDENE" - Large

Designer:	Arthur Gredington
Height:	5 ¾", 14.6 cm
Colours:	White with black spot - gloss; matt
Issued:	1. Gloss - 1941-1994
	2. Matt - 1970-1994

Description	U.K. £	U.S. $	Can. $
1. Gloss	45.00	125.00	125.00
2. Matt	40.00	125.00	125.00

Note: For the small size see no. 1763.

Model No. 962
AIREDALE TERRIER "CAST IRON MONARCH"

Designer:	Arthur Gredington
Height:	5 ½", 14.0 cm
Colours:	Black and tan - gloss; matt
Issued:	1. Gloss - 1941-1989
	2. Matt - 1987-1989

Description	U.K. £	U.S. $	Can. $
1. Gloss	45.00	150.00	200.00
2. Matt	40.00	150.00	200.00

Model No. 963
WIRED-HAIRED TERRIER
"TALAVERA ROMULUS"

Designer:	Arthur Gredington	
Height:	5 ¾", 14.6 cm	
Colours:	White, light sandy brown and black - gloss	
Issued:	1941-1984	

Description	U.K. £	U.S. $	Can. $
Gloss	45.00	175.00	250.00

Model No. 964
SMOOTH-HAIRED TERRIER
"ENDON BLACK ROD"

Designer:	Arthur Gredington	
Height:	5 ½", 14.0 cm	
Colours:	White with black patches - gloss	
Issued:	1941-1973	

Description	U.K. £	U.S. $	Can. $
Gloss	175.00	395.00	450.00

Model No. 965
BULLDOG "BASFORD BRITISH MASCOT" - Large

Designer:	Arthur Gredington	
Height:	5 ½", 14.0 cm	
Colours:	Brindle, tan and white - gloss; matt	
Issued:	1. Gloss - 1941-1990	
	2. Matt - 1987-1989	

Description	U.K. £	U.S. $	Can. $
1. Gloss	65.00	150.00	175.00
2. Matt	60.00	100.00	175.00

Note: For small size see no. 1731.

Model No. 966
IRISH SETTER "SUGAR OF WENDOVER"

Designer:	Arthur Gredington	
Height:	5 ¾", 14.6 cm	
Colours:	Red brown - gloss; matt	
Issued:	1. Gloss - 1941-1989	
	2. Matt - 1987-1989	

Description	U.K. £	U.S. $	Can. $
1. Gloss	45.00	100.00	90.00
2. Matt	40.00	100.00	100.00

Model No. 967

COCKER SPANIEL "HORSESHOE PRIMULA"

Designer: Arthur Gredington
Height: 5 ¾", 14.6 cm

			Price	
Colours	Issued	U.K. £	U.S. $	Can. $
Golden brown - gloss	1941-1994	40.00	75.00	95.00
Golden brown - matt	1987-1994	35.00	70.00	100.00
Black - gloss	1965-1982	65.00	80.00	125.00
Black and white - gloss	1970-1982	75.00	90.00	135.00
Liver and white - gloss	1970-1994	50.00	75.00	100.00
Liver and white - matt	1987-1994	45.00	75.00	100.00

Model No. 968
GREAT DANE "RULER OF OUBOURGH"

Designer:	Arthur Gredington
Height:	7", 17.8 cm
Colours:	Light sandy brown - gloss; matt
Issued:	1. Gloss - 1941-1994
	2. Matt - 1987-1994

Description	U.K. £	U.S. $	Can. $
1. Gloss	55.00	150.00	125.00
2. Matt	50.00	100.00	125.00

Model No. 969
ALSATIAN "ULRICA OF BRITTAS" - Large

Designer:	Arthur Gredington
Height:	5 ¾", 14.6 cm
Colours:	Black and light brown - gloss; matt
Issued:	1. 1942-1994
	2. 1970-1994

Description	U.K. £	U.S. $	Can. $
1. Gloss	50.00	110.00	120.00
2. Matt	45.00	80.00	95.00

Note: For small size see no. 1762.

Model No. 970
BULL TERRIER "ROMANY RHINESTONE" - Large

Designer:	Arthur Gredington
Height:	6 ½", 16.5 cm
Colours:	1. Brindle and white - gloss
	2. White - gloss; matt
Issued:	1. Gloss - 1942-1975
	2a. Gloss - 1942-1994
	2b. Matt - 1987-1994

Description	U.K. £	U.S. $	Can. $
1. Brindle/white	150.00	350.00	375.00
2a. White - gloss	45.00	100.00	150.00
2b. White - matt	40.00	120.00	150.00

Model No. 971
SEALYHAM "FORESTEDGE FOXGLOVE"

Designer:	Arthur Gredington
Height:	4 ¼", 10.8 cm
Colours:	White - gloss
Issued:	1942-1967

Description	U.K. £	U.S. $	Can. $
Gloss	95.00	250.00	275.00

Model No. 972
GREYHOUND "JOVIAL ROGER"

Designer: Arthur Gredington
Height: 6", 15.0 cm
Colours: Light sandy brown - gloss; matt
Issued: 1.   Gloss - 1942-1990
              2.   Matt - 1970-1990

Description	U.K. £	U.S. $	Can. $
1. Gloss	60.00	150.00	200.00
2. Matt	45.00	80.00	175.00

Model No. 973
ENGLISH SETTER "BAYLDONE BARONET"

Designer: Arthur Gredington
Height: 5 ½", 14.0 cm
Colours: Speckled grey - gloss; matt
Issued: 1.   Gloss - 1942-1989
              2.   Matt - 1987-1989

Description	U.K. £	U.S. $	Can. $
1. Gloss	45.00	125.00	150.00
2. Matt	40.00	100.00	125.00

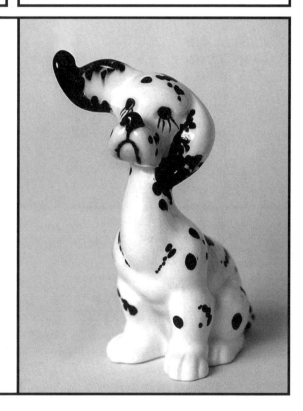

Model No. 1002
PUPPIT DOG

Designer: Arthur Gredington
Height: 4 ¾", 12.1 cm
Colours: White with black markings - gloss
Issued: 1944-1969
Series: Fun Models

Description	U.K. £	U.S. $	Can. $
Gloss	65.00	125.00	175.00

Model No. 1054
SPANIEL HOLDING "MY PLATE"

Designer: Arthur Gredington
Height: 4 ¼", 12.1 cm
Colours: White and brown - gloss
Issued: 1947-1967
Series: Fun Models

Description	U.K. £	U.S. $	Can. $
Gloss	75.00	125.00	200.00

Model No. 1055A
CAIRN TERRIER
First Version - With ball on left leg

Designer: Arthur Gredington
Height: 4", 10.1 cm
Colours: Beige with brown "stripes," red ball - gloss
Issued: 1946-1969

Description	U.K. £	U.S. $	Can. $
With ball	65.00	295.00	250.00

Note: Also found with ball on right leg.

Model No. 1055B
CAIRN TERRIER
Second Version - Without ball

Designer: Arthur Gredington
Height: 4", 10.1 cm
Colours: Beige with brown "stripes" - gloss
Issued: 1946-1969

Description	U.K. £	U.S. $	Can. $
Without ball	75.00	295.00	250.00

Model No. 1057
SPANIEL - Running

Designer: Arthur Gredington
Height: 3 ¾", 9.5 cm
Colours: White with golden tan patches - gloss
Issued: 1946-1967

Description	U.K. £	U.S. $	Can. $
Gloss	65.00	175.00	225.00

Model No. 1058
DOG WITH COLLAR "SCAMP"

Designer: Arthur Gredington
Height: 4 ½", 11.9 cm
Colours: Tan - gloss
Issued: 1948-1973
Seies: Fun Models

Description	U.K. £	U.S. $	Can. $
Gloss	65.00	110.00	175.00

Model No. 1059
PEKINESE - Begging

Designer: Arthur Gredington
Height: 4 ¼", 10.8 cm
Colours: Golden tan - gloss
Issued: 1946-1967

Description	U.K. £	U.S. $	Can. $
Gloss	65.00	195.00	175.00

Model No. 1060
RED SETTER - Lying

Designer: Arthur Gredington
Height: 3", 7.6 cm
Colours: Deep red brown - gloss
Issued: 1946-1973

Description	U.K. £	U.S. $	Can. $
Gloss	65.00	175.00	175.00

Model No. 1061
TERRIER - Lying

Designer:	Arthur Gredington	
Height:	2", 5.0 cm	
Colours:	White with light tan patches - gloss	
Issued:	1946-1973	

Description	U.K. £	U.S. $	Can. $
Gloss	65.00	195.00	200.00

Model No. 1062
TERRIER- Walking

Designer:	Arthur Gredington	
Height:	4", 10.1 cm	
Colours:	White with light tan and black patches - gloss	
Issued:	1946-1973	

Description	U.K. £	U.S. $	Can. $
Gloss	65.00	195.00	225.00

Model No. 1088
COMICAL DACHSHUND

Designer:	Miss Jones	
Height:	3 ½", 8.9 cm	
Colours:	White and brown - gloss	
Issued:	1947-1973	
Series:	Fun Models	

Description	U.K. £	U.S. $	Can. $
Gloss	65.00	125.00	180.00

Model No. 1202
BOXER "BLUE MOUNTAIN GRETA" - Large

Designer:	Arthur Gredington	
Height:	5 ½", 14.0 cm	
Colours:	1. Brindle - gloss; matt	
	2. Tan - gloss	
Issued:	1a. Gloss - 1950-1989	
	1b. Matt - 1987-1989	
	2. Gloss - 1973-1975	

Description	U.K. £	U.S. $	Can. $
1a. Brindle - gloss	50.00	85.00	135.00
1b. Brindle - matt	45.00	85.00	135.00
2. Tan - gloss	75.00	125.00	175.00

Model No. 1220
ENGLISH SETTER

Designer:	Arthur Gredington
Height:	8", 20.3 cm
Colours:	Speckled grey - gloss
Issued:	1951-1973

Description	U.K. £	U.S. $	Can. $
Gloss	200.00	550.00	600.00

Model No. 1239
DOG WITH RUFF - Begging

Designer:	Arthur Gredington
Height:	2 ½", 6.4 cm
Colours:	White and light tan - gloss
Issued:	1952-1967

Description	U.K. £	U.S. $	Can. $
Gloss	50.00	100.00	150.00

Note: Originally issued in combination as model no. 1086 "Clown and Dog."

Model No. 1240
DOG - Seated

Designer:	Arthur Gredington
Height:	2", 5.0 cm
Colours:	White and light tan - gloss
Issued:	1952-1952

Description	U.K. £	U.S. $	Can. $
Gloss	50.00	100.00	175.00

Note: Originally produced in combination as model no. 1096 "Sportsman."

Model No. 1241
DOG - Howling

Designer:	Arthur Gredington
Height:	1 ¼", 3.2 cm
Colours:	White and light tan - gloss
Issued:	1952-1952

Description	U.K. £	U.S. $	Can. $
Gloss	35.00	100.00	175.00

Note: Originally produced in combination as model no. 909 "Puppy Love" (Hummel 1).

Model No. 1242
DOG - Barking

Designer:	Arthur Gredington
Height:	1 ¼", 3.2 cm
Colours:	White and light tan - gloss
Issued:	1952-1952

Description	U.K. £	U.S. $	Can. $
Gloss	35.00	100.00	175.00

Note: Originally issued in combination as model no. 906 "Strolling Along" (Hummel 5).

Model No. 1294
POODLE "EBONIT AV BARBETT"

Designer:	Arthur Gredington	
Height:	5 ¾", 14.0 cm	
Colours:	1.	Black - gloss; matt
	2.	White - gloss
Issued:	1.	1953-1967
	2.	1953-1967

Description	U.K. £	U.S. $	Can. $
1a. Black - gloss	200.00	350.00	450.00
1b. Black - matt	200.00	350.00	450.00
2. White- gloss	200.00	350.00	450.00

Model No. 1299A
CORGI "BLACK PRINCE" - Large

Designer:	Arthur Gredington
Height:	5 ½", 14.0 cm
Colours:	Black, tan and white - gloss
Issued:	1953-1982
Varieties:	1299B

Description	U.K. £	U.S. $	Can. $
Gloss	70.00	225.00	275.00

Note: For small size see no. 1736.

Model No. 1299B
CORGI - Large

Designer:	Arthur Gredington	
Height:	5 ½", 14.0 cm	
Colours:	1.	Golden brown - gloss
	2.	Golden brown - matt
Issued:	1.	1953-1994
	2.	1987-1994
Varieties:	1299A	

Description	U.K. £	U.S. $	Can. $
1. Gloss	40.00	100.00	150.00
2. Matt	35.00	100.00	150.00

Note: For small size see no. 1736.

Model No. 1378

OLD ENGLISH DOGS
Left and right facing pairs

Designer: Unknown
Series: Mantelpiece Dogs

Colourway	Height	Issued	U.K. £	Price U.S. $	Can. $
Red and gold - gloss	13 ¼", 33.6 cm	1955-1973	120.00	200.00	275.00
White and gold - gloss	13 ¼", 33.6 cm	1955-1976	55.00	100.00	130.00
Red and gold - gloss	11 ½", 29.2 cm	1955-1972	110.00	175.00	225.00
White and gold - gloss	11 ½", 29.2 cm	1955-1972	45.00	80.00	110.00
Red and gold - gloss	10", 25.4 cm	1955-1973	100.00	160.00	200.00
White and gold - gloss	10", 25.4 cm	1955-1989	40.00	70.00	95.00
Red and gold - gloss	9", 22.9 cm	1955-1973	90.00	140.00	175.00
White and gold - gloss	9", 22.9 cm	1955-1989	35.00	60.00	80.00
Red and gold - gloss	7 ½", 19.1 cm	1955-1973	80.00	130.00	175.00
White and gold - gloss	7 ½", 19.1 cm	1955-1989	30.00	50.00	70.00
Red and gold - gloss	5 ½", 14.0 cm	1955-1973	70.00	120.00	160.00
White and gold - gloss	5 ½", 14.0 cm	1955-1989	25.00	45.00	60.00
Red and gold - gloss	3 ½", 8.9 cm	1955-1973	60.00	100.00	130.00
White and gold - gloss	3 ½", 8.9 cm	1955-1989	15.00	30.00	40.00

Note: Transferred to R.D. backstamp (DA89-98) 08/89.
Note: Also seen in Opaque white glaze.

Model No. 1386

POODLE

Designer: Arthur Gredington
Height: 3 ½", 8.9 cm

Colourway	Issued	U.K. £	Price U.S. $	Can. $
Brown - gloss	1953-1973	50.00	85.00	115.00
Black - gloss	1955-1990	25.00	45.00	60.00
Black - matt	1988-1989	20.00	45.00	60.00
White - gloss	1955-1990	25.00	45.00	60.00
White - matt	1984-1989	20.00	45.00	60.00

The only

magazine

Packed full of news, features, profiles and information.

for collectors!

A monthly magazine for collecting enthusiasts. From affordable antiques like Royal Doulton, to modern collectables such as Lilliput, Wade, Disneyana or sports memorabilia, Collect it! covers it - and gives you extensive valuation listings and a fact file to back up any collection.

Available at major newsagents. For more information and subscriptions call: +44 1344 868280 or fax +44 1344 861777. Email: collectit@dial.pipex.com

Model No. 1460
DACHSHUND - Seated

Designer: Arthur Gredington
Height: 2 ¾", 7.0 cm
Colours: 1.   Black and tan - gloss or matt
            2.   Tan - gloss or matt
Issued: 1a. Gloss - 1956 to the present
           1b. Matt - 1984-1989
           2a. Gloss - 1956-1990
           2b. Matt - 1984-1990

Description	U.K. £	U.S. $	Can. $
1a. Black/tan - gloss	13.50	N/A	N/A
1b. Black/tan - matt	20.00	40.00	50.00
2a. Tan - gloss	25.00	40.00	50.00
2b. Tan - matt	20.00	40.00	50.00

Model No. 1461
DACHSHUND - Begging

Designer: Arthur Gredington
Height: 4", 10.1 cm
Colours: 1.   Tan - gloss
            2.   Black and tan - gloss
Issued: 1.   1957-1975
           2.   1957-1980

Description	U.K. £	U.S. $	Can. $
1. Tan	50.00	80.00	125.00
2. Black and tan	45.00	75.00	160.00

Model No. 1548

LABRADOR "SOLOMON OF WENDOVER"- Large

Designer: Arthur Gredington
Height: 5 ½", 14.0 cm

Colourway	Issued	U.K. £	Price U.S. $	Can. $
Golden yellow - gloss	1958-1994	45.00	75.00	90.00
Golden yellow - matt	1970-1994	40.00	75.00	80.00
Black - gloss	1958-1994	45.00	75.00	100.00
Black - matt	1987-1994	40.00	75.00	90.00

Note: For small size see no. 1956.

Model No. 1731
BULLDOG "BOSUN" - Small

Designer: Unknown
Height: 2 ½", 6.4 cm
Colours: Tan and white - gloss; matt
Issued: 1. Gloss - 1960-1977
2. Matt - 1984-1989

Description	U.K. £	U.S. $	Can. $
1. Gloss	13.00	35.00	30.00
2. Matt	20.00	35.00	50.00

Note: For large size see no. 965.

Model No. 1736
CORGI - Small

Designer: Unknown
Height: 2 ¾", 7.0 cm
Colours: Golden brown - gloss; matt
Issued: 1. Gloss - 1961-1996
2. Matt - 1984-1989

Description	U.K. £	U.S. $	Can. $
1. Gloss	15.00	35.00	40.00
2. Matt	15.00	35.00	55.00

Note: For large size see no. 1299.

Model No. 1738
PUP WITH BONE

Designer: Harry Sales
Height: 3 ¾", 9.5 cm
Colours: White - gloss
Issued: 1961-1967
Series: Fun Models

Description	U.K. £	U.S. $	Can. $
Gloss	75.00	160.00	275.00

Model No. 1753
BULL TERRIER - Small

Designer: Arthur Gredington
Height: 3 ½", 8.9 cm
Colours: White with bright tan patches - gloss
Issued: 1961-1971

Description	U.K. £	U.S. $	Can. $
Gloss	85.00	225.00	250.00

Note: For large size see no. 970.

Model No. 1754

COCKER SPANIEL

Designer: Arthur Gredington
Height: 3", 7.6 cm

Colourway	Issued	U.K. £	Price U.S. $	Can. $
Black and white - gloss	1961-1996	15.00	25.00	35.00
Black and white - matt	1984-1989	12.00	25.00	50.00
Liver and white - gloss	1961-1997	13.00	25.00	35.00
Liver and white - matt	1984-1989	12.00	25.00	50.00

Model No. 1762A
ALSATIAN
First Version - 'Wolf-like,' tail not fully attached to leg

Designer:	Mr. Garbet
Height:	3 ¼", 8.3 cm
Colours:	Black and cream - gloss
Issued:	1961-1963

Description	U.K. £	U.S. $	Can. $
Gloss	50.00	80.00	115.00

Model No. 1762B
ALSATIAN - Small
Second Version - 'Fine head,' tail attached to leg

Designer:	Arthur Gredington
Height:	3 ¼", 8.3 cm
Colours:	Black and cream - gloss
Issued:	1963-1966

Description	U.K. £	U.S. $	Can. $
Gloss	40.00	65.00	90.00

Note: For large size see no. 969.

Model No. 1763
DALMATION - Small

Designer:	Mr. Garbet	
Height:	3 ½", 8.9 cm	
Colours:	White with black spots - gloss; matt	
Issued:	1.	Gloss - 1961 to the present
	2.	Matt - 1984-1989

Description	U.K. £	U.S. $	Can. $
1. Gloss	13.50	N/A	N/A
2. Matt	12.00	30.00	45.00

Note: For large size see no. 961.

Model No. 1786A
WHIPPET "WINGED FOOT MARKSMAN OF ALLWAYS"
First Version - Tail curls between legs

Designer:	Arthur Gredington
Height:	4 ½", 11.9 cm
Colours:	Light sandy brown - gloss
Issued:	1961-Unknown

Description	U.K. £	U.S. $	Can. $
Gloss	120.00	195.00	400.00

Model No. 1786B
WHIPPET "WINGED FOOT MARKSMAN
OF ALLWAYS"
Second Version - Tail attached to leg

Designer: Arthur Gredington
Height: 4 ½", 11.9 cm
Colours: Light sandy brown - gloss; matt
Issued: 1.   Gloss - Unknown-1989
              2.   Matt - 1987-1989

Description	U.K. £	U.S. $	Can. $
1. Gloss	55.00	100.00	200.00
2. Matt	50.00	100.00	225.00

Model No. 1791
COLLIE "LOCHINVAR OF LADYPARK" - Large

Designer: Arthur Gredington
Height: 5 ¾", 14.6 cm
Colours: Golden brown and white - gloss; matt
Issued: 1.   Gloss - 1961-1994
              2.   Matt - 1970-1994

Description	U.K. £	U.S. $	Can. $
1. Gloss	45.00	95.00	125.00
2. Matt	40.00	70.00	100.00

Note: For small size see no. 1814.

Model No. 1792
SHEEPDOG - Large

Designer: Arthur Gredington
Height: 5 ½", 14.0 cm
Colours: Black and white - gloss; matt
Issued: 1.   Gloss - 1961-1994
              2.   Matt - 1987-1994

Description	U.K. £	U.S. $	Can. $
1. Gloss	45.00	75.00	110.00
2. Matt	40.00	60.00	100.00

Note: For small size see no. 1854.

Model No. 1814
COLLIE - Small

Designer: Arthur Gredington
Height: 3 ¼", 8.3 cm
Colours: Golden brown and white - gloss
Issued: 1962-1975

Description	U.K. £	U.S. $	Can. $
Gloss	45.00	95.00	115.00

Note: For large size see no. 1791.

Model No. 1824
DOG - Singing

Designer:	Albert Hallam
Height:	1 ½", 3.8 cm
Colours:	Tan - gloss
Issued:	1962-1971
Series:	Bedtime Chorus

Description	U.K. £	U.S. $	Can. $
Gloss	65.00	125.00	200.00

Model No. 1852
BOXER - Small

Designer:	Arthur Gredington
Height:	3", 7.6 cm
Colours:	Tan - gloss
Issued:	1962-1975

Description	U.K. £	U.S. $	Can. $
Gloss	45.00	85.00	100.00

Note: For large size see no. 1202.

Model No. 1854
SHEEPDOG - Small

Designer:	Arthur Gredington
Height:	3", 7.6 cm
Colours:	Black and white - gloss; matt
Issued:	1. Gloss - 1962 to the present
	2. Matt - 1987-1989

Description	U.K. £	U.S. $	Can. $
1. Gloss	13.50	N/A	N/A
2. Matt	12.00	25.00	45.00

Note: For large size see no. 1792.

Model No. 1855
RETRIEVER

Designer:	Arthur Gredington
Height:	3 ¼", 8.3 cm
Colours:	Light golden brown - gloss
Issued:	1962-1975

Description	U.K. £	U.S. $	Can. $
Gloss	45.00	75.00	110.00

Model No. 1871
POODLE

Designer:	Arthur Gredington
Height:	4 ¼", 10.8 cm
Colours:	White, red bow - gloss
Issued:	1963-1967
Series:	Advertising ware "Dubonnet"

Description	U.K. £	U.S. $	Can. $
Gloss	85.00	160.00	225.00

Model No. 1872
BULLDOG

Designer:	Arthur Gredington
Height:	3 ¾", 9.5 cm
Colours:	White, pale tan ear and around eyes - gloss
Issued:	1963-1967
Series:	Advertising ware "Dubonnet"

Description	U.K. £	U.S. $	Can. $
Gloss	85.00	160.00	225.00

Model No. 1918
ASHTRAY WITH DOG

Designer:	Albert Hallam	
Height:	11" x 8", 27.9 x 20.3 cm	
Colours:	1.	Pale brown bowl with animal - gloss
	2.	Pale blue bowl with animal - gloss
Issued:	1963-1971	

Description	U.K. £	U.S. $	Can. $
1. Pale brown	70.00	125.00	175.00
2. Pale blue	125.00	250.00	350.00

Note: This ashtray was available with any small dog attached to it. Model shown is no. 1762.

Model No. 1932
DACHSHUND - Ashtray

Designer:	Albert Hallam	
Height:	8" x 3", 20.3 x 7.6 cm	
Colours:	1.	Black and tan dog on charcoal base - gloss
	2.	Tan dog on charcoal base - gloss
Issued:	1962-1969	

Description	U.K. £	U.S. $	Can. $
1. Black/tan	70.00	160.00	175.00
2. Tan	70.00	160.00	175.00

Model No. 1933A
BEAGLE "WENDOVER BILLY" - Large

Designer: Arthur Gredington
Height: 5 ½", 14.0 cm
Colours: Black, tan and white - gloss or matt
Issued: 1. 1964-1989
           2. 1987-1989
Varieties: 1933B

Description	U.K. £	U.S. $	Can. $
1. Gloss	50.00	100.00	115.00
2. Matt	45.00	100.00	115.00

Note: For small size see no. 1939.

Model No. 1933B
BEAGLE "WENDOVER BILLY" - on wooden plinth

Designer: Arthur Gredington
Height: 6", 15.0 cm
Colours: Black, tan and white - matt
Issued: 1970-1989
Series: Connoisseur Dogs
Varieties: 1933A

Description	U.K. £	U.S. $	Can. $
Matt	65.00	150.00	150.00

Model No. 1939
BEAGLE "WENDOVER BILLY" - Small

Designer: Arthur Gredington
Height: 3", 7.6 cm
Colours: Black, tan and white - gloss or matt
Issued: 1. Gloss - 1964 to the present
           2. Matt - 1984-1989

Description	U.K. £	U.S. $	Can. $
1. Gloss	13.50	N/A	N/A
2. Matt	15.00	25.00	45.00

Note: For large size see no. 1933A.

Model No. 1944
YORKSHIRE TERRIER - Lying

Designer: Arthur Gredington
Height: 3 ½", 8.9 cm
Colours: Grey and tan - gloss
Issued: 1964-1976

Description	U.K. £	U.S. $	Can. $
Gloss	55.00	125.00	150.00

Model No. 1956

LABRADOR - Small

Designer: Arthur Gredington
Height: 3 ¼″, 8.3 cm

Colourway	Issued	U.K. £	Price U.S. $	Can. $
Black - gloss	1964 to the present	11.00	N/A	N/A
Black - matt	1984-1989	10.00	25.00	50.00
Golden brown - gloss	1964 to the present	11.00	N/A	N/A
Golden brown - matt	1984-1989	10.00	25.00	50.00

Note: For large size see no. 1548.

Model No. 1982A
STAFFORDSHIRE BULL TERRIER
"BANDITS BRINTIGA"

Designer:	Arthur Gredington
Height:	4 ¾", 12.1 cm
Colours:	Dark brindle - gloss
Issued:	1964-1969

Description	U.K. £	U.S. $	Can. $
Gloss	200.00	250.00	400.00

Model No. 1982B
STAFFORDSHIRE BULL TERRIER

Designer:	Arthur Gredington
Height:	4 ¾", 12.1 cm
Colours:	Tan and white - gloss
Issued:	1964-1969

Description	U.K. £	U.S. $	Can. $
Gloss	200.00	250.00	400.00

Model No. 1990
OLD ENGLISH SHEEPDOG

Designer:	Mr. Mortimer
Height:	12 ½", 31.7 cm
Colours:	Black, grey and white - gloss
Issued:	1964-1970
Series:	Advertising ware "Dulux"

Description	U.K. £	U.S. $	Can. $
Gloss	450.00	795.00	1,200.00

Model No. 1997
PUG "CUTMIL CUTIE" - Large

Designer: Arthur Gredington
Height: 4 ½", 11.9 cm
Colours: Light sandy brown - gloss or matt
Issued: 1. Gloss - 1965-1982
             2. Matt - 1970-1982

Description	U.K. £	U.S. $	Can. $
1. Gloss	50.00	150.00	225.00
2. Matt	45.00	125.00	225.00

Model No. 1998
PUG - Small

Designer: Arthur Gredington
Height: 2 ½", 6.4 cm
Colours: Light sandy brown - gloss or matt
Issued: 1. Gloss - 1966-1990
             2. Mattt - 1984-1989

Description	U.K. £	U.S. $	Can. $
1. Gloss	30.00	50.00	85.00
2. Matt	25.00	50.00	85.00

Note: This model has also been seen with head forward.

Model No. 2023
JACK RUSSELL TERRIER - Large

Designer: Arthur Gredington
Height: 5", 12.7 cm
Colours: White body, tan/black head - gloss or matt
Issued: 1. Gloss - 1965-1994
             2. Matt - 1987-1994

Description	U.K. £	U.S. $	Can. $
1. Gloss	45.00	75.00	125.00
2. Matt	40.00	70.00	125.00

Note: For small size see no. 2109.

Model No. 2037
SCOTTIE

Designer: Arthur Gredington
Height: 4 ½", 11.9 cm
Colours: Black - gloss or matt
Issued: 1. Gloss - 1965-1990
             2. Matt - 1987-1989

Description	U.K. £	U.S. $	Can. $
1. Gloss	45.00	100.00	150.00
2. Matt	40.00	85.00	150.00

Model No. 2038
WEST HIGHLAND TERRIER

Designer: Arthur Gredington
Height: 4 ¾", 12.1 cm
Colours: White - gloss or matt
Issued: 1.   Gloss - 1965-1994
            2.   Matt - 1987-1989

Description	U.K. £	U.S. $	Can. $
1. Gloss	40.00	75.00	125.00
2. Matt	35.00	75.00	125.00

Model No. 2045A
BASSET HOUND "FOCHNO TRINKET"

Designer: Arthur Gredington
Height: 5", 12.7 cm
Colours: Black, white and tan - gloss or matt
Issued: 1.   Gloss - 1965-1994
            2.   Matt - 1987-1994

Description	U.K. £	U.S. $	Can. $
1. Gloss	45.00	100.00	150.00
2. Matt	40.00	100.00	150.00

Model No. 2045B
BASSET HOUND "FOCHNO TRINKET"
- on wooden plinth

Designer: Arthur Gredington
Height: 6", 15.0 cm
Colours: Black, white and tan - matt
Issued: 1970-1989
Series: Connoisseur Dogs

Description	U.K. £	U.S. $	Can. $
Matt	70.00	150.00	175.00

Model No. 2102
YORKSHIRE TERRIER LAUGHING

Designer: Albert Hallam
Height: 3", 7.6 cm
Colours: Tan - gloss
Issued: 1967-1972
Series: Fun Models

Description	U.K. £	U.S. $	Can. $
Gloss	65.00	125.00	200.00

Model No. 2107A
KING CHARLES SPANIEL "BLENHEIM"

Designer: Arthur Gredington
Height: 5 ¼", 13.3 cm
Colours: Tan and white - gloss or matt
Issued: 1. Gloss - 1967-1994
             2. Matt - 1987-1994

Description	U.K. £	U.S. $	Can. $
1. Gloss	45.00	85.00	150.00
2. Matt	40.00	85.00	150.00

Model No. 2107B
KING CHARLES SPANIEL
"JOSEPHINE OF BLAGREAVES"

Designer: Arthur Gredington
Height: 5 ¼", 13.3 cm
Colours: Black, tan and white - gloss or matt
Issued: 1. Gloss - 1967-1994
             2. Matt - 1987-1994

Description	U.K. £	U.S. $	Can. $
1. Gloss	45.00	85.00	150.00
2. Matt	40.00	85.00	150.00

Model No. 2108
POODLE "IVANOLA GOLD DIGGER"

Designer: Arthur Gredington
Height: 5 ¾", 14.6 cm
Colours: White, blue bow - gloss
Issued: 1967-1971

Description	U.K. £	U.S. $	Can. $
Gloss	200.00	350.00	450.00

Model No. 2109
JACK RUSSELL TERRIER - Small

Designer: Arthur Gredington and
             Albert Hallam
Height: 2 ½", 6.4 cm
Colours: White with tan head - gloss or matt
Issued: 1. Gloss - 1967 to the present
             2. Matt - 1984-1989

Description	U.K. £	U.S. $	Can. $
1. Gloss	13.50	N/A	N/A
2. Matt	12.00	25.00	40.00

Note: For large size see no. 2023.

Model No. 2112
CAIRN TERRIER

Designer:	Arthur Gredington and Albert Hallam	
Height:	2 ¾", 7.0 cm	
Colours:	Dark cream - gloss or matt	
Issued:	1. Gloss - 1967-1995	
	2. Matt - 1984-1989	

Description	U.K. £	U.S. $	Can. $
1. Gloss	20.00	30.00	45.00
2. Matt	15.00	30.00	45.00

Model No. 2130
DOG PRAYING

Designer:	Albert Hallam
Height:	3", 7.6 cm
Colours:	Blue - gloss
Issued:	1967-1972
Series:	Fun Models

Description	U.K. £	U.S. $	Can. $
Gloss	55.00	125.00	200.00

Model No. 2221
ST. BERNARD "CORNA GARTH STROLLER"

Designer:	Albert Hallam	
Height:	5 ½", 14.0 cm	
Colours:	Dark brown, tan and white - gloss or matt	
Issued:	1. Gloss - 1968-1989	
	2. Matt - 1970-1989	

Description	U.K. £	U.S. $	Can. $
1. Gloss	65.00	125.00	100.00
2. Matt	60.00	125.00	100.00

Model No. 2232
OLD ENGLISH SHEEPDOG

Designer:	Albert Hallam
Height:	11 ½", 29.2 cm
Colours:	Grey and white - gloss
Issued:	1968-1989
Series:	Fireside Models

Description	U.K. £	U.S. $	Can. $
Gloss	90.00	200.00	350.00

Note: Transferred to the R.D. backstamp (DA84) 08/89.

Model No. 2235
BASSETHOUND - Wall Plaque

Designer:	Graham Tongue
Height:	6 ¼" x 4 ½", 15.9 x 11.9 cm (concave)
Colours:	Tan and white head black satin surround - gloss
Issued:	1968-Unknown
Series:	Wall Plaques

Description	U.K. £	U.S. $	Can. $
Gloss	85.00	150.00	200.00

Model No. 2262
FOXHOUND
Second Version - Thin legs and tail

Designer:	Graham Tongue
Height:	2 ½", 6.4 cm
Colours:	White, tan and black - gloss or matt
Issued:	1. Gloss - 1969-1997
	2. Matt - 1984-1989
Varieties:	941

Description	U.K. £	U.S. $	Can. $
1. Gloss	12.00	30.00	40.00
2. Matt	15.00	35.00	60.00

Model No. 2263
FOXHOUND
Second Version - Thin legs and tail

Designer:	Graham Tongue
Height:	3", 7.6 cm
Colours:	White, tan and black - gloss or matt
Issued:	1. Gloss - 1969-1997
	2. Matt - 1984-1989
Varieties:	942

Description	U.K. £	U.S. $	Can. $
1. Gloss	12.00	30.00	40.00
2. Matt	15.00	35.00	60.00

Model No. 2264
FOXHOUND
Second Version - Thin legs and tail

Designer:	Graham Tongue
Height:	3", 7.6 cm
Colours:	White, tan and black - gloss or matt
Issued:	1. Gloss - 1969-1997
	2. Matt - 1984-1989
Varieties:	944

Description	U.K. £	U.S. $	Can. $
1. Gloss	12.00	30.00	40.00
2. Matt	15.00	35.00	60.00

Model No. 2265
FOXHOUND
Second Version - Thin legs and tail

Designer:	Graham Tongue
Height:	2 ¾", 7.0 cm
Colours:	White, tan and black - gloss or matt
Issued:	1. Gloss - 1969-1997
	2. Matt - 1984-1989
Varieties:	943

Description	U.K. £	U.S. $	Can. $
1. Gloss	12.00	30.00	40.00
2. Matt	15.00	35.00	60.00

Model No. 2268
POODLE - Wall Plaque

Designer:	Graham Tongue
Height:	6" x 4 ½", 15.9 x 11.9 cm (Concave)
Colours:	Unknown - gloss
Issued:	1968-Unknown
Series:	Wall Plaques

Description	U.K. £	U.S. $	Can. $
Gloss	95.00	175.00	250.00

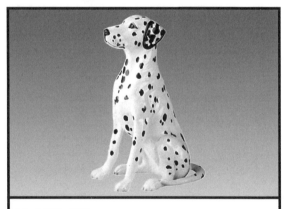

Model No. 2271
DALMATIAN

Designer:	Graham Tongue
Height:	13 ¾", 34.9 cm
Colours:	White with black spots - gloss
Issued:	1969-1989
Series:	Fireside Models

Description	U.K. £	U.S. $	Can. $
White/black	85.00	195.00	300.00

Note: Transferred to R.D.backstamp (DA85) 08/89.

Model No. 2285
AFGHAN HOUND "HAJUBAH OF DAVIEN"

Designer:	Graham Tongue
Height:	5 ½", 14.0 cm
Colours:	Golden and dark brown - gloss or matt
Issued:	1. Gloss - 1969-1994
	2. Matt - 1987-1989

Description	U.K. £	U.S. $	Can. $
1. Gloss	45.00	95.00	85.00
2. Matt	40.00	95.00	85.00

Model No. 2286
DACHSHUND

Designer:	Albert Hallam
Height:	10 ½", 26.7 cm
Colours:	1. Black and tan - gloss
	2. Tan - gloss
Issued:	1. 1969-1981
	2. 1969-1981
Series:	Fireside Models

Description	U.K. £	U.S. $	Can. $
1. Black/tan	120.00	225.00	300.00
2. Tan	120.00	225.00	300.00

Model No. 2287
GOLDEN RETRIEVER "CABUS CADET"

Designer:	Graham Tongue
Height:	5 ½", 14.0 cm
Colours:	Light golden brown - gloss or matt
Issued:	1. Gloss - 1969-1994
	2. Matt - 1987-1994

Description	U.K. £	U.S. $	Can. $
1. Gloss	45.00	85.00	135.00
2. Matt	40.00	85.00	135.00

Model No. 2299
DOBERMAN PINSCHER "ANNASTOCK LANCE"

Designer:	Graham Tongue
Height:	5 ¾", 14.6 cm
Colours:	Black and tan - gloss or matt
Issued:	1. Gloss - 1970-1994
	2. Matt - 1987-1994

Description	U.K. £	U.S. $	Can. $
1. Gloss	45.00	125.00	110.00
2. Matt	40.00	125.00	110.00

Model No. 2300
BEAGLE
Designer: Albert Hallam
Height: 12 ¾", 32.4 cm
Colours: Black, tan and white - gloss
Issued: 1969-1983
Series: Fireside Models

Description	U.K. £	U.S. $	Can. $
Gloss	175.00	295.00	450.00

Model No. 2314
LABRADOR
Designer: Graham Tongue
Height: 13 ½", 34.3 cm
Colours: 1. Golden brown - gloss
        2. Black - gloss
Issued: 1970-1989
Series: Fireside Models

Description	U.K. £	U.S. $	Can. $
1. Golden brown	125.00	225.00	350.00
2. Black	110.00	225.00	375.00

Note: Transferred to R.D. backstamp (DA 86) 08/89.

Model No. 2339
POODLE
Designer: Graham Tongue
Height: 5 ¾", 14.6 cm
Colours: 1. Black - gloss
        2. White - gloss
Issued: 1971-1983

Description	U.K. £	U.S. $	Can. $
1. Black	65.00	110.00	150.00
2. White	65.00	110.00	150.00

Model No. 2377
YORKSHIRE TERRIER

Designer:	Graham Tongue
Height:	10 ¼", 26.0 cm
Colours:	Grey and tan - gloss
Issued:	1971-1989
Series:	Fireside Models

Description	U.K. £	U.S. $	Can. $
Gloss	100.00	225.00	375.00

Note: Transferred to R.D. backstamp (DA87) 08/89.

Model No. 2410
ALSATIAN

Designer:	Graham Tongue
Height:	14", 35.5 cm
Colours:	Dark and sandy brown - gloss
Issued:	1972-1989
Series:	Fireside Models

Description	U.K. £	U.S. $	Can. $
Gloss	125.00	225.00	375.00

Note: Transferred to R.D. backstamp (DA88) 08/89.

Model No. 2448
LAKELAND TERRIER

Designer:	Albert Hallam
Height:	3 ¼", 8.3 cm
Colours:	Pale tan and black - gloss or matt
Issued:	1. Gloss - 1973 to the present
	2. Matt - 1984-1989

Description	U.K. £	U.S. $	Can. $
1. Gloss	11.00	N/A	N/A
2. Matt	12.00	35.00	50.00

Model No. 2454
CHIHUAHUA - Lying on cushion

Designer:	Albert Hallam
Height:	2 ¾", 7.0 cm
Colours:	Cream dog, maroon cushion - gloss or matt
Issued:	1. Gloss - 1973-1996
	2. Matt - 1984-1989

Description	U.K. £	U.S. $	Can. $
1. Gloss	15.00	25.00	35.00
2. Matt	15.00	30.00	40.00

Model No. 2581
COLLIE - on wooden plinth

Designer:	Graham Tongue
Height:	8", 20.3 cm
Colours:	Golden brown and white - matt
Issued:	1979-1989
Series:	Connoisseur Dogs

Description	U.K. £	U.S. $	Can. $
Matt	75.00	125.00	175.00

Note: Transferred to R.D. backstamp (DA24) 08/89.

Model No. 2587
ALSATIAN - on wooden plinth

Designer:	Graham Tongue
Height:	9", 22.9 cm
Colours:	Dark and sandy brown - matt
Issued:	1979-1989
Series:	Connoisseur Dogs

Description	U.K. £	U.S. $	Can. $
Matt	75.00	125.00	175.00

Note: Transferred to R.D. backstamp (DA26) 08/89.

Model No. 2929
COLLIE - Wall Plaque

Designer:	Unknown
Height:	Unknown
Colours:	Golden brown and white - matt
Issued:	1986-1989
Series:	Best of Breed

Description	U.K. £	U.S. $	Can. $
Matt	25.00	50.00	75.00

Note: Head from model no. 2581 mounted on wood.

Model No. 2932
ALSATIAN - Wall Plaque

Designer:	Unknown
Height:	Unknown
Colours:	Black and cream - matt
Issued:	1986-1989
Series:	Best of Breed

Description	U.K. £	U.S. $	Can. $
Matt	25.00	50.00	75.00

Note: Head from model no. 2587 mounted on wood.

Model No. 2946
MEAL TIME

Designer:	Unknown	
Height:	3 ½", 8.9 cm	
Colours:	White and tan - gloss	
Issued:	1986-1989	
Series:	Playful Puppies	

Description	U.K. £	U.S. $	Can. $
Gloss	50.00	75.00	125.00

Note: Taken from Royal Doulton HN 1158.

Model No. 2947
GNAWING

Designer:	Unknown	
Height:	4 ¼", 10.8 cm	
Colours:	White and tan - gloss	
Issued:	1986-1989	
Series:	Playful Puppies	

Description	U.K. £	U.S. $	Can. $
Gloss	50.00	75.00	125.00

Note: Taken from Royal Doulton HN 1159.

Model No. 2948
PLAY TIME

Designer:	Unknown	
Height:	3 ¾", 9.5 cm	
Colours:	White and tan - gloss	
Issued:	1986-1989	
Series:	Playful Puppies	

Description	U.K. £	U.S. $	Can. $
Gloss	50.00	75.00	125.00

Note: Taken from Royal Doulton HN 2664.

Model No. 2949
JUGGLING

Designer:	Unknown	
Height:	3", 7.6 cm	
Colours:	White and tan - gloss	
Issued:	1986-1989	
Series:	Playful Puppies	

Description	U.K. £	U.S. $	Can. $
Gloss	50.00	75.00	125.00

Note: Taken from Royal Doulton HN 1103.

Model No. 2950
NAP TIME

Designer: Unknown
Height: 4 ½", 11.9 cm
Colours: White and tan - gloss
Issued: 1986-1989
Series: Playful Puppies

Description	U.K. £	U.S. $	Can. $
Gloss	60.00	75.00	125.00

Note: Taken from Royal Doulton HN 1099.

Model No. 2951
CAUGHT IT

Designer: Unknown
Height: 2 ¾", 7.0 cm
Colours: White and tan - gloss
Issued: 1986-1989
Series: Playful Puppies

Description	U.K. £	U.S. $	Can. $
Gloss	50.00	75.00	125.00

Note: Taken from Royal Doulton HN 1097.

Model No. 2980
SPANIEL - on plinth

Designer: Alan Maslankowski
Height: 8 ¼", 21.0 cm
Colours: Black; black and white; golden; liver and white; white - matt
Issued: 1987-1989
Series: Spirited Dogs

Description	U.K. £	U.S. $	Can. $
1. Black or white	50.00	125.00	175.00
2. Black/white	80.00	125.00	175.00
3. Golden	80.00	125.00	175.00
4. Liver/white	80.00	125.00	175.00

Model No. 2982
PEKINESE - Begging

Designer: Alan Maslankowski
Height: 5 ½", 14.0 cm
Colours: Cream - gloss or matt
Issued: 1987-1989
Series: Good Companions

Description	U.K. £	U.S. $	Can. $
1. Gloss	55.00	100.00	150.00
2. Matt	50.00	100.00	150.00

Note: Transferred to R.D. backstamp (DA113) gloss.

Model No. 2984
NORFOLK TERRIER

Designer:	Alan Maslankowski
Height:	4", 10.1 cm
Colours:	Brown - gloss or matt
Issued:	1987-1989
Series:	Good Companions

Description	U.K. £	U.S. $	Can. $
1. Gloss	50.00	85.00	130.00
2. Matt	45.00	85.00	130.00

Note: Transferred to R.D. backstamp (DA114) gloss.

Model No. 2985
POODLE - on cushion

Designer:	Alan Maslankowski
Height:	5 ½", 14.0 cm
Colours:	White poodle, turquoise cushion - gloss or matt
Issued:	1987-1989
Series:	Good Companions

Description	U.K. £	U.S. $	Can. $
1. Gloss	65.00	85.00	150.00
2. Matt	60.00	85.00	150.00

Note: Transferred to R.D. backstamp (DA115) in gloss.

Model No. 2986

SETTER - on ceramic plinth

Designer: Graham Tongue
Height: 8 ½", 21.6 cm
Series: See below

Colours	Issued	Series	U.K. £	Price U.S. $	Can. $
Black - matt	1987-1989	Spirited Dogs	50.00	100.00	225.00
Gordon Setter					
black and tan - matt	1988-1989	Spirited Dogs	80.00	150.00	250.00
Bronze	1989-1993	Britannia	75.00	115.00	175.00
Red Setter					
deep red brown - matt	1987-1989	Spirited Dogs	80.00	150.00	250.00
White - matt	1987-1989	Spirited Dogs	50.00	100.00	125.00
English Setter					
white and liver - matt	1987-1989	Spirited Dogs	80.00	150.00	225.00

Model No. 3011

POINTER

Designer: Graham Tongue
Height: 8 ½", 21.6 cm
Series: See below

Colours	Issued	Series	U.K. £	Price U.S. $	Can. $
Black - matt	1987-1989	Spirited Dogs	50.00	85.00	175.00
Bronze finish	1989-1993	Britannia	70.00	120.00	165.00
White - matt	1987-1989	Spirited Dogs	50.00	85.00	125.00
White/brown - matt	1987-1989	Spirited Dogs	65.00	110.00	175.00

Note: Transferred to R.D. backstamp (DA110) 08/89 - white/brown in matt.

Model No. 3056
ROTTWEILER

Designer: Alan Maslankowski
Height: 5 ¼", 13.3 cm
Colours: Black and tan - gloss or matt
Issued: 1.   Gloss - 1988-1989
            2.   Matt - 1988-1989

Description	U.K. £	U.S. $	Can. $
1. Gloss	55.00	85.00	125.00
2. Matt	50.00	85.00	125.00

Note: Transferred to R.D. backstamp (DA 99) in gloss.

Model No. 3058
OLD ENGLISH SHEEP DOG - Walking

Designer: Warren Platt
Height: 5 ½", 14.0 cm
Colours: Grey and white - gloss or matt
Issued: 1988-1989

Description	U.K. £	U.S. $	Can. $
1. Gloss	55.00	85.00	125.00
2. Matt	50.00	85.00	125.00

Note: Transferred to R.D. backstamp (DA100) in gloss.

Model No. 3060
STAFFORDSHIRE BULL TERRIER

Designer: Alan Maslankowski
Height: 4", 10.1 cm
Colours: 1.   White and tan - gloss or matt
            2.   Brindle - gloss or matt
Issued: 1988-1989

Description	U.K. £	U.S. $	Can. $
1a. White/tan - gloss	55.00	85.00	175.00
1b. White/tan - matt	50.00	85.00	150.00
2a. Brindle - gloss	55.00	85.00	175.00
2b. Brindle - matt	50.00	85.00	150.00

Note: Transferred to R.D. backstamp (DA101) in gloss.

Model No. 3062A
LABRADOR - on ceramic plinth

Designer: Alan Maslankowski
Height: 6 ½", 16.5 cm
Colours: 1.   Black - matt
            2.   Golden - matt
Issued: 1988-1989
Series: Spirited Dogs
Varieties: 3062B

Description	U.K. £	U.S. $	Can. $
1. Black	60.00	110.00	150.00
2. Golden	70.00	120.00	175.00

Note: Transferred to R.D. backstamp (DA111) in golden.

Model No. 3062B
LABRADOR - Standing

Designer:	Alan Maslankowski	
Height:	5″, 12.7 cm	
Colours:	Chocolate brown - gloss	
Issued:	1993 in a limited edition of 93	
Varieties:	3062A	

Description	U.K. £	U.S. $	Can. $
Gloss	100.00	195.00	300.00

Note: Produced for the B.C.C. with a special BCC backstamp.

Model No. 3066
RETRIEVER - on ceramic plinth

Designer:	Graham Tongue		
Height:	7 ½″, 19.1 cm		
Colours:	1. Golden - matt	2. Bronze finish	
Issued:	1. 1988-1989	2. 1989-1989	
Series:	1. Spirited Dogs	2. Britannia	

Description	U.K. £	U.S. $	Can. $
1. Golden	75.00	150.00	225.00
2. Bronze	65.00	150.00	225.00

Note: Transferred to R.D. backstamp (DA112) in golden.

Model No. 3070
AFGHAN HOUND - Running

Designer:	Alan Maslankowski
Height:	5 ½″, 14.0 cm
Colours:	Light brown and cream - gloss or matt
Issued:	1988-1989

Description	U.K. £	U.S. $	Can. $
1. Gloss	55.00	100.00	200.00
2. Matt	50.00	100.00	200.00

Note: Transferred to R.D. backstamp (DA102) in gloss.

Model No. 3073
ALSATIAN - Standing

Designer:	Alan Maslankowski
Height:	5 ¾″, 14.6 cm
Colours:	Black and light brown - gloss or matt
Issued:	1988-1989

Description	U.K. £	U.S. $	Can. $
1. Gloss	55.00	95.00	165.00
2. Matt	50.00	95.00	165.00

Note: Transferred to R.D. backstamp (DA103) in gloss.

Model No. 3080
SHETLAND SHEEPDOG - Seated

Designer:	Alan Maslankowski
Height:	5 ½", 14.0 cm
Colours:	Golden brown and white - gloss or matt
Issued:	1988-1989
Series:	Good Companions

Description	U.K. £	U.S. $	Can. $
1. Gloss	85.00	150.00	200.00
2. Matt	80.00	150.00	200.00

Note: Transferred to R.D. backstamp (DA117) in gloss.

Model No. 3081
BOXER - Standing

Designer:	Alan Maslankowski
Height:	5 ½", 14.0 cm
Colours:	Golden brown and white - gloss or matt
Issued:	1988-1989

Description	U.K. £	U.S. $	Can. $
1. Gloss	50.00	100.00	150.00
2. Matt	45.00	100.00	150.00

Note: Transferred to R.D. backstamp (DA104) in gloss.

Model No. 3082
CAIRN TERRIER - Standing

Designer:	Warren Platt
Height:	4 ¾", 12.1 cm
Colours:	Light brown - gloss or matt
Issued:	1988-1989
Series:	Good Companions

Description	U.K. £	U.S. $	Can. $
1. Gloss	45.00	85.00	125.00
2. Matt	40.00	85.00	125.00

Note: Transferred to R.D. backstamp (DA118) in gloss.

Model No. 3083
YORKSHIRE TERRIER - Seated

Designer:	Warren Platt
Height:	5 ½", 14.0 cm
Colours:	Grey and light brown - gloss and matt
Issued:	1988-1989
Series:	Good Companions

Description	U.K. £	U.S. $	Can. $
1. Gloss	45.00	85.00	125.00
2. Matt	40.00	85.00	125.00

Note: Transferred to R.D. backstamp (DA119) in gloss.

Model No. 3103
DACHSHUND - Standing

Designer:	Alan Maslankowski
Height:	4 ¼", 10.8 cm
Colours:	1. Black and tan - gloss or matt
	2. Tan - gloss or matt
Issued:	1987-1989, transferred to DA116
Series:	Good Companions

Description	U.K. £	U.S. $	Can. $
1a. Black/tan - gloss	45.00	75.00	110.00
1b. Black/tan - matt	40.00	75.00	110.00
2a. Tan - gloss	45.00	75.00	110.00
2b. Tan - matt	40.00	75.00	110.00

Model No. 3121
DOBERMAN

Designer:	Alan Maslankowski
Height:	5 ¼", 13.3 cm
Colours:	Black and tan - gloss or matt
Issued:	1988-1989

Description	U.K. £	U.S. $	Can. $
1. Gloss	50.00	85.00	125.00
2. Matt	45.00	85.00	125.00

Note: Transferred to R.D. backstamp (DA105) in gloss.

Model No. 3129
ROUGH COLLIE

Designer:	Warren Platt
Height:	5 ½", 14.0 cm
Colours:	Golden brown and white - gloss or matt
Issued:	1988-1989

Description	U.K. £	U.S. $	Can. $
1. Gloss	45.00	85.00	150.00
2. Matt	40.00	85.00	140.00

Note: Transferred to R.D. backstamp (DA106) in gloss.

Model No. 3135
SPRINGER SPANIEL

Designer:	Amanda Hughes-Lubeck
Height:	5", 12.7 cm
Colours:	Dark brown and white - gloss or matt
Issued:	1988-1989

Description	U.K. £	U.S. $	Can. $
1. Gloss	65.00	115.00	175.00
2. Matt	60.00	115.00	150.00

Note: Transferred to R.D. backstamp (DA107) in gloss.

Model No. 3149
WEST HIGHLAND TERRIER - Seated

Designer: Martyn Alcock
Height: 5″, 12.7 cm
Colours: White - gloss or matt
Issued: 1989-1989
Series: Good Companions

Description	U.K. £	U.S. $	Can. $
1. Gloss	45.00	75.00	145.00
2. Matt	40.00	75.00	125.00

Note: Transferred to R.D. backstamp (DA120) in gloss.

Model No. 3155
CAVALIER KING CHARLES SPANIEL - Standing

Designer: Warren Platt
Height: 5 ½″, 14.0 cm
Colours: 1. Black, tan and white - gloss or matt
     2. Tan and white - gloss or matt
Issued: 1989-1989, transferred to DA121 - gloss
Series: Good Companions

Description	U.K. £	U.S. $	Can. $
1a. Gloss	65.00	115.00	175.00
1b. Matt	60.00	115.00	135.00
2a. Gloss	65.00	115.00	175.00
2b. Matt	60.00	115.00	135.00

Model No. 3258
ALSATIAN - Standing

Designer: Unknown
Height: 4 ¼″, 10.8 cm
Colours: Black and cream - gloss
Issued: 1991-1997

Description	U.K. £	U.S. $	Can. $
Gloss	15.00	25.00	35.00

Model No. 3260
ROTTWEILER - Standing

Designer: Unknown
Height: 3 ½″, 8.9 cm
Colours: Black and tan - gloss
Issued: 1991 to the present

Description	U.K. £	U.S. $	Can. $
Gloss	13.50	N/A	N/A

Model No. 3262
YORKSHIRE TERRIER - Standing

Designer:	Unknown
Height:	3 ½", 8.9 cm
Colours:	Grey and sandy brown - gloss
Issued:	1991-1997

Description	U.K. £	U.S. $	Can. $
Gloss	12.00	20.00	30.00

Model No. 3270
GOLDEN RETRIEVER - Standing

Designer:	Unknown
Height:	2 ¾", 7.0 cm
Colours:	Pale golden brown - gloss
Issued:	1991 to the present

Description	U.K. £	U.S. $	Can. $
Gloss	11.00	N/A	N/A

Model No. 3375
HOUNDS - Seated

Designer:	Martyn Alcock
Height:	2 ¼", 5.7 cm
Colours:	Black, tan and white - gloss
Issued:	1993-1997

Description	U.K. £	U.S. $	Can. $
Gloss	15.00	25.00	40.00

Model No. 3376
GOLDEN RETRIEVERS - Seated

Designer:	Martyn Alcock
Height:	2", 5.0 cm
Colours:	Golden brown - gloss
Issued:	1993-1997

Description	U.K. £	U.S. $	Can. $
Gloss	15.00	25.00	40.00

Model No. 3377
COCKER SPANIEL - Standing

Designer: Amanda Hughes-Lubeck
Height: 3″, 7.6 cm
Colours: Golden brown - gloss
Issued: 1993-1997

Description	U.K. £	U.S. $	Can. $
Gloss	12.00	25.00	42.00

Model No. 3378
ALSATIAN - Lying

Designer: Amanda Hughes-Lubeck
Height: 2 ½″, 6.4 cm
Colours: Black and cream - gloss
Issued: 1993 to the present

Description	U.K. £	U.S. $	Can. $
Gloss	11.00	N/A	42.00

Model No. 3379
BULLDOG - Seated

Designer: Warren Platt
Height: 2 ½″, 6.4 cm
Colours: White with pale tan patch - gloss
Issued: 1993 to the present

Description	U.K. £	U.S. $	Can. $
Gloss	11.00	N/A	42.00

Model No. 3380
JACK RUSSELL TERRIER - Standing

Designer: Warren Platt
Height: 2 ½″, 6.4 cm
Colours: White with pale brown ears and patches
on head - gloss
Issued: 1993-1997

Description	U.K. £	U.S. $	Can. $
Gloss	12.00	25.00	42.00

Model No. 3381
RETRIEVER - Standing

Designer:	Warren Platt
Height:	2", 5.0 cm
Colours:	Golden brown - gloss
Issued:	1993-1997

Description	U.K. £	U.S. $	Can. $
Gloss	12.00	25.00	42.00

Model No. 3382
SCOTTISH TERRIER - Standing

Designer:	Martyn Alcock
Height:	3", 7.6 cm
Colours:	Black - gloss
Issued:	1993 to the present

Description	U.K. £	U.S. $	Can. $
Gloss	11.00	N/A	42.00

Model No. 3383
COCKER SPANIELS - Seated

Designer:	Martyn Alcock
Height:	2", 5.0 cm
Colours:	Golden brown - gloss
Issued:	1993-1997

Description	U.K. £	U.S. $	Can. $
Gloss	15.00	25.00	42.00

Model No. 3384
BULLDOGS - Seated

Designer:	Martyn Alcock
Height:	2 ¼", 5.7 cm
Colours:	White with pale tan patches - gloss
Issued:	1994 to the present

Description	U.K. £	U.S. $	Can. $
Gloss	13.50	N/A	42.00

Model No. 3385
DALMATIAN - Standing

Designer:	Amanda Hughes-Lubeck
Height:	3", 7.6 cm
Colours:	White with black spots - gloss
Issued:	1994-1997

Description	U.K. £	U.S. $	Can. $
Gloss	18.00	30.00	42.00

Model No. 3436
CAVALIER KING CHARLES SPANIEL - Seated

Designer:	Amanda Hughes-Lubeck
Height:	2 ½", 6.4 cm
Colours:	White with golden brown patches - gloss
Issued:	1994 to the present

Description	U.K. £	U.S. $	Can. $
Gloss	11.00	N/A	42.00

Model No. 3467
WEST HIGHLAND WHITE TERRIERS - Seated

Designer:	Amanda Hughes-Lubeck
Height:	2", 5.0 cm
Colours:	White - gloss
Issued:	1994 to the present

Description	U.K. £	U.S. $	Can. $
Gloss	13.50	N/A	42.00

Model No. 3468
OLD ENGLISH SHEEPDOGS - Seated

Designer:	Warren Platt
Height:	2", 5.0 cm
Colours:	Grey and white - gloss
Issued:	1995 to the present

Description	U.K. £	U.S. $	Can. $
Gloss	13.50	N/A	53.00

Model No. 3475
BOXERS - One seated, one lying

Designer: Amanda Hughes-Lubeck
Height: 2 ¼", 5.7 cm
Colours: Tan - gloss
Issued: 1995 to the present

Description	U.K. £	U.S. $	Can. $
Gloss	15.00	N/A	58.00

Model No. 3490
ROTTWEILERS - One seated, one lying

Designer: Warren Platt
Height: 2", 5.0 cm
Colours: Black and tan - gloss
Issued: 1995-1997

Description	U.K. £	U.S. $	Can. $
Gloss	16.00	35.00	58.00

Chapter Five

FARM ANIMALS - CATTLE

As the number of Beswick collectors grows dramatically, this particular section of Beswick animals has become more popular. This is mainly due to the accurate reproduction of champion-stock animals, where meticulous attention to detail by the designers and modellers at the Beswick factory, and now the Beswick Studio of Royal Doulton, has produced some superb models over the years.

This is very noticeable with the Hereford Cattle, since as the breed standard has changed, the models have been updated. Just compare the models of the early Herefords with the ones that followed; they are very different in shape.

It is also interesting to note that when the calves were discontinued in the mid 1970s, with the exception of the Friesian, public pressure brought about their reintroduction ten years later. Although the later models were altered from the originals, they can all live together as one happy family. Thus, for example, Aberdeen Angus Cattle becomes a set of four rather than just three.

The models of the best-known breeds have survived to the present, but the lesser-known breeds, such as the Galloways, sadly had a short production run and now, as a result, are highly sought after by collectors.

The Connoisseur Range of cattle on polished wooden bases is truly impressive. With a satin matt finish, more detail can generally be achieved than on the gloss models—this, of course, was reflected in the retail price.

After nearly forty years, 1997 was the last year Farm Animals were in production.

MODEL NUMBER INDEX

Model No. 854
HEREFORD CALF

Designer:	Arthur Gredington
Height:	4 ½", 11.9 cm
Colour:	1. Brown and white - gloss
	2. Roan - gloss
	3. Blue
Issued:	1940-c.1957

Description	U.K. £	U.S. $	Can. $
1. Brown/white	150.00	250.00	350.00
2. Roan	150.00	250.00	350.00
3. Blue	200.00	350.00	450.00

Model No. 899
HEREFORD COW
First Version - Horns are upright

Designer:	Arthur Gredington
Height:	5", 12.7 cm
Colour:	Brown and white - gloss
Issued:	1941-1941
Varieties:	948 (Horns point forward)

Description	U.K. £	U.S. $	Can. $
Gloss	275.00	450.00	650.00

Note: Model no. 899 was remodelled in 1941 and became model no. 948.

Model No. 901A
HEREFORD CALF
First Version - Mouth open

Designer:	Arthur Gredington
Height:	4", 10.1 cm
Colour:	1. Roan and white - gloss
	2. Tan and white - gloss
Issued:	1940-Unknown
Varieties:	901B (mouth closed)

Description	U.K. £	U.S. $	Can. $
1. Roan/white	200.00	350.00	500.00
2. Tan/white	200.00	350.00	450.00

Model No. 901B
HEREFORD CALF
Second Version - Mouth closed

Designer:	Arthur Gredington
Height:	3 ¾", 9.5 cm
Colour:	Brown and white - gloss
Issued:	Unknown-c.1957
Varieties:	901A (mouth open)

Description	U.K. £	U.S. $	Can. $
Gloss	75.00	150.00	225.00

Model No. 948
HEREFORD COW
Second Version - Horns point forward

Designer:	Arthur Gredington
Height:	5", 12.7 cm
Colour:	Brown and white - gloss
Issued:	1941-c.1957
Varieties:	899 (horns are upright)

Description	U.K. £	U.S. $	Can. $
Gloss	200.00	350.00	475.00

Note: Model no. 948 was remodelled in 1941 from model no. 899.

Model No. 949
HEREFORD BULL

Designer:	Arthur Gredington
Height:	5 ¾", 14.6 cm
Colour:	Brown and white - gloss
Issued:	1941-c.1957

Description	U.K. £	U.S. $	Can. $
Gloss	175.00	275.00	375.00

Model No. 1248A
GUERNSEY COW
First Version - Horns and ears separate

Designer:	Arthur Gredington
Height:	4 ¼", 10.8 cm
Colour:	Golden brown and white - gloss
Issued:	1952-1953
Varieties:	1248B (Horns and ears moulded together)

Description	U.K. £	U.S. $	Can. $
Gloss	175.00	300.00	450.00

Note: Modelled from the Standard of the Guernsey Cattle Society.

Model No. 1248B
GUERNSEY COW
Second Version - Horns and ears are moulded together

Designer:	Arthur Gredington
Height:	4 ¼", 10.8 cm
Colour:	Golden brown and white - gloss or matt
Issued:	1. Gloss - 1953-1989
	2. Matt - 1985-1989
Varieties:	1248A (Horns and ears separate)

Description	U.K. £	U.S. $	Can. $
1. Gloss	80.00	150.00	250.00
2. Matt	70.00	125.00	200.00

Model No. 1248B/1249A
GUERNSEY COW AND CALF - on wooden plinth

Designer:	Arthur Gredington
Height:	4 ¼", 10.8 cm
Colour:	Golden brown and white - matt
Issued:	c.1988

Description	U.K. £	U.S. $	Can. $
Matt	175.00	275.00	375.00

Note: Cow is no. 1248B; Calf is no. 1249A. Issued as a special commission for the Guernsey Cattle Society c.1988

Model No. 1249A
GUERNSEY CALF

Designer:	Arthur Gredington		
Height:	2 ¾", 7.0 cm		
Colour:	Golden brown and white - gloss or matt		
Issued:	1.	Gloss - 1952-1975	
	2.	Matt - 1987-1989	
Reissued:	3.	Gloss - 1985-1989	

Description	U.K. £	U.S. $	Can. $
1. Gloss	40.00	65.00	90.00
2. Matt	25.00	50.00	75.00
3. Gloss reissued	30.00	55.00	75.00

Model No. 1249B
AYRSHIRE CALF

Designer:	Arthur Gredington		
Height:	2 ¾", 7.0 cm		
Colour:	Brown and white - gloss or matt		
Modelled:	1952		
Issued:	1.	Gloss - 1956-1975	
	2.	Matt - 1987-1989	
Reissued:	3.	Gloss - 1985-1990	

Description	U.K. £	U.S. $	Can. $
1. Gloss	40.00	65.00	90.00
2. Matt	25.00	50.00	75.00
3. Gloss reissued	30.00	55.00	75.00

Model No. 1249C
FRIESIAN CALF

Designer:	Arthur Gredington		
Height:	2 ¾", 7.0 cm		
Colour:	Black and white - gloss or matt		
Modelled:	1952		
Issued:	1.	Gloss - 1956-1997	
	2.	Matt - 1987-1989	

Description	U.K. £	U.S. $	Can. $
1. Gloss	17.00	30.00	50.00
2. Matt	25.00	45.00	60.00

Model No. 1249D
JERSEY CALF

Designer:	Arthur Gredington
Height:	2 ¾", 6.4 cm
Colour:	Light brown with shading darker around the head - gloss or matt
Issued:	1. 1956-1975
	2. 1987-1989
Reissued:	3. 1985-1997

Description	U.K. £	U.S. $	Can. $
1. Gloss	40.00	65.00	90.00
2 Matt	25.00	45.00	60.00
3. Gloss reissued	20.00	35.00	45.00

Model No. 1249E
HEREFORD CALF

Designer:	Arthur Gredington
Height:	2 ¾", 7.0 cm
Colour:	Brown and white - gloss
Modelled:	1952
Issued:	This model was especially commissioned, sometime between 1975 and 1985, when the only calf in production was the Friesian.

Description	U.K. £	U.S. $	Can. $
Gloss	80.00	125.00	175.00

Model No. 1345
JERSEY COW CH. "NEWTON TINKLE"

Designer:	Arthur Gredington
Height:	4 ¼", 10.8 cm
Colour:	Light brown with shading darker around the head - gloss or matt
Issued:	1. Gloss - 1954-1997
	2. Matt - 1985-1989

Description	U.K. £	U.S. $	Can. $
1. Gloss	30.00	50.00	75.00
2. Matt	50.00	120.00	175.00

Model No. 1345/1249D
JERSEY COW AND CALF - on wooden plinth

Designer:	Arthur Gredington
Height:	5 ¼", 13.3 cm
Colour:	Light brown with shading especially around the head - gloss
Issued:	1993-1996
Series:	Plinthed Animals

Description	U.K. £	U.S. $	Can. $
Gloss	60.00	100.00	130.00

Note: Cow is no. 1345; Calf is no. 1249D.

Model No. 1350
AYRSHIRE COW CH. "ICKHAM BESSIE"

Designer:	Arthur Gredington
Height:	5", 12.7 cm
Colour:	Brown and white - gloss or matt
Issued:	1. Gloss - 1954-1990
	2. Matt - 1985-1989

Description	U.K. £	U.S. $	Can. $
1. Gloss	90.00	150.00	250.00
2. Matt	80.00	150.00	225.00

Model No. 1360
HEREFORD COW

Designer:	Arthur Gredington
Height:	4 ¼", 10.8 cm
Colour:	Brown and white - gloss or matt
Issued:	1. Gloss - 1954-1997
	2. Matt - 1985-1989

Description	U.K. £	U.S. $	Can. $
1. Gloss	30.00	50.00	75.00
2. Matt	60.00	120.00	175.00

Note: Modelled from the standard of the Hereford Cattle Society.

Model No. 1360/1827C
HEREFORD COW AND CALF - on wooden plinth

Designer:	Graham Tongue
Height:	7", 17.8 cm
Colour:	Brown and white - gloss
Issued:	1993-1996
Series:	Plinthed Animals

Description	U.K. £	U.S. $	Can. $
Gloss	55.00	90.00	125.00

Note: Cow is no. 1360; Calf is no. 1827C.

Model No. 1362A
FRIESIAN COW
CH. "CLAYBURY LEEGWATER"

Designer:	Arthur Gredington
Height:	4 ½", 11.9 cm
Colour:	Black and white - gloss or matt
Issued:	1. Gloss - 1954-1997
	2. Matt - 1985-1989
Varieties:	1362B

Description	U.K. £	U.S. $	Can. $
1. Gloss	30.00	50.00	75.00
2. Matt	60.00	12000	175.00

Model No. 1362B
RED FRIESIAN COW

Designer:	Arthur Gredington
Height:	4 ½", 11.9 cm
Colour:	Brown and white - gloss
Modelled:	1954
Issued:	1992 in an edition of 130
Varieties:	1362A

Description	U.K. £	U.S. $	Can. $
Gloss	700.00	1,250.00	1,500.00

Note: Produced for the Beswick Collectors Circle with special B.C.C. and Beswick backstamps.

Model No. 1362/1249C
FRIESIAN COW AND CALF - on wooden plinth

Designer:	Graham Tongue
Height:	5 ½", 14.0 cm
Colour:	Black and white - gloss
Issued:	1993-1996
Series:	Plinthed Animals

Description	U.K. £	U.S. $	Can. $
Gloss	60.00	100.00	150.00

Note: Cow is no. 1362; Calf is no. 1249C.

Model No. 1363A
HEREFORD BULL
First Version - Horns pertrude from ears

Designer:	Arthur Gredington
Height:	4 ½", 10.8 cm
Colour:	Brown and white - gloss
Issued:	1955-unknown

Description	U.K. £	U.S. $	Can. $
Gloss	50.00	100.00	150.00

Model No. 1363B
HEREFORD BULL
Second Version - Horns flush to ears

Designer:	Arthur Gredinton
Height:	4 ½", 10.8 cm
Colour:	Brown and white - gloss or matt
Issued:	1. Gloss - Unknown-1997
	2. Matt - 1985-1989

Description	U.K. £	U.S. $	Can. $
1. Gloss	30.00	55.00	75.00
2. Matt	60.00	100.00	150.00

Note: Modelled from the standard of the Hereford Cattle Society. This model has also appeared as a money-box.

Model No. 1363C
HEREFORD BULL - on wooden plinth

Designer: Arthur Gredington
Height: 5 ½″, 14.0 cm
Colour: Brown and white - satin matt
Modelled: 1955
Issued: 1968-1975
Series: Connoisseur

Description	U.K. £	U.S. $	Can. $
Satin matt	175.00	300.00	400.00

Note: Issued on a teak stand. The base was changed to polished wood in 1974.

Model No. 1406A
ABERDEEN ANGUS CALF

Designer: Arthur Gredington
Height: 3″, 7.6 cm
Colour: Black - gloss
Issued: 1956-1975

Description	U.K. £	U.S. $	Can. $
Gloss	125.00	200.00	300.00

Model No. 1406B
HEREFORD CALF

Designer: Arthur Gredington
Height: 3″, 7.6 cm
Colour: Brown and white - gloss
Issued: 1956-1975

Description	U.K. £	U.S. $	Can. $
Gloss	150.00	250.00	350.00

Model No. 1406C
DAIRY SHORTHORN CALF

Designer: Arthur Gredington
Height: 3″, 7.6 cm
Colour: Brown and white with shading - gloss
Issued: 1956-1973

Description	U.K. £	U.S. $	Can. $
Gloss	450.00	750.00	950.00

Model No. 1422
JERSEY BULL CH. "DUNSLEY COY BOY"

Designer:	Arthur Gredington
Height:	4 ½", 11.9 cm
Colour:	Light brown with shading and darker head - gloss or matt
Issued	1. Gloss - 1956-1997
	2. Matt - 1985-1989

Description	U.K. £	U.S. $	Can. $
1. Gloss	30.00	55.00	75.00
2. Matt	50.00	110.00	150.00

Model No. 1439A
FRIESIAN BULL
CH. "CODDINGTON HILT BAR"

Designer:	Arthur Gredington
Height:	4 ¾", 12.1 cm
Colour:	Black and white - gloss or matt
Issued:	1. Gloss - 1956-1997
	2. Matt - 1985-1989

Description	U.K. £	U.S. $	Can. $
1. Gloss	36.00	60.00	80.00
2. Matt	50.00	110.00	150.00

Model No. 1439B
FRIESIAN BULL - on teak plinth

Designer:	Arthur Gredington
Height:	5 ½", 14.0 cm
Colour:	Black and white - satin matt
Modelled:	1956
Issued:	1968-1973
Varieties:	1439A
Series:	Connoisseur Cattle

Description	U.K. £	U.S. $	Can. $
Satin matt	175.00	300.00	450.00

Model No. 1439C
RED FRIESIAN BULL

Designer:	Arthur Gredington
Height:	4 ¾", 12.1 cm
Colour:	Brown and white - gloss
Modelled:	1956
Issued:	1992 in an edition of 129

Description	U.K. £	U.S. $	Can. $
Gloss	750.00	1,250.00	1,500.00

Note: Produced for the Beswick Collectors Circle with special B.C.C. and Beswick backstamps.

Model No. 1451
GUERNSEY BULL
CH. "SABRINA'S SIR RICHMOND 14ᵗʰ"

Designer:	Colin Melbourne
Height:	4 ¾", 11.9 cm
Colour:	Tan/brown and white - gloss or matt
Issued:	1. Gloss - 1956-1989
	2. Matt - 1985-1989

Description	U.K. £	U.S. $	Can. $
1. Gloss	100.00	175.00	250.00
2. Matt	100.00	175.00	250.00

Photograph not
available at press time

Model No. 1454A
AYRSHIRE BULL CH. "WHITEHILL MANDATE"
First Version

Designer:	Colin Melbourne
Height:	5 ¼", 13.3 cm
Colour:	Brown and white with shading - gloss
Issued:	1956-1957

Description	U.K. £	U.S. $	Can. $
Gloss		Rare	

Model No. 1454B
AYRSHIRE BULL CH. "WHITEHILL MANDATE"
Second Version

Designer:	Colin Melbourne
Height:	5 ¼", 13.3 cm
Colour:	Brown, white and shaded - gloss or matt
Issued:	1. Gloss - 1957-1990
	2. Matt - 1985-1989

Description	U.K. £	U.S. $	Can. $
1. Gloss	100.00	175.00	250.00
2. Matt	100.00	175.00	250.00

Model No. 1504
DAIRY SHORTHORN BULL
CH. "GWERSYLT LORD OXFORD 74ᵗʰ"

Designer:	Arthur Gredington
Height:	5", 12.7 cm
Colour:	Brown and white with shading - gloss
Issued:	1957-1973

Description	U.K. £	U.S. $	Can. $
Gloss	500.00	900.00	1,250.00

Model No. 1510
DAIRY SHORTHORN COW
CH. "EATON WILD EYES 91 ST"

Designer: Arthur Gredington
Height: 4 ¾", 12.1 cm
Colour: Brown and white with shading - gloss
Issued: 1957-1973

Description	U.K. £	U.S. $	Can. $
Gloss	700.00	1,250.00	1,500.00

Model No. 1562
ABERDEEN ANGUS BULL

Designer: Arthur Gredington
Height: 4 ½", 11.9 cm
Colour: Black - gloss or matt
Issued: 1. Gloss - 1958-1989
2. Matt - 1985-1989

Description	U.K. £	U.S. $	Can. $
1. Gloss	150.00	250.00	350.00
2. Matt	125.00	250.00	350.00

Note: This model was approved by a panel of judges of the Breed Society.

Model No. 1563
ABERDEEN ANGUS COW

Designer: Arthur Gredington
Height: 4 ¼", 10.8 cm
Colour: Black - gloss or matt
Issued: 1. Gloss - 1959-1989
2. Matt - 1985-1989

Description	U.K. £	U.S. $	Can. $
1. Gloss	150.00	250.00	350.00
2. Matt	125.00	250.00	350.00

Note: This model was approved by a panel of judges of the Breed Society.

Model No. 1740
HIGHLAND COW

Designer: Arthur Gredington
Height: 5 ¼", 3.3 cm
Colour: Tan and brown - gloss or matt
Issued: 1. Gloss - 1961-1990
2. Matt - 1985-1989

Description	U.K. £	U.S. $	Can. $
1. Gloss	95.00	175.00	250.00
2. Matt	90.00	175.00	250.00

Photograph not
available at press time

Model No. 1746A
GALLOWAY BULL

Designer:	Arthur Gredington
Height:	4 ½", 11.9 cm
Colour:	Black - gloss
Modelled:	1961
Issued:	1962-1969
Varieties:	1746B, 1746C

Description	U.K. £	U.S. $	Can. $
Gloss	1,000.00	1,500.00	2,000.00

Model No. 1746B
GALLOWAY BULL - BELTED

Designer:	Arthur Gredington
Height:	4 ½", 11.9 cm
Colour:	Black and white - gloss
Modelled:	1961
Issued:	1963-1969
Varieties:	1746A, 1746C

Description	U.K. £	U.S. $	Can. $
Gloss	1,200.00	2,000.00	2,750.00

Model No. 1746C
GALLOWAY BULL - SILVER DUNN

Designer:	Arthur Gredington
Height:	4 ½", 11.9 cm
Colour:	Fawn and brown - gloss
Modelled:	1961
Issued:	1962-1969
Varieties:	1746A, 1746B

Description	U.K. £	U.S. $	Can. $
Gloss	950.00	1,500.00	2,000.00

Model No. 1827A
ABERDEEN ANGUS CALF

Designer:	Arthur Gredington
Height:	3", 7.6 cm
Colour:	Black - gloss or matt
Issued:	1. Gloss - 1985-1989
	2. Matt - 1987-1989

Description	U.K. £	U.S. $	Can. $
1. Gloss	125.00	200.00	275.00
2. Matt	100.00	200.00	275.00

Model No. 1827B
CHAROLAIS CALF

Designer: Arthur Gredington
Height: 3", 7.6 cm
Colour: Cream - gloss or matt
Issued: 1. Gloss - 1985-1997
           2. Matt - 1987-1989

Description	U.K. £	U.S. $	Can. $
1. Gloss	15.00	25.00	35.00
2. Matt	30.00	50.00	75.00

Model No. 1827C
HEREFORD CALF

Designer: Arthur Gredington
Height: 3", 7.6 cm
Colour: Brown and white - gloss or matt
Issued: 1. Gloss - 1985-1997
           2. Matt - 1987-1989

Description	U.K. £	U.S. $	Can. $
1. Gloss	15.00	25.00	35.00
2. Matt	30.00	50.00	75.00

Model No. 1827D
HIGHLAND CALF

Designer: Arthur Gredington
Height: 3", 7.6 cm
Colour: Tan/brown - gloss or matt
Issued: 1. Gloss - 1962-1990
           2. Matt - 1987-1989

Description	U.K. £	U.S. $	Can. $
1. Gloss	45.00	75.00	100.00
2. Matt	35.00	75.00	100.00

Model No. 2008
HIGHLAND BULL

Designer: Arthur Gredington
Height: 5", 12.7 cm
Colour: Tan/brown - gloss or matt
Issued: 1. Gloss - 1965-1990
           2. Matt - 1985-1989

Description	U.K. £	U.S. $	Can. $
1. Gloss	150.00	250.00	350.00
2. Matt	135.00	250.00	350.00

Model No. 2463
CHAROLAIS BULL

Designer:	Alan Maslankowski
Height:	5", 12.7 cm
Colour:	Cream - gloss or matt
Modelled:	1973
Issued:	1. Gloss - 1979-1997
	2. Matt - 1985-1989

Description	U.K. £	U.S. $	Can. $
1. Gloss	35.00	55.00	80.00
2. Matt	50.00	120.00	175.00

Model No. A2463
CHAROLAIS BULL - on wooden plinth

Designer:	Alan Maslankowski
Height:	5 ½", 14.0 cm
Colour:	Cream - satin matt
Modelled:	1973
Issued:	1975-1979
Series:	Connoisseur Cattle

Description	U.K. £	U.S. $	Can. $
Satin matt	175.00	300.00	400.00

Photograph not
available at press time

Model No. A2542A
HEREFORD BULL - on wooden plinth

Designer:	Graham Tongue
Height:	7 ½", 19.1 cm
Colour:	Brown and white - satin matt
Modelled:	1975
Issued:	1976-1989
Series:	Connoisseur Cattle

Description	U.K. £	U.S. $	Can. $
Satin matt	135.00	225.00	300.00

Note: Transferred to R.D.backstamp (DA19) 08/89.

Model No. A2542B
HEREFORD BULL - on ceramic base

Designer:	Graham Tongue
Height:	7 ½", 19.1 cm
Colour:	Bronze, black shading - satin
Modelled:	1975
Issued:	1989-1992
Series:	Britannia Collection

Description	U.K.£	U.S.$	Can.$
Satin	150.00	250.00	350.00

Photograph not
available at press time

Model No. 2549A
POLLED HEREFORD BULL

Designer: Graham Tongue
Height: 5", 12.7 cm
Colour: Brown, white ringed nose - gloss or matt
Modelled: 1975
Issued: 1.   Gloss - 1977-1997
              2.   Matt - 1985-1989

Description	U.K. £	U.S. $	Can. $
1. Gloss	60.00	100.00	125.00
2. Matt	70.00	115.00	150.00

Model 2549B
POLLED HEREFORD BULL

Designer: Graham Tongue
Height: 5", 12.7 cm
Colour: Bronze, black shading - satin
Modelled: 1975
Issued: 1989-1992
Series: Britannia Collection

Description	U.K.£	U.S.$	Can.$
Satin	100.00	200.00	300.00

Model No. A2574
POLLED HEREFORD BULL - on wooden plinth

Designer: Graham Tongue
Height: 7 ½", 19.1 cm
Colour: Brown and white - satin matt
Modelled: 1976
Issued: 1977-1989
Series: Connoisseur Cattle

Description	U.K. £	U.S. $	Can. $
Satin matt	135.00	225.00	300.00

Note: Transferred to R.D. backstamp (DA21) 08/89.

Model No. A2580
FRIESIAN BULL - on wooden plinth

Designer: Graham Tongue
Height: 7 ½", 19.1 cm
Colour: Black and white - satin matt
Modelled: 1976
Issued: 1978-1989
Series: Connoisseur Cattle

Description	U.K. £	U.S. $	Can. $
Satin matt	135.00	225.00	300.00

Note: Transferred to R.D. backstamp (DA23) 08/89.

Model No. A2600
CHAROLAIS BULL - on wooden plinth

Designer:	Graham Tongue
Height:	7 ½", 19.1 cm
Colour:	Cream - satin matt
Issued:	1971-1979
Series:	Connoisseur Cattle

Description	U.K. £	U.S. $	Can. $
Satin matt	135.00	225.00	350.00

Note: Transferred R.D. to backstamp (DA27) 08/89.

Model No. A2607
FRIESIAN COW - on wooden plinth

Designer:	Graham Tongue
Height:	7 ½", 19.1 cm
Colour:	Black and white - satin matt
Modelled:	1977
Issued:	1979-1989
Series:	Connoisseur Cattle

Description	U.K. £	U.S. $	Can. $
Satin matt	135.00	225.00	300.00

Note: Transferred to R.D. backstamp (DA29) 08/89.

Model No. A2607/2690
FRIESIAN COW AND CALF - on wooden plinth

Designer:	Graham Tongue
Height:	6 ½", 16.5 cm
Colour:	Black and white - satin matt
Modelled:	Cow - 1977; Calf - 1982
Issued:	1982-1989
Series:	Connoisseur Cattle

Description	U.K. £	U.S. $	Can. $
Satin matt	175.00	300.00	375.00

Note: Cow is no. A2607; Calf is no. 2690, never issued individually. Transferred to R.D. backstamp (DA3) 08/89.

Model No. A2648/2652
CHAROLAIS COW AND CALF - on wooden plinth

Designer:	Graham Tongue
Height:	7 ¼", 18.4 cm
Colour:	Cream - satin matt
Modelled:	1979
Issued:	1981-1989
Series:	Connoisseur

Description	U.K. £	U.S. $	Can. $
Satin matt	175.00	300.00	400.00

Note: Cow is no. A2648; Calf is no. 2652 which was never issued individually. Transferred to R.D. backstamp (DA33) 08/89.

Model No. A2667/2669
HEREFORD COW AND CALF - on wooden plinth

Designer:	Graham Tongue
Height:	7", 17.8 cm
Colour:	Brown and white - satin matt
Modelled:	1980
Issued:	1981-1989
Series:	Connoisseur

Description	U.K. £	U.S. $	Can. $
Satin matt	175.00	300.00	400.00

Note: Cow is no. A2667; Calf is no. 2669, which was never issued individually. Transferred to R.D. backstamp (DA34) 08/89.

Model No. 2690
RED FRIESIAN CALF

Designer:	Graham Tongue
Height:	2 ¼", 5.7 cm
Colour:	Brown and white - gloss
Modelled:	1980
Issued:	1992 in a special edition of 132

Description	U.K. £	U.S. $	Can. $
Gloss	·	400.00	675.00	900.00

Note: Produced as a free standing model, in this special colourway for The Beswick Collectors Circle. The B.C.C. backstamp appears in addition to the normal Beswick Backstamp.

Model No. 2792
DAISY THE COW CREAMER

Designer:	Graham Tongue
Height:	5 ¾", 14.6 cm
Colour:	A variety of floral decorations, blue flowers or yellow being the most common, but all on a white background
Issued:	1982-1989
Series:	Fun models

Description	U.K. £	U.S. $	Can. $
1. Blue	50.00	125.00	150.00
2. Yellow	50.00	125.00	150.00

Model No. 3075
CHAROLAIS COW

Designer:	Unknown
Height:	5", 12.7 cm
Colour:	Cream - gloss or matt
Modelled:	1987
Issued:	1. Gloss - 1988-1997
	2. Matt - 1988-1989

Description	U.K. £	U.S. $	Can. $
1. Gloss	30.00	50.00	80.00
2. Matt	45.00	95.00	125.00

Model No. 3075/1827B
CHAROLAIS COW AND CALF - on wooden plinth

Designer: Unknown
Height: 6", 15.0 cm
Colour: Cream - gloss
Issued: 1993-1996

Description	U.K. £	U.S. $	Can. $
Gloss	55.00	95.00	125.00

Note: Cow is no. 3075; Calf is no. 1827B.

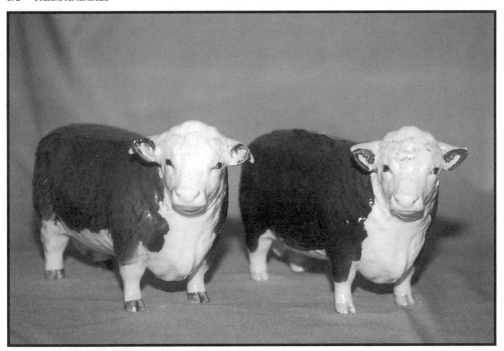

Model 1363A Version One (left) and Model 1363B Version Two (right)

Model 1363A Version One (left) and Model 1363B Version Two (right)

FARM ANIMALS
OTHERS

It is surprising that this section was never expanded to include rare breeds, but it does include most of the animals one expects to find on a farm, besides cattle.

With the exception of the earlier models, the majority of the animals in this group are realistically portrayed. Examples of this are the goat and kid, which make a delightful pair, and the donkeys, as popular now as they ever were.

Model No. 323
LAMB ON BASE

Designer: Miss Greaves
Height: 7 ½", 19.1 cm
Colour: 1. Cream - satin matt
2. Blue - gloss
3. Natural - satin matt
Issued: c.1935-by 1954

Description	U.K. £	U.S. $	Can. $
1. Cream	125.00	250.00	350.00
2. Blue	195.00	375.00	475.00
3. Natural	195.00	375.00	475.00
Note: Modelled in Deco style.			

Model No. 369
DONKEY

Designer: Miss Greaves
Height: 8", 20.3 cm
Colour: 1. Cream - satin matt
2. Blue - gloss
3. Natural - satin matt
Issued: 1936-by 1954

Description	U.K. £	U.S. $	Can. $
1. Cream	125.00	250.00	350.00
2. Blue	195.00	375.00	475.00
3. Natural	195.00	375.00	475.00
Note: Modelled in Deco style.			

Model No. 398
GOAT

Designer: Mr. Owen
Height: 4 ½", 11.9 cm
Colour: 1. Blue - gloss
2. Green - satin matt
3. White - satin matt
Issued: 1936-by 1954

Description	U.K. £	U.S. $	Can. $
1. Blue	50.00	95.00	125.00
2. Green	35.00	60.00	75.00
3. White	35.00	60.00	75.00

Model No. 832
PIG

Designer: Arthur Gredington
Height: 3 ¾", 9.5 cm
Colour: White and pink with grey patches - gloss
Issued: 1940-1971
Set: 833, 834

Description	U.K. £	U.S. $	Can. $
Gloss	40.00	70.00	95.00

Model No. 833
PIGLET - Running

Designer: Arthur Gredington
Height: 1 ¾", 4.5 cm
Colour: White and pink with grey patches - gloss
Issued: 1940-1971
Set: 832, 834

Description	U.K. £	U.S. $	Can. $
Gloss	25.00	40.00	60.00

Model No. 834
PIGLET - Trotting

Designer: Arthur Gredington
Height: 1 ½", 3.8 cm
Colour: White and pink with grey patches - gloss
Issued: 1940-1971
Set: 832, 833

Description	U.K. £	U.S. $	Can. $
Gloss	25.00	40.00	60.00

Photograph not
available at press time

Model No. 897
DONKEY FOAL

Designer: Arthur Gredington
Height: Unknown
Colour: Natural - gloss
Issued: 1941-Unknown

Description	U.K. £	U.S. $	Can. $
Gloss		Extremely Rare	

Note: Probably not put into production under this
number, see no. 950.

Model No. 935
SHEEP

Designer: Arthur Gredington
Height: 3 ½", 8.9 cm
Colour: White - gloss
Issued: 1941-1971
Set: 936, 937, 938

Description	U.K. £	U.S. $	Can. $
Gloss	30.00	50.00	70.00

Model No. 936
LAMB

Designer:	Arthur Gredington
Height:	3 ¼", 8.3 cm
Colour:	White - gloss
Issued:	1941-1971
Set:	935, 937, 938

Description	U.K. £	U.S. $	Can. $
Gloss	18.00	30.00	45.00

Model No. 937
LAMB

Designer:	Arthur Gredington
Height:	2", 5.0 cm
Colour:	White - gloss
Issued:	1941-1971
Set:	935, 936, 938

Description	U.K. £	U.S. $	Can. $
Gloss	18.00	30.00	45.00

Model No. 938
LAMB

Designer:	Arthur Gredington
Height:	2", 5.0 cm
Colour:	White - gloss
Issued:	1941-1971
Set:	935, 936, 937

Description	U.K. £	U.S. $	Can. $
Gloss	18.00	30.00	45.00

Model No. 950
DONKEY FOAL

Designer:	Arthur Gredington
Height:	5", 12.7 cm
Colour:	Grey-brown - gloss
Issued:	1941-1962

Description	U.K. £	U.S. $	Can. $
Gloss	90.00	150.00	200.00

Model No. 1035
GOAT

Designer:	Arthur Gredington		
Height:	5 ½", 14.0 cm		
Colour:	Tan - gloss		
Issued:	1945-1971		
Set:	1036		

Price	U.K. £	U.S. $	Can. $
Gloss	100.00	175.00	250.00

Model No. 1036
KID

Designer:	Arthur Gredington		
Height:	2 ½", 6.4 cm		
Colour:	Tan - gloss		
Issued:	1945-1971		
Set:	1035		

Price	U.K. £	U.S. $	Can. $
Gloss	65.00	120.00	165.00

Model No. 1364A
DONKEY
First Version

Designer:	Mr. Orwell
Height:	4 ½", 11.9 cm
Colour:	Natural - gloss
Issued:	1955-1955

Description	U.K. £	U.S. $	Can. $
Gloss		Extremely Rare	

Model No. 1364B
DONKEY
Second Version

Designer:	Mr. Orwell		
Height:	4 ½", 11.9 cm		
Colour:	Natural - gloss or matt		
Issued:	1. Gloss - 1955 to the present		
	2. Matt - 1987-1989		

Description	U.K. £	U.S. $	Can. $
1. Gloss	17.50	N/A	N/A
2. Matt	35.00	80.00	100.00

Model No. 1452A
SOW CH "WALL QUEEN 40th"

Designer:	Arthur Gredington
Height:	2 ¾", 7.0 cm
Colour:	White - gloss or matt
Issued:	1. Gloss - 1956 to the present
	2. Matt - 1987-1989

Description	U.K. £	U.S. $	Can. $
1. Gloss	17.50	N/A	N/A
2. Matt	25.00	40.00	60.00

Photograph not
available at press time

Model No. 1452B
SOW - on wooden plinth

Designer:	Arthur Gredington
Height:	3 ¾", 9.5 cm
Colour:	White - gloss
Issued:	1993-1995

Description	U.K. £	U.S. $	Can. $
Gloss	30.00	50.00	65.00

Model No. 1453A
BOAR Ch. "WALL CHAMPION BOY 53rd"

Designer:	Arthur Gredington
Height:	2 ¾", 7.0 cm
Colour:	White - gloss or matt
Issued:	1. Gloss - 1956 to the present
	2. Matt - 1987-1989

Description	U.K. £	U.S. $	Can. $
1. Gloss	17.50	N/A	N/A
2. Matt	25.00	40.00	60.00

Photograph not
available at press time

Model No. 1453B
BOAR - on wooden plinth

Designer:	Arthur Gredington
Height:	3 ¾", 9.5 cm
Colour:	White - gloss
Issued:	1993 -1995

Description	U.K. £	U.S. $	Can. $
Gloss	30.00	50.00	65.00

Model No. 1511
WESSEX SADDLEBACK SOW
 "MERRYWOOD SILVER WINGS 56th"

Designer:	Colin Melbourne	
Height:	2 ¾", 7.0 cm	
Colour:	Black and white - gloss	
Issued:	1957-1969	
Set:	1512	

Description	U.K. £	U.S. $	Can. $
Gloss	350.00	575.00	775.00

Model No. 1512
WESSEX SADDLEBACK BOAR
 "FARACRE VISCOUNT 3rd"

Designer:	Colin Melbourne	
Height:	2 ¾", 7.0 cm	
Colour:	Black and white - gloss	
Issued:	1957-1969	
Set:	1511	

Description	U.K. £	U.S. $	Can. $
Gloss	350.00	575.00	775.00

Model No. 1760
PIGGY BANK

Designer:	Albert Hallam	
Height:	8 ½", 21.6 cm	
Colour:	White, grey and pink - gloss	
Issued:	1961-1967	
Series:	Fun Models	

Description	U.K. £	U.S. $	Can. $
Various	85.00	150.00	200.00

Model No. 1765
BLACK-FACED SHEEP

Designer:	Mr. Garbet	
Height:	3 ¼", 8.3 cm	
Colour:	Black and white - gloss or matt	
Modelled:	1961	
Issued:	1. Gloss - 1963 to the present	
	2. Matt - 1987-1989	
Set:	1828	

Description	U.K. £	U.S. $	Can. $
1. Gloss	15.00	N/A	N/A
2. Matt	20.00	40.00	60.00

Model No. 1765/1828
BLACK-FACED SHEEP AND LAMB
- on wooden plinth

Designer:	Mr. Garbet and Arthur Gredington
Height:	3 ¾", 9.5 cm
Colour:	Black and white - gloss
Issued:	1993-1996

Description	U.K. £	U.S. $	Can. $
Gloss	30.00	50.00	85.00

Note: Sheep is no. 1765; Lamb is no. 1828.

Model No. 1828
BLACK-FACED LAMB

Designer:	Arthur Gredington
Height:	2 ½", 6.4 cm
Colour:	Black and white - gloss or matt
Modelled:	1962
Issued:	1. Gloss - 1963 to the present
	2. Matt - 1987-1989
Set:	1765

Description	U.K. £	U.S. $	Can. $
1. Gloss	10.00	N/A	N/A
2. Matt	15.00	25.00	35.00

Model No. 1917
MERINO RAM

Designer:	Arthur Gredington
Height:	4 ¼", 10.8 cm
Colour:	Grey with white face - gloss
Modelled:	1963
Issued:	1964-1967

Description	U.K. £	U.S. $	Can. $
Gloss	275.00	475.00	650.00

Model No. 2103
LAUGHING PIGS

Designer:	Albert Hallam
Height:	2 ¾", 7.0 cm
Colour:	White and pink - gloss
Modelled:	1967
Issued:	1968-1971
Series:	Fun Models

Description	U.K. £	U.S. $	Can. $
Gloss	85.00	150.00	225.00

Model No. 2110
DONKEY FOAL

Designer:	Graham Tongue
Height:	4 ½", 11.9 cm
Colour:	Grey-brown - gloss or matt
Modelled:	1967
Issued:	1. Gloss - 1968 to the present
	2. Matt - 1987-1989

Description	U.K. £	U.S. $	Can. $
1. Gloss	15.00	N/A	N/A
2. Matt	20.00	35.00	45.00

Model No. 2267
DONKEY

Designer:	Albert Hallam and Graham Tongue
Height:	5 ½", 14.0 cm
Colour:	Grey-brown - gloss or matt
Modelled:	1969
Issued:	1. Gloss - 1970 to the present
	2. Matt - 1987-1989

Description	U.K. £	U.S. $	Can. $
1. Gloss	20.00	N/A	N/A
2. Matt	35.00	55.00	80.00

Model No. 2294
PIGLET CANDLEHOLDER

Designer:	Harry Sales
Length:	11" x 3 ½", 27.9 x 8.9 cm
Colour:	1. Blue and white - gloss
	2. Brown - gloss
Modelled:	1969
Issued:	1970-1972
Series:	Fun Models

Description	U.K. £	U.S. $	Can. $
1. Blue/white	65.00	125.00	175.00
2. Brown	50.00	100.00	125.00

Note: This candlestick has four candle holders.

Model No. 2746
PIG AND PIGLET "Piggy Back"

Designer:	Graham Tongue
Length:	6 ½", 16.5 cm
Colour:	Pink and white - gloss
Modelled:	1981
Issued:	1983-1994
Series:	Fun Models

Description	U.K. £	U.S. $	Can. $
Gloss	40.00	70.00	95.00

Model No. 3071
BLACK-FACED RAM

Designer:	Mr. Chawner
Height:	3 ¼", 8.3 cm
Colour:	Black and white - gloss or matt
Modelled:	1987
Issued:	1. Gloss - 1988 to the present
	2. Matt - 1988-1989

Description	U.K. £	U.S. $	Can. $
1. Gloss	20.00	N/A	N/A
2. Matt	30.00	50.00	65.00

Model No. 3071/1765
"EWE AND I" - on ceramic plinth

Designer:	Unknown
Height:	4 ½", 11.9 cm
Base:	7 ½", 19.1 cm
Colour:	Black and white - gloss
Issued:	Unknown

Description	U.K. £	U.S. $	Can. $
Gloss	75.00	125.00	175.00

Note: Ram is no. 3071; Sheep is no. 1765.
Produced as a special commission.

Chapter Six

FISH

All but two of these fish models are realistically portrayed. The detail on many of them is amazing, for example the Golden Trout. So many colours were used, and the result is simply stunning.

The only stylized version of a fish is one from the Moda series. All the rest are supported on bases, although their fins are still vulnerable to damage. Very few, therefore, have survived intact to the present, and as a result they are particularly hard to find in mint condition, although restored ones do appear.

INDEX BY MODEL NUMBER

Model No. 1032

TROUT

Designer:	Arthur Gredington
Height:	6 ¼", 15.9 cm
Colour:	Brown and dark green - gloss
Issued:	1945-1975

Model		Price	
No.	U.K. £	U.S. $	Can. $
1032	75.00	175.00	250.00

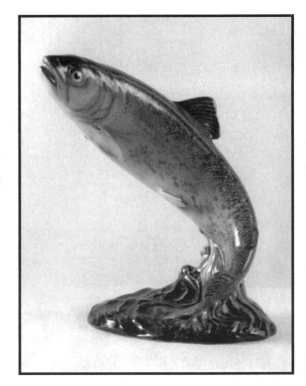

Model No. 1047

ANGEL FISH

Designer:	Arthur Gredington
Height:	7 ¼", 18.4 cm
Colour:	Silver, red and green-brown - gloss
Issued:	1946-1967

Model		Price	
No.	U.K. £	U.S. $	Can. $
1047	175.00	400.00	600.00

Model No. 1232

OCEANIC BONITO

Designer:	Arthur Gredington
Height:	7 ¼", 18.4 cm
Colour:	Blue, silver and green - gloss
Issued:	1952-1968

Model		Price	
No.	U.K. £	U.S. $	Can. $
1232	250.00	425.00	575.00

Model No. 1233

ATLANTIC SALMON

Designer:	Arthur Gredington
Height:	6 ½", 16.5 cm
Colour:	Blue, silver and green - gloss
Issued:	1952-1970

Model		Price	
No.	U.K. £	U.S. $	Can. $
1233	140.00	275.00	400.00

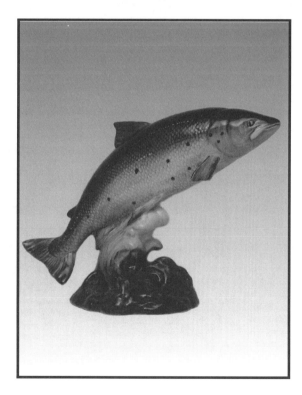

Model No. 1235

BARRACUDA

Designer: Arthur Gredington
Colour: Blue and silver

Model No.	Finish	Height	Intro.	Disc.	U.K. £	Price U.S. $	Can. $
1235	Gloss	4 ¾", 12.1 cm	1952	1968	250.00	425.00	575.00

Model No. 1243

MARLIN

Designer: Arthur Gredington
Colour: Blue, grey and green

Model No.	Finish	Height	Intro.	Disc.	U.K. £	Price U.S. $	Can. $
1243	Gloss	5 ½", 14.0 cm	1952	1970	350.00	650.00	850.00

Model No. 1246

GOLDEN TROUT

Designer: Arthur Gredington
Colour: Blue, yellow and green

Model No.	Finish	Height	Intro.	Disc.	U.K. £	Price U.S. $	Can. $
1246	Gloss	6", 15.0 cm	1952	1970	125.00	300.00	400.00

Model No. 1266

LARGE-MOUTHED BLACK BASS

Designer: Arthur Gredington
Colour: Yellow, black, beige and blue

Model No.	Finish	Height	Intro.	Disc.	U.K. £	Price U.S. $	Can. $
1266	Gloss	5", 12.7 cm	1952	1968	225.00	400.00	525.00

Model No. 1304

FISH TRAY/TRINKET DISH

Designer: Arthur Gredington
Colour: Blues, yellow, browns and pink with black - gloss

Model No.	Finish	Length	Intro.	Disc.	U.K.£	Price U.S.$	Can. $
1304	Gloss	5", 12.7 cm	1953	1966	50.00	100.00	150.00

Model No. 1390

TROUT

Designer: Arthur Gredington
Colour: Brown and dark green - gloss
Height: 4", 10.1 cm
Issued: 1955-1975

Model No.	U.K. £	Price U.S. $	Can. $
1390	55.00	130.00	175.00

Model No. 1485

BLACK BASS

Designer: Colin Melbourne
Height: 6", 15.0 cm
Colour: Brown and dark green - gloss
Issued: 1957-1968

Model No.	Price		
	U.K. £	U.S. $	Can. $
1485	225.00	400.00	525.00

Note: Illustration courtesy of Royal Doulton.

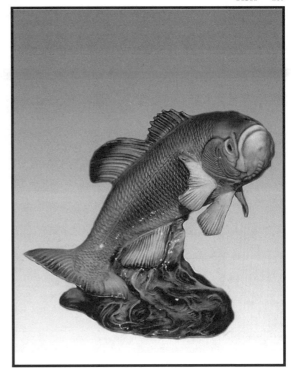

Model No. 1599

TROUT (Ash Bowl)

Designer: Graham Tongue
Height: 5", 12.7 cm
Colour: Brown fish, turquoise-blue bowl - gloss
Issued: 1959-1970

Model No.	Price		
	U.K. £	U.S. $	Can. $
1599	100.00	250.00	350.00

Model No. 1874

ROACH

Designer: Arthur Gredington
Colour: Turquoise and browns

Model No.	Finish	Length	Intro.	Disc.	U.K. £	Price U.S. $	Can. $
1874	Gloss	6 ¼", 15.9 cm	1963	1971	160.00	275.00	375.00

Model No. 1875

PERCH

Designer: Arthur Gredington
Colour: Greens and browns

Model No.	Finish	Length	Intro.	Disc.	U.K. £	Price U.S. $	Can. $
1875	Gloss	6 ¼", 15.9 cm	1963	1971	150.00	275.00	375.00

Model No. 2066

SALMON

Designer: Graham Tongue
Height: 8", 20.3 cm
Colour: Browns and silver - gloss
Issued: 1966-1975

| Model | | Price | |
No.	U.K. £	U.S. $	Can. $
2066	175.00	325.00	450.00

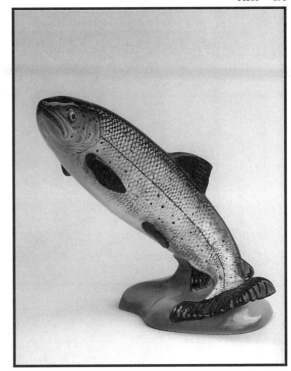

Model No. 2087

TROUT

Designer: Graham Tongue
Height: 6", 15.0 cm
Colour: Brown with red-brown spots - gloss
Issued: 1967-1975

| Model | | Price | |
No.	U.K. £	U.S. $	Can. $
2087	150.00	275.00	400.00

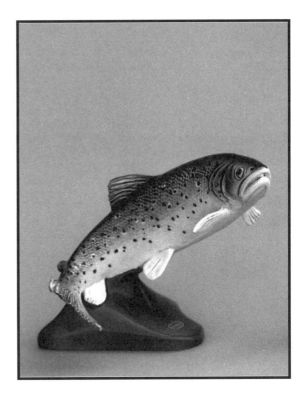

Model No 2254   **FISH (Stylized Model)**

Designer: Harry Sales
Colour: Dark and light blue
Series: Moda

Model No.	Finish	Height	Intro.	Disc.	U.K. £	Price U.S. $	Can. $
2254	Gloss	4 ½", 11.9 cm	1968	1971	115.00	195.00	275.00

Chapter Seven
HORSES

Beswick is most readily associated with the production of accurately modelled horses. Indeed horses form the largest section by far of all the Beswick range. From 1939 to 1989, Beswick produced over 150 different horse models, the vast majority available in several colourways and in gloss or matt finishes. Although each model had a shape number, many were only listed in price lists and catalogues as horse, mare or foal, which left less knowledgeable collectors and dealers with a considerable identification problem! Some horses do have their names incorporated into their backstamp (for example, the Mountain and Moorland ponies) or numbers imprinted into their base (such as the lying down foal, 915), and of course those with riders are easy to sort out. But those that remain need careful examination to determine exactly which models they are.

A further consideration is colour. Initially Beswick produced horses in dark chestnut, light brown, dark brown, rocking horse grey and even in blue gloss. Later brown, painted white, opaque, palomino, chestnut and light grey glosses were added to the range, and most of the initial colourways were dropped. Special colours were also used for specific models, such as on the 2282 Fjord. From 1970 onwards, matt finishes were introduced in various colours: brown, grey, palomino, white and black. Within each colour there can be considerable variations, from a light tone with shading to an all-over, solid, one-tone version of the same colour. Avid collectors will value the former, which usually indicates an earlier example, painted when more attention was paid to details like well-painted eyes and pink mouths.

The Beswick stable comprises the full spectrum of the equine world, from childrens ponies, specific breeds, famous racehorses, to the giant Shires, whilst the Colin Melbourne series adds a contemporary touch to the collection.

Arthur Gredington modelled Beswicks first realistic horse in 1939 when he modelled the first version of the 1938 Derby winner, Bois Roussel. Although a handful of other modellers made contributions to the horse models it was Arthur Gredington who was responsible for the vast majority until he retired in 1968. Graham Tongue then took over, adding many more horses to the range, including a new bronze finish for the Britannia Series. In August 1989 all except three Beswick horses became Doulton Animals and so from that date, although they continued to be produced in the Beswick factory, they were backstamped with the name of the parent company, Royal Doulton. In 1994 to mark the Beswick Centenary it was a horse model that was chosen as a special piece to represent Beswick. This was the large rearing model of Downland Cancara. Graham Tongue modelled this magnificent horse. In 1995 Cancara was issued with a Royal Doulton backstamp and the three remaining Beswick horses were completely withdrawn.

1996 saw the revival of the Beswick backstamp on horses when the 1642 Dartmoor pony stallion was commissioned by Doug Middleweek in bright bay gloss as "Warlord." Warlord was followed at the end of 1997 with a brand new model of a Dartmoor Mare "Another Bunch." The set will be completed in 1998 with the "birth" of their foal.

Since the publication of the 2nd edition there have been several interesting "finds" made. These have included the 953 mare and foal in brown matt and further shapes other than those previously listed have been found in opaque. In addition a small number of pieces have been discovered in black gloss, suggesting that at some point Beswick could have produced trial runs in this colourway. The most unusual and attractive colourway found during this period is the 818 Shire in "pearl" or "iron grey" gloss. This is a dark grey with white star shaped dapples all over and has been seen with a black or white mane and tail. Research at the Beswick factory found an entry in the decoration book which suggested a production date of about 1952. As there is no mention of this colourway in price lists these Shires could therefore have been a "special run" or commission.

Note: DA numbers are given for easy cross-reference with *The Charlton Standard Catalogue of Royal Doulton Animals.*

Model No. 701

BOIS ROUSSEL
RACEHORSE

There are two varieties of Bois Roussell. The first version was introduced in 1939.

FIRST VERSION : The tail is attached to the hind legs all the way down and the legs are long and thick.

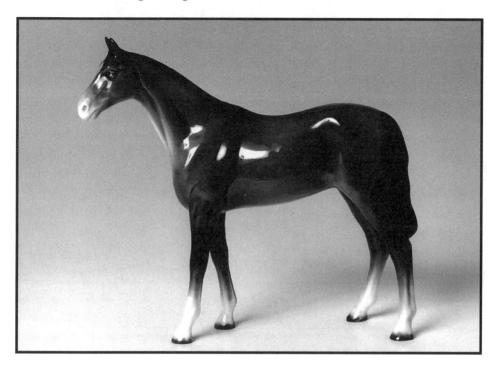

Designer: Arthur Gredington
Height: 8", 20.3 cm

Colourway	Finish	Intro.	Disc.	U.K. £	U.S. $	Can. $
Blue	Gloss	1939	1947	Extremely Rare		
Light brown	Gloss	1940	1947	275.00	475.00	625.00
Dark brown	Gloss	1940	1947	350.00	600.00	800.00
Dark chestnut	Gloss	1939	1947	350.00	750.00	1,000.00
Rocking horse grey	Gloss	c.1940	1947	500.00	850.00	1,250.00

SECOND VERSION: In 1947 Bois Roussel was remodelled with only the tail-end attached to the leg.

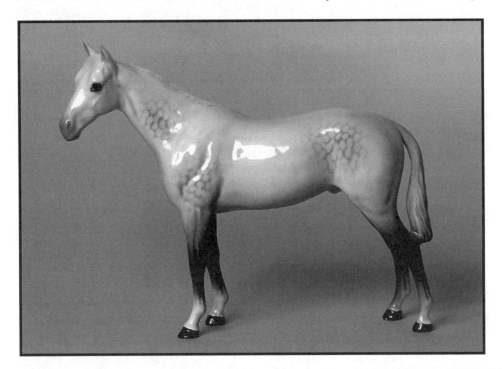

Colourway	Finish	DA #	Intro.	Disc.	U.K. £	U.S. $	Can. $
Brown	Gloss	42	1947	1989	45.00	100.00	125.00
Brown	Matt	42	1979	1989	55.00	100.00	125.00
Chestnut	Gloss	—	1958	1967	350.00	600.00	800.00
Grey	Gloss	42	1960	1989	80.00	175.00	250.00
Grey	Matt	—	1970	1989	75.00	175.00	250.00
Opaque	Gloss	—	1960	1967	225.00	375.00	525.00
Painted white	Gloss	—	1952	1967	250.00	425.00	575.00
Palomino	Gloss	—	1960	1989	80.00	175.00	250.00
Palomino	Matt	—	1970	1983	75.00	175.00	250.00
Rocking horse grey	Gloss	—	1947	1962	400.00	675.00	950.00
White	Matt	—	1970	1982	100.00	150.00	200.00

SERIES: On ceramic stand or wooden plinths

The stand was shape no. 1809, modelled by Albert Hallam in 1963.

Colourway/stand/finish	Intro.	Disc.	U.K. £	U.S. $	Can. $
Brown/brown ceramic/gloss	c.1963	Unknown	150.00	250.00	400.00
Brown/copper lustre ceramic/gloss	c.1963	Unknown	165.00	275.00	450.00
Chestnut/ceramic/gloss	c.1963	Unknown	375.00	650.00	1,000.00
Brown/wooden plinth/matt	c.1989	c.1989	75.00	125.00	200.00

Model No. 728

FOAL
(Comical Type)

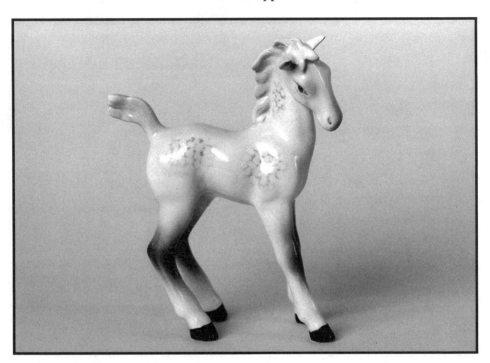

Designer: Arthur Gredington
Height: 5", 12.7 cm

Colourway	Finish	Intro.	Disc.	U.K. £	U.S. $	Can. $
Blue	Gloss	1939	1954	Extremely Rare		
Brown	Gloss	1940	1971	35.00	65.00	90.00
Chestnut	Gloss	1958	1966	200.00	375.00	550.00
Dark chestnut	Gloss	1939	1954	Extremely Rare		
Grey	Gloss	1961	1971	95.00	150.00	200.00
Opaque	Gloss	1961	1971	125.00	200.00	300.00
Painted white	Gloss	1961	1966	175.00	300.00	400.00
Palomino	Gloss	1961	1971	95.00	150.00	225.00
Rocking horse grey	Gloss	c.1940	1962	250.00	425.00	600.00
Stone/ivory	Satin	Unknown	1954	95.00	200.00	300.00
White	Matt	1970	1970	65.00	135.00	200.00

Model No. 763/1421

FOAL
(Small, Stretched, Upright)

First Version: Long ears

Second Version: Short ears

Designer: Arthur Gredington
Height: 3 ½", 8.9 cm

FIRST VERSION: Long ears, thick legs. When viewed from the back legs almost touch. Tail is straight.

Colourway	Finish	Intro.	Disc.	U.K. £	U.S. $	Can. $
Blue	Gloss	1940	Unknown	Extremely Rare		
Brown	Gloss	1940	Unknown	35.00	60.00	80.00
Rocking horse grey	Gloss	c.1940	Unknown	225.00	375.00	500.00

SECOND VERSION: Short ears, thick legs, but an overall smaller model. Tail is straight.

Colourway	Finish	Intro.	Disc.	U.K. £	U.S. $	Can. $
Blue	Gloss	Unknown	1956	Extremely Rare		
Brown	Gloss	Unknown	1956	35.00	60.00	80.00
Painted white	Gloss	Unknown	1956	150.00	250.00	350.00
Rocking horse grey	Gloss	Unknown	1956	225.00	375.00	500.00

THIRD VERSION: Very thin legs with off hind stretched out well behind the near hind. Tail is slightly bent.

In 1956 model no. 763 was completely remodelled by Arthur Gredington, but the model no. 763 was retained.

Colourway	Finish	Intro.	Disc.	U.K. £	U.S. $	Can. $
Brown	Gloss	1956	1976	35.00	55.00	75.00
Chestnut	Gloss	1958	1967	180.00	350.00	500.00
Grey	Gloss	1961	1976	65.00	110.00	150.00
Opaque	Gloss	1961	1973	90.00	175.00	275.00
Painted white	Gloss	1962	1967	150.00	250.00	350.00
Palomino	Gloss	1956	1976	60.00	110.00	150.00
Rocking horse grey	Gloss	1956	1961	225.00	400.00	600.00
White	Matt	1970	1976	50.00	85.00	110.00

Model No. 766

FOAL - TROTTING
(With Or Without Base)

Photograph not
available at press time

Designer: Arthur Gredington
Height: 3 ¾", 9.5 cm

VARIATION No. 1. *Free standing*

Colourway	Finish	Intro.	Disc.	U.K. £	U.S. $	Can. $
Blue	Gloss	*1940*	*By 1954*			
Light brown	Gloss	*1940*	*By 1954*			
Dark brown	Gloss	*1940*	*By 1954*	All colourways are		
Dark chestnut	Gloss	*1940*	*By 1954*	extremely rare		
Rocking horse grey	Gloss	1940	By 1954			

VARIATION No. 2. *On ceramic base*

Colourway	Finish	Intro.	Disc.	U.K. £	U.S. $	Can. $
Blue	Gloss	1940	By 1954			
Light brown	Gloss	1940	By 1954	All colourways are		
Dark brown	Gloss	1940	By 1954	extremely rare		
Dark chestnut	Gloss	1940	By 1954			

Model No. 815

FOAL
(Small, Stretched, Facing Right)

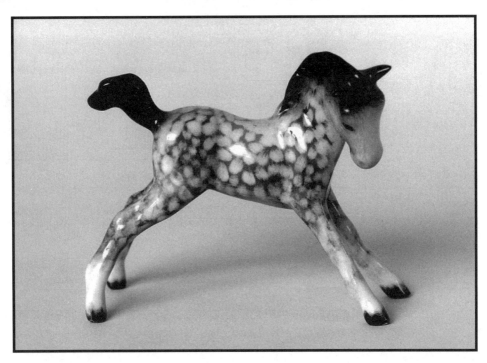

Designer:	Arthur Gredington
Height:	3 ¼", 8.3 cm

Colourway	Finsh	DA #	Intro.	Disc.	U.K. £	U.S. $	Can. $
Blue	Gloss	—	1940	1954	Extremely Rare		
Brown	Gloss	74	1940	1989	20.00	35.00	50.00
Brown	Matt	74	1979	1989	20.00	35.00	50.00
Chestnut	Gloss	—	1958	1967	195.00	325.00	450.00
Dark chestnut	Gloss	—	1940	1954	Extremely Rare		
Grey	Gloss	74	*1961*	1989	30.00	50.00	70.00
Opaque	Gloss	—	*1961*	1973	90.00	150.00	200.00
Painted white	Gloss	—	1962	1967	150.00	250.00	350.00
Palomino	Gloss	—	*1961*	1989	25.00	40.00	60.00
Rocking horse grey	Gloss	—	c.1940	1962	225.00	375.00	500.00
White	Matt	—	1970	1982	40.00	70.00	90.00

Model No. 818   **SHIRE MARE**

In recognition of 50 years of production of model number 818 a black gloss shire mare was commissioned by the Beswick Collectors Circle in 1990. Approximately 135 of these were issued with a gold backstamp for Circle Members.

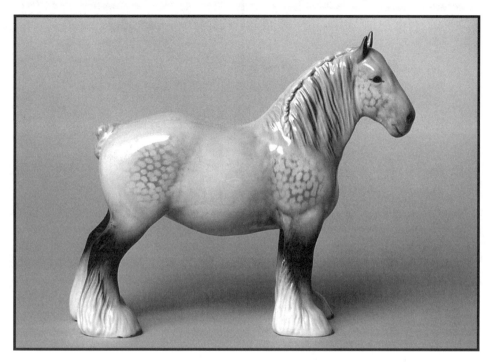

Designer: Arthur Gredington
Height: 8 ½", 21.6 cm

FIRST VERSION: Without Harness

Colourway	Finish	DA#	Intro.	Disc.	U.K. £	U.S. $	Can. $
Black - yellow ribbon	Gloss	—	Unknown	Unknown	600.00	950.00	1,250.00
Black - blue/yellow ribbons - Gloss		—	1990	1990	600.00	950.00	1,250.00
Brown	Gloss	43	1940	1989	40.00	70.00	150.00
Brown	Matt	43	1979	1989	60.00	100.00	175.00
Chestnut	Gloss	—	1958	1967	500.00	800.00	1,100.00
Grey	Gloss	—	*1961*	1989	95.00	200.00	300.00
Opaque	Gloss	—	*1961*	1973	200.00	325.00	450.00
Painted white	Gloss	—	*1961*	1970	350.00	600.00	800.00
Palomino	Gloss	—	*1961*	1973	300.00	500.00	675.00
Piebald	Gloss	—	Unknown	Unknown	600.00	950.00	1,250.00
Rocking horse grey	Gloss	—	c.1940	1962	425.00	700.00	975.00
Skewbald	Gloss	—	Unknown	Unknown	600.00	950.00	1,250.00
White	Matt	—	1970	1982	100.00	150.00	200.00

SECOND VERSION: Dressed; Series — Harnessed Horses

Colourway	Finish	Intro.	Disc.	U.K. £	U.S. $	Can. $
Brown	Gloss	1974	1982	125.00	250.00	375.00
Grey	Gloss	1974	1982	150.00	300.00	425.00

Model No. 836

FOAL
(Large, Stretched)

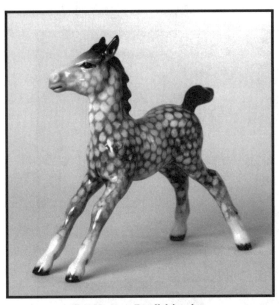

First Version: Parallel fore legs

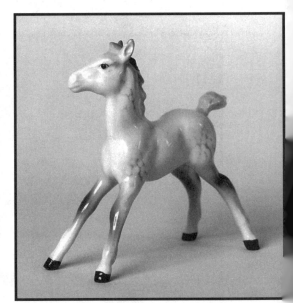

Second Version: Splayed fore legs

Designer: Arthur Gredington
Height: 5", 12.7 cm

FIRST VERSION: Parallel fore legs.

Colourway	Finish	Intro.	Disc.	U.K. £	U.S. $	Can.
Blue	Gloss	Unknown	Unknown	Extremely Rare		
Brown	Gloss	1940	Unknown	45.00	80.00	100.0
Brown	Matt	1979	Unknown	45.00	80.00	110.0
Chestnut	Gloss	1961	Unknown	225.00	400.00	525.0
Grey	Gloss	1961	Unknown	55.00	125.00	200.0
Opaque	Gloss	1961	Unknown	95.00	175.00	275.
Painted white	Gloss	1961	Unknown	175.00	325.00	475.
Palomino	Gloss	1961	Unknown	55.00	125.00	225.
Pink	Gloss	Unknown	Unknown	Extremely Rare		
Rocking horse grey	Gloss	1961	Unknown	275.00	450.00	625.
White	Matt	1970	Unknown	45.00	125.00	200.

SECOND VERSION: Splayed fore legs.

Colourway	Finish	Intro.	Disc.	U.K. £	U.S. $	Can
Brown	Gloss	Unknown	1984	35.00	60.00	70
Brown	Matt	Unknown	1984	35.00	60.00	70
Chestnut	Gloss	Unknown	1967	225.00	400.00	525
Grey	Gloss	Unknown	1983	55.00	100.00	150
Opaque	Gloss	Unknown	1973	95.00	150.00	225
Painted white	Gloss	Unknown	1967	175.00	275.00	375
Palomino	Gloss	Unknown	1984	55.00	100.00	150
White	Matt	Unknown	1982	45.00	100.00	150

Model No. 855   **STOCKY JOGGING MARE**

FIRST VERSION: Modelled September 1940. Near fore leg is raised off the ground, near hind leg is under the body. Tail attached to the leg all the way down. Legs rather crudely modelled.

Designer: Arthur Gredington
Height: 6", 5.0 cm

Colourway	Finish	Intro.	Disc.	U.K. £	U.S. $	Can. $
Blue	Gloss	1940	1941			
Dark brown	Gloss	1940	1941	All colourways are		
Light brown	Gloss	1940	1941	extremely rare		
Dark chestnut	Gloss	1940	1941			

SECOND VERSION: Modelled September 1941. Near fore leg is raised off the ground, near hind leg is under the body. Tail arched away from the leg. More shape to the joints of the legs.

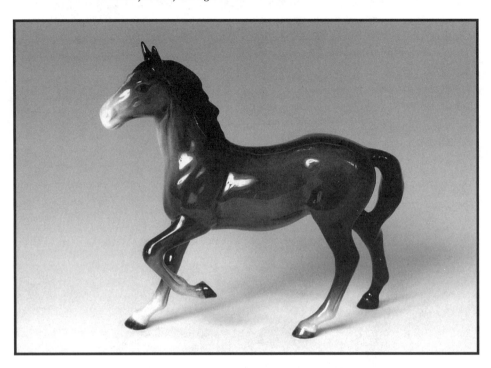

Colourway	Finish	Intro.	Disc.	U.K. £	U.S. $	Can. $
Blue	Gloss	1941	1947		Extremely Rare	
Dark brown	Gloss	1941	1947	350.00	575.00	775.00
Light brown	Gloss	1941	1947	350.00	575.00	775.00
Dark chestnut	Gloss	1941	1947		Extremely Rare	
Rocking horse grey	Gloss	1941	1947		Extremely Rare	

THIRD VERSION: Shape no. 1090 was modelled in 1947 but retained the number 855.
Off fore leg raised from the ground, off hind leg under the body.
Tail more arched from the body. Head lowered. A chunkier model.

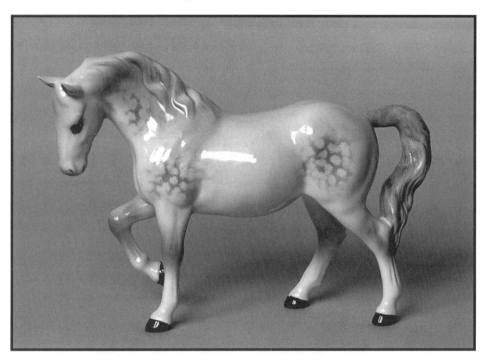

Colourway	Finish	DA #	Intro.	Disc.	U.K. £	U.S. $	Can. $
Blue	Gloss	—	1947	Unknown	350.00	700.00	1,000.00
Brown	Gloss	44	1947	1989	45.00	85.00	100.00
Chestnut	Gloss	—	1958	1967	300.00	600.00	800.00
Grey	Gloss	—	1961	1989	75.00	125.00	200.00
Opaque	Gloss	—	1961	1973	200.00	375.00	700.00
Painted white	Gloss	—	1961	1967	275.00	500.00	750.00
Palomino	Gloss	—	1961	1989	75.00	125.00	200.00
Rocking horse grey	Gloss	—	c.1947	1962	350.00	700.00	1,000.00
White	Matt	—	1970	1982	100.00	175.00	250.00

Model No. 868

HUNTSMAN
(On Rearing Horse)

STYLE ONE: On rearing horse

*FIRST VERSION: Huntsman is sitting straight up and his lower legs are also vertical.
His coat is cut away at the waist. He is riding a common headed horse.*

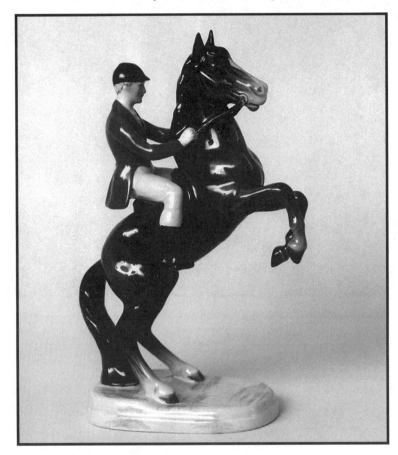

Designer: Arthur Gredington
Height: 10", 25.4 cm

COLOURWAY No. 1. Orangey red coat, cream breeches.

Colourway	Finish	Intro.	Disc.	U.K. £	U.S. $	Can. $
Brown	Gloss	1940	1952	350.00	600.00	800.00
Dark chestnut	Gloss	1940	1952		Extremely Rare	
Rocking horse grey	Gloss	c.1940	1952		Extremely Rare	

COLOURWAY No. 2. Scarlet coat and white breeches.

Colourway	Finish	Intro.	Disc.	U.K. £	U.S. $	Can. $
Brown	Gloss	1940	1952	325.00	550.00	750.00
Rocking horse grey	Gloss	c.1948	1952		Extremely Rare	

SECOND VERSION: Huntsman is leaning back slightly. His coat is not cut away at the waist. The horse's head has an Arab appearance (dished profile).

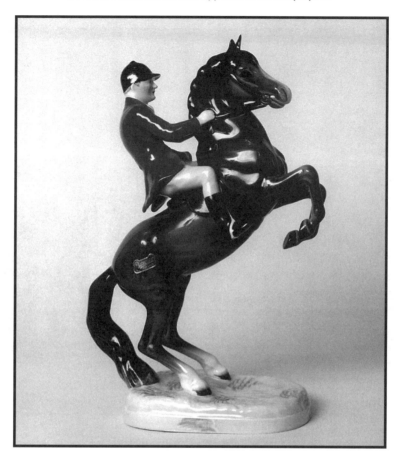

Colourway	Finish	Intro.	Disc.	U.K. £	U.S. $	Can. $
Brown	Gloss	1952	1995	125.00	200.00	275.00
Chestnut	Gloss	1958	1967	775.00	1,300.00	1,500.00
Grey	Gloss	1962	1972	550.00	925.00	1,250.00
Opaque	Gloss	1971	1973	250.00	475.00	700.00
Painted white	Gloss	1965	1971	350.00	600.00	850.00
Palomino	Gloss	*1961*	1972	775.00	1,300.00	1,500.00
Rocking horse grey	Gloss	*1952*	*1962*	900.00	1,500.00	2,000.00
White	Matt	1971	1981	175.00	300.00	400.00

SERIES: Britannia Collection

Colourway	Finish	Intro.	Disc.	U.K. £	U.S. $	Can. $
Bronze	Satin	1989	1993	150.00	275.00	375.00

Model No. 915

FOAL
(Lying)

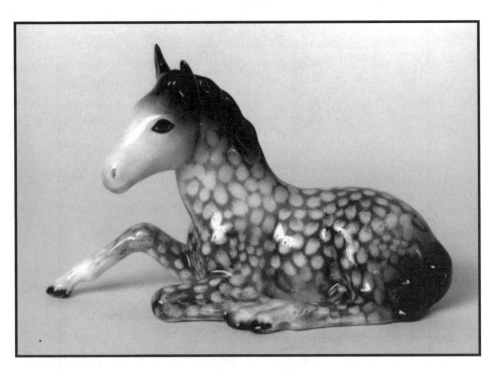

Designer: Arthur Gredington
Height: 3 ¼", 8.3 cm

Colourway	Finish	DA #	Intro.	Disc.	U.K. £	U.S. $	Can. $
Brown	Gloss	75	1941	1989	20.00	35.00	50.00
Brown	Matt	75	1979	1989	25.00	45.00	60.00
Chestnut	Gloss	—	1958	1967	195.00	325.00	475.00
Grey	Gloss	75	*1961*	1989	40.00	65.00	90.00
Opaque	Gloss	—	*1961*	1973	90.00	150.00	200.00
Painted white	Gloss	—	1962	1967	175.00	300.00	400.00
Palomino	Gloss	—	*1961*	1989	40.00	65.00	90.00
Rocking horse grey	Gloss	—	c.1942	*1962*	225.00	400.00	525.00
White	Matt	—	1970	1982	45.00	75.00	100.00

Model No. 939   ## GIRL ON JUMPING HORSE

The horse used for model 939 is also that used for model 982 "Huntswoman."

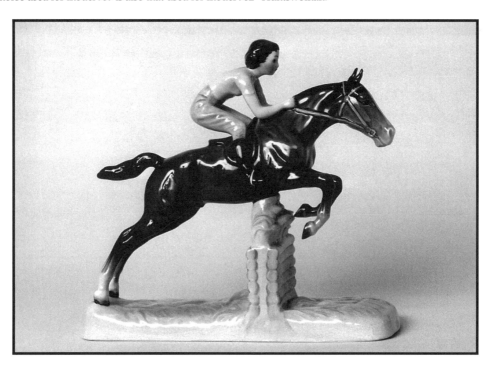

Designer: Arthur Gredington
Height: 9 ¾", 24.7 cm

Colourway	Finish	Intro.	Disc.	U.K. £	U.S. $	Can. $
Brown	Gloss	1941	1965	250.00	450.00	650.00

Model No. 946

FOAL
(Grazing)

First Version: Off-side hooves almost touch   Second Version: Legs well separated

Designer: Arthur Gredington
Height: 3 ¼", 8.3 cm

FIRST VERSION: Has common head and the off-side hooves almost touch.

Colourway	Finish	Intro.	Disc.	U.K. £	U.S. $	Can. $
Light brown	Gloss	1941	1955	45.00	75.00	100.00
Dark brown	Gloss	1941	1955	45.00	75.00	100.00
Rocking horse grey	Gloss	1941	1955	375.00	600.00	800.00

SECOND VERSION: Much finer head with the legs being well separated.

Colourway	Finish	DA #	Intro.	Disc.	U.K. £	U.S. $	Can. $
Brown	Gloss	76	1955	1989	20.00	35.00	50.00
Brown	Matt	76	1979	1989	25.00	45.00	60.00
Chestnut	Gloss	—	1958	1967	195.00	325.00	475.00
Grey	Gloss	76	*1961*	1989	35.00	60.00	85.00
Opaque	Gloss	—	*1961*	1967	90.00	175.00	250.00
Painted white	Gloss	—	*1961*	1967	175.00	300.00	400.00
Palomino	Gloss	76	*1961*	1989	30.00	65.00	85.00
Rocking horse grey	Gloss	—	1955	1962	325.00	550.00	725.00
White	Matt	—	1970	1982	45.00	100.00	125.00

Model No. 947

FOAL
(Large, Head Down)

This model in the dun colourway, along with the Mare (976), was the 1997 Beswick Collectors Club Special. They show both the "Beswick" and BCC97 backstamps. The Foal (dun) was issued in a limited edition of 730.

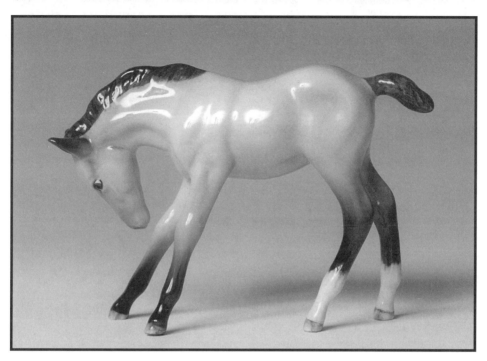

Designer: Arthur Gredington
Height: 4 ½", 11.9 cm

Colourway	Finish	DA #	Intro.	Disc.	U.K. £	U.S. $	Can. $
Brown	Gloss	77	1941	1989	20.00	35.00	50.00
Brown	Matt	77	1979	1989	25.00	45.00	60.00
Chestnut	Gloss	—	1958	1967	200.00	350.00	550.00
Dun (BCC97)	Gloss	—	1997	1997	75.00	150.00	225.00
Grey	Gloss	—	*1961*	1983	40.00	100.00	150.00
Opaque	Gloss	—	*1961*	1973	95.00	175.00	250.00
Painted white	Gloss	—	1962	1967	195.00	325.00	450.00
Palomino	Gloss	—	*1961*	1983	35.00	60.00	85.00
Rocking horse grey	Gloss	—	c.1942	1962	275.00	475.00	625.00
White	Matt	—	1970	1982	50.00	85.00	110.00

Model No. 951

SHIRE FOAL
(Large)

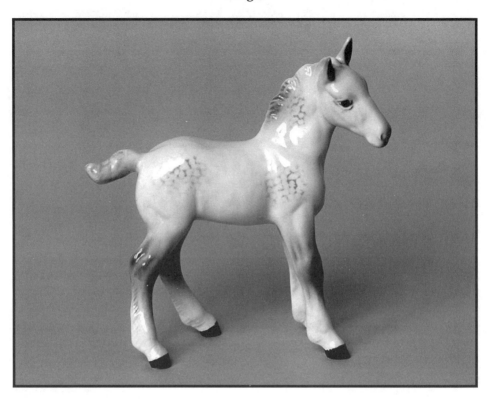

Designer: Arthur Gredington
Height: 6 ¼", 15.9 cm

Colourway	Finish	Intro.	Disc.	U.K. £	U.S. $	Can. $
Blue	Gloss	1941	Unknown		Extremely Rare	
Brown	Gloss	1941	1971	50.00	85.00	110.00
Chestnut	Gloss	1958	1967	350.00	600.00	800.00
Grey	Gloss	*1961*	1971	150.00	250.00	350.00
Opaque	Gloss	*1961*	1971	125.00	200.00	275.00
Painted white	Gloss	1962	1967	250.00	425.00	575.00
Palomino	Gloss	*1961*	1971	150.00	250.00	350.00
Rocking horse grey	Gloss	1941	1962	425.00	750.00	1,000.00
White	Matt	1970	1970	100.00	150.00	225.00

Model No. 953　　　　　　　　**MARE AND FOAL ON BASE**

The mare is a modern 976 with the foal and the base varying.

FIRST VERSION: The foal has its tail and near fore leg slightly raised.
The base was rectangular.

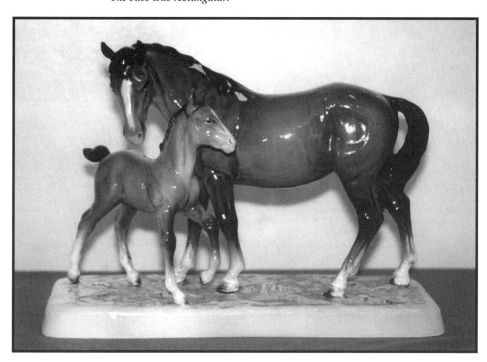

Designer:　Arthur Gredington
Height:　　7 ¾", 19.7 cm

Colourway	Finish	Intro.	Disc.	U.K. £	U.S. $	Can. $
Brown	Gloss	1941	1949		Extremely Rare	
Rocking horse grey	Gloss	1941	1949		Extremely Rare	

SECOND VERSION: Foal has all four legs attached to an irregularly shaped base and the tail hangs straight down.

Model 953, Second Version

Model 953, Third Version

Colourway	Finish	Intro.	Disc.	U.K. £	U.S. $	Can. $
Brown	Gloss	1949	1983	125.00	275.00	425.00
Chestnut	Gloss	1958	1967	500.00	850.00	1,100.00
Grey	Gloss	1958	1972	500.00	850.00	1,100.00
Opaque	Gloss	1971	1973	250.00	425.00	575.00
Painted white	Gloss	1962	1967	450.00	750.00	1,000.00
Palomino	Gloss	*1958*	1972	425.00	725.00	975.00
Rocking horse grey	Gloss	*1950*	1962	700.00	1,200.00	1,500.00
White	Matt	1971	1981	150.00	250.00	350.00

THIRD VERSION: Foal is model no. 1813, second version, on an irregularly shaped base.

Colourway	Finish	Intro.	Disc.	U.K. £	U.S. $	Can. $
Brown mare with an orangey bay foal	Gloss	1981	1983	100.00	250.00	375.00
Brown mare and foal, green matt base	Matt	*1981*	*1983*	125.00	250.00	375.00

Model No. 975   **CANTERING SHIRE**

This model in the black colourway was the 1996 Beswick Collectors Club Special.

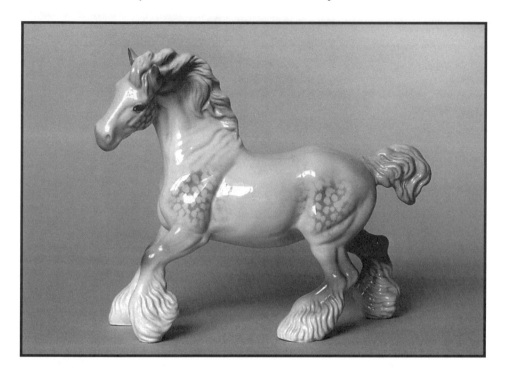

Designer: Arthur Gredington
Height: 8 ¾", 22.2 cm

Colourway	Finish	DA #	Intro.	Disc.	U.K. £	U.S. $	Can. $
Black (BCC96)	Gloss	—	1996	1996	150.00	250.00	350.00
Brown	Gloss	45	1943	1989	55.00	95.00	125.00
Brown	Matt	—	1980	1989	65.00	100.00	150.00
Chestnut	Gloss	—	1958	1967	500.00	850.00	1,100.00
Grey	Gloss	—	*1961*	1989	95.00	200.00	300.00
Opaque	Gloss	—	1966	1967	200.00	350.00	500.00
Painted white	Gloss	—	1962	1967	350.00	600.00	800.00
Palomino	Gloss	—	*1961*	1970	300.00	500.00	700.00
Rocking horse grey	Gloss	—	*c.1944*	*1962*	500.00	850.00	1,100.00
White	Matt	—	1971	1982	100.00	150.00	225.00

Note: Also known in flambé.

Model No. 976

MARE
(Facing Left)

This model and the foal (947) in dun gloss were the 1997 Beswick Collectors Club Special. They have both the "Beswick" and BCC97 backstamps. The Mare was issued in a limited edition of 710.

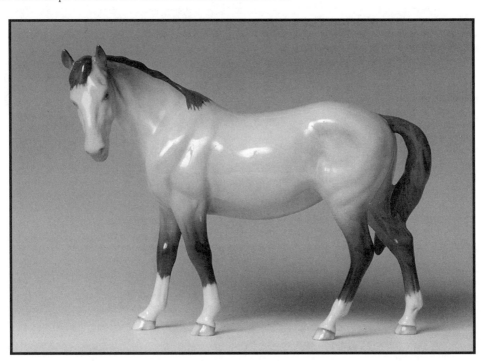

Designer: Arthur Gredington
Height: 6 ¾", 17.2 cm

Colourway	Finish	DA #	Intro.	Disc.	U.K. £	U.S. $	Can. $
Brown	Gloss	46	1941	1989	45.00	75.00	110.00
Brown	Matt	46	1979	1989	55.00	125.00	150.00
Chestnut	Gloss	—	1958	1967	375.00	650.00	875.00
Dun (BCC97)	Gloss	—	1997	1997	150.00	275.00	375.00
Grey	Gloss	46	1962	1989	75.00	150.00	225.00
Opaque	Gloss	—	1961	1973	175.00	300.00	400.00
Painted white	Gloss	—	1961	1967	325.00	550.00	750.00
Palomino	Gloss	—	1961	1983	90.00	150.00	225.00
Rocking horse grey	Gloss	—	c.1942	1962	400.00	675.00	950.00
White	Matt	—	1970	1982	95.00	150.00	200.00

Model No. 982   **HUNTSWOMAN**

The horse used for model 982 is the same as that used for model 939 "Girl on Jumping Horse."

Designer: Arthur Gredington
Height: 10", 25.4 cm

Colourway	Finish	Intro.	Disc.	U.K. £	U.S. $	Can. $
Brown	Gloss	1942	1967	250.00	575.00	850.00

Model No. 996

FOAL
(Small, Gambolling left)

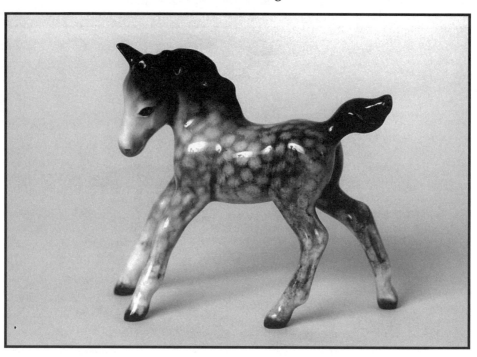

Designer: Arthur Gredington
Height: 3 ¼", 8.3 cm

Colourway	Finish	Intro.	Disc.	U.K. £	U.S. $	Can. $
Brown	Gloss	1943	1976	30.00	50.00	65.00
Chestnut	Gloss	1958	1967	195.00	325.00	450.00
Grey	Gloss	*1961*	1976	45.00	125.00	175.00
Opaque	Gloss	*1961*	1973	90.00	175.00	225.00
Painted white	Gloss	*1961*	1967	175.00	300.00	400.00
Palomino	Gloss	*1961*	1976	45.00	125.00	175.00
Rocking horse grey	Gloss	*c.1944*	*1962*	225.00	375.00	525.00
White	Matt	1970	1976	45.00	125.00	175.00

Model No. 997

FOAL
(Small, Stretched, Facing Left)

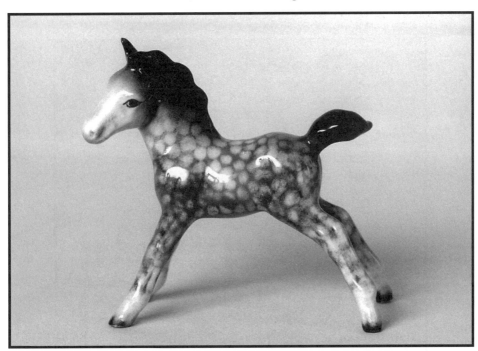

Designer: Arthur Gredington
Height: 3 ¼", 8.3 cm

Colourway	Finish	DA #	Intro.	Disc.	U.K. £	U.S. $	Can. $
Brown	Gloss	78	1943	1989	25.00	45.00	60.00
Brown	Matt	78	1979	1989	30.00	50.00	65.00
Chestnut	Gloss	—	1958	1967	180.00	300.00	475.00
Grey	Gloss	78	*1961*	1989	40.00	70.00	95.00
Opaque	Gloss	—	*1961*	1973	85.00	150.00	200.00
Painted white	Gloss	—	*1961*	1967	165.00	275.00	375.00
Palomino	Gloss	—	*1961*	1989	40.00	90.00	120.00
Rocking horse grey	Gloss	—	*c.1944*	1962	200.00	350.00	550.00
White	Matt	—	1970	1982	40.00	90.00	120.00

Model No. 1014

WELSH COB
(Rearing)

FIRST VERSION: The tail is attached to the ceramic base.

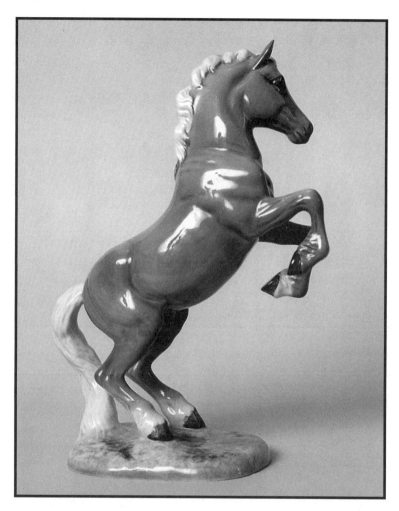

Designer: Arthur Gredington
Height: 10 ¼", 26.0 cm

Colourway	Finish	Intro.	Disc.	U.K. £	U.S. $	Can. $
Black	Gloss	Unknown	Unknown	175.00	300.00	400.00
Brown	Gloss	1944	Unknown	95.00	250.00	375.00
Chestnut	Gloss	1958	Unknown	450.00	750.00	1,200.00
Grey	Gloss	*1961*	Unknown	375.00	650.00	1,100.00
Opaque	Gloss	*1961*	Unknown	225.00	375.00	500.00
Painted white	Gloss	*1962*	Unknown	400.00	675.00	900.00
Palomino	Gloss	*1961*	Unknown	325.00	550.00	750.00
Rocking horse grey	Gloss	*c.1945*	Unknown	550.00	925.00	1,400.00
White	Matt	1970	Unknown	150.00	250.00	350.00

SECOND VERSION: Tail hangs loose.

Colourway	Finish	DA #	Intro.	Disc.	U.K. £	U.S. $	Can. $
Black	Gloss		*c.1990*	*c.1990*	150.00	300.00	500.00
Brown	Gloss	41	Unknown	1989	95.00	250.00	375.00
Chestnut	Gloss	—	Unknown	1967	450.00	750.00	1,200.00
Grey	Gloss	—	Unknown	1973	375.00	650.00	1,100.00
Grey	Matt	—	Unknown	1983	175.00	350.00	550.00
Opaque	Gloss	—	Unknown	1973	225.00	375.00	500.00
Painted white	Gloss	—	Unknown	1967	400.00	675.00	900.00
Palomino	Gloss	—	Unknown	1973	325.00	550.00	750.00
White	Matt	—	Unknown	1983	150.00	250.00	350.00

Model No. 1033

SHETLAND PONY
(Woolly Shetland Mare)

Designer: Arthur Gredington
Height: 5 ¾", 14.6 cm

Colourway	Finish	Intro.	Disc.	U.K. £	U.S. $	Can. $
Brown	Gloss	1945	1989	45.00	75.00	110.00
Chestnut	Gloss	Unknown	Unknown	450.00	750.00	1,000.00
Dapple grey	Gloss	Unknown	Unknown	375.00	650.00	850.00
Palomino	Gloss	Unknown	Unknown	375.00	650.00	850.00
White	Matt	1973	1982	65.00	110.00	150.00

Model No. 1034   **SHETLAND FOAL**

Designer: Arthur Gredington
Height: 3 ¾", 9.5 cm

Colourway	Finish	DA #	Intro.	Disc.	U.K. £	U.S. $	Can. $
Brown	Gloss	79	1945	1989	30.00	50.00	75.00
Brown	Matt	79	1979	1989	25.00	50.00	75.00
White	Matt	—	1973	1982	40.00	75.00	90.00

Model No. 1037

RACEHORSE AND JOCKEY
(Walking Racehorse)

The jockey's silks, for an extra payment, could be decorated as the purchaser wished. A great many colourways and number cloths could exist.

Colourway No. 1 - Stripes on saddlecloth   Colourway No. 2 - Number on saddlecloth

Designer: Arthur Gredington
Height: 8 ½", 21.6 cm

STYLE ONE: Walking Racehorse

Colourway No. 1. Stripes on saddlecloth

Colourway	Finish	Intro.	Disc.	U.K. £	U.S. $	Can. $
Brown	Gloss	1945	Unknown	250.00	450.00	675.00

Colourway No. 2. Number on saddlecloth

Colourway	Finish	Intro.	Disc.	U.K. £	U.S. $	Can. $
Brown	Gloss	Unknown	1976	225.00	400.00	625.00

Model No. 1050   **GRAZING SHIRE**

Designer: Arthur Gredington
Height: 5 ½", 14.0 cm

Colourway	Finish	Intro.	Disc.	U.K. £	U.S. $	Can. $
Brown	Gloss	1946	1970	95.00	200.00	300.00
Chestnut	Gloss	1958	1967	475.00	800.00	1,100.00
Grey	Gloss	1962	1970	550.00	950.00	1,250.00
Opaque	Gloss	*1961*	1970	225.00	400.00	575.00
Painted white	Gloss	1962	1967	600.00	1,000.00	1,350.00
Palomino	Gloss	*1961*	1970	500.00	850.00	1,150.00
Rocking horse grey	Gloss	*c.1947*	1962	750.00	1,250.00	1,750.00

Model No. 1053

SHIRE FOAL
(Small)

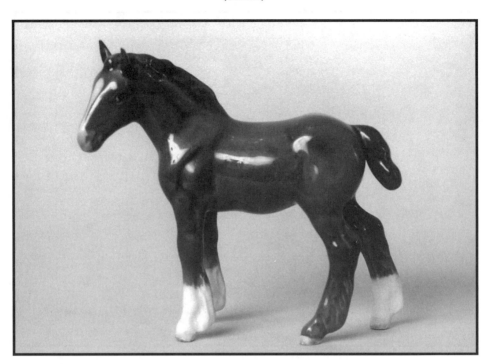

| Designer: | Arthur Gredington |
| Height: | 5", 12.7 cm |

Colourway	Finish	Intro.	Disc.	U.K. £	U.S. $	Can. $
Brown	Gloss	1946	1984	40.00	70.00	90.00
Brown	Matt	1979	1984	35.00	70.00	90.00
Chestnut	Gloss	1958	1967	325.00	550.00	750.00
Grey	Gloss	*1961*	1973	150.00	250.00	350.00
Opaque	Gloss	*1961*	1973	125.00	250.00	350.00
Painted white	Gloss	1962	1967	250.00	425.00	575.00
Palomino	Gloss	*1961*	1973	150.00	250.00	350.00
Rocking horse grey	Gloss	*c.1947*	1962	400.00	675.00	900.00
White	Matt	1970	1982	95.00	165.00	200.00

Model No. 1084

FOAL
(Medium, Almost Stood Square)

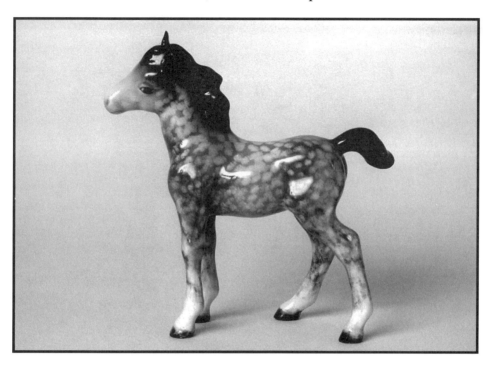

Designer: Arthur Gredington
Height: 4 ½", 11.9 cm

Colourway	Finish	Intro.	Disc.	U.K. £	U.S. $	Can. $
Brown	Gloss	1947	1984	30.00	50.00	70.00
Brown	Matt	1979	1983	25.00	50.00	70.00
Chestnut	Gloss	1958	1967	275.00	450.00	625.00
Grey	Gloss	*1961*	1973	95.00	150.00	200.00
Opaque	Gloss	*1961*	1973	90.00	175.00	250.00
Painted white	Gloss	*1961*	1967	185.00	325.00	475.00
Palomino	Gloss	*1961*	1973	80.00	150.00	200.00
Rocking horse grey	Gloss	*c.1948*	1962	325.00	550.00	750.00
White	Matt	1970	1982	75.00	125.00	150.00

Model No. 1085

FOAL
(Medium, Head Down)

Designer:	Arthur Gredington
Height:	3 ½", 8.9 cm

Colourway	Finish	Intro.	Disc.	U.K. £	U.S. $	Can. $
Brown	Gloss	1947	1971	45.00	75.00	115.00
Chestnut	Gloss	1958	1967	300.00	500.00	675.00
Grey	Gloss	*1961*	1971	125.00	210.00	275.00
Opaque	Gloss	*1961*	1971	100.00	150.00	250.00
Painted white	Gloss	*1961*	1967	200.00	350.00	450.00
Palomino	Gloss	*1961*	1971	100.00	150.00	225.00
Rocking horse grey	Gloss	*c.1948*	1962	350.00	600.00	800.00
White	Matt	1970	1970	85.00	150.00	200.00

Model No. 1145

KNIGHT IN ARMOUR
(The Earl of Warwick)

Designer: Arthur Gredington
Height: 10 ¾", 27.8 cm

Colourway	Finish	Intro.	Disc.	U.K. £	U.S. $	Can. $
Grey	Gloss	1949	1973	1,000.00	1,750.00	2,500.00

Model No. 1182   SWISH TAIL HORSE

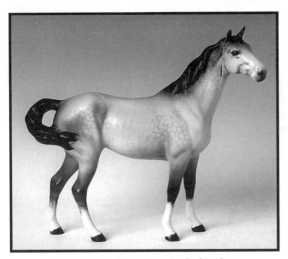

First Version: The tail is attached to the
quarter almost parallel to the ground

Second Version: The tail is slightly lower
down and only to the edge of the quarters

Designer: Arthur Gredington
Height: 8 ¾", 22.2 cm

FIRST VERSION: The tail is attached to the quarters almost parallel to the ground.

Colourway	Finish	Intro.	Disc.	U.K. £	U.S. $	Can. $
Brown	Gloss	1950	c.1982	75.00	130.00	175.00
Brown	Matt	1970	c.1982	65.00	125.00	175.00
Chestnut	Gloss	1958	1967	375.00	650.00	850.00
Grey	Gloss	1961	c.1982	85.00	150.00	225.00
Grey	Matt	1970	c.1982	85.00	150.00	225.00
Opaque	Gloss	*1961*	1973	200.00	350.00	450.00
Painted white	Gloss	*1961*	1967	325.00	550.00	750.00
Palomino	Gloss	*1961*	c.1982	85.00	150.00	225.00
Palomino	Matt	1970	c.1982	85.00	150.00	225.00
Rocking horse grey	Gloss	*c.1951*	1962	400.00	675.00	900.00
White	Matt	1970	c.1982	95.00	150.00	200.00

SECOND VERSION: The tail is attached slightly lower down and only to the edge of the quarters.

Colourway	Finish	DA #	Intro.	Disc.	U.K. £	U.S. $	Can. $
Brown	Gloss	48	c.1982	1989	55.00	95.00	125.00
Brown	Matt	48	c.1982	1989	45.00	75.00	100.00
Grey	Gloss	—	c.1982	1989	65.00	125.00	175.00
Grey	Matt	—	c.1982	1989	65.00	125.00	175.00
Palomino	Gloss	—	c.1982	1983	65.00	125.00	175.00
Palomino	Matt	—	c.1982	1983	65.00	125.00	175.00
White	Matt		c.1982	1982	75.00	130.00	175.00

Model No. 1197

PONY
(Head Up)

Designer: Arthur Gredington
Height: 5 ½", 14.0 cm

Colourway	Finish	Intro.	Disc.	U.K. £	U.S. $	Can. $
Brown	Gloss	1950	1975	65.00	125.00	175.00
Chestnut	Gloss	1958	1967	325.00	550.00	750.00
Grey	Gloss	1962	1975	95.00	200.00	300.00
Opaque	Gloss	*1961*	1973	150.00	300.00	400.00
Painted white	Gloss	*1961*	1967	275.00	475.00	625.00
Palomino	Gloss	*1961*	1975	85.00	175.00	275.00
Piebald	Gloss	Unknown	Unknown	Extremely Rare		
Rocking horse grey	Gloss	*c.1951*	1962	350.00	600.00	800.00
White	Matt	1970	1975	85.00	175.00	275.00

Model No. 1261

PALOMINO
(Prancing Arab Type)

There are two versions of model no. 1261, the first has a more defined, thicker tail, the second has a thinner tail. At the present time dates cannot be determined as to when the mould was changed.

Model No. 1261 First Version   First Version - Thicker tail   Second Version - Thinner tail

Designer: Arthur Gredington
Height: 6 ¾", 17.2 cm

FIRST VERSION: *Thicker tail with more definition.*

Colourway	Finish	Intro.	Disc.	U.K. £	U.S. $	Can. $
Brown	Gloss	*1961*	Unknown	65.00	125.00	165.00
Brown	Matt	1970	Unknown	60.00	125.00	165.00
Chestnut	Gloss	1958	1967	325.00	550.00	750 00
Grey	Gloss	*1961*	Unknown	85.00	150.00	200.00
Grey	Matt	1970	Unknown	80.00	150.00	200.00
Opaque	Gloss	*1961*	1973	150.00	250.00	350.00
Painted white	Gloss	*1961*	1967	225.00	375.00	500.00
Palomino	Gloss	1952	Unknown	80.00	150.00	200.00
Palomino	Matt	1970	Unknown	65.00	125.00	150.00
Rocking horse grey	Gloss	*c.1956*	1962	350.00	600.00	800.00
White	Matt	1970	Unknown	85.00	150.00	200.00

SECOND VERSION: *Thinner tail with little definition.*

Colourway	Finish	DA #	Intro.	Disc.	U.K. £	U.S. $	Can. $
Brown	Gloss	49	Unknown	1989	45.00	75.00	125.00
Brown	Matt	49	Unknown	1989	40.00	75.00	125.00
Grey	Gloss	49	Unknown	1989	65.00	125.00	175.00
Grey	Matt	—	Unknown	1989	60.00	125.00	175.00
Palomino	Gloss	49	Unknown	1989	60.00	125.00	175.00
Palomino	Matt	—	Unknown	1989	45.00	75.00	125.00
White	Matt	—	Unknown	1982	65.00	125.00	175.00

Model No. 1265   **ARAB XAYAL**

The charcoal grey colourway with four white socks is the authentic colouring for " Xayal. " The charcoal grey colourway varies from black to charcoal grey.

Arab " Xayal "

Arab " Xayal " Connoisseur Horse

Designer: Arthur Gredington
Height: 6 ¼", 15.9 cm

Colourway	Finish	Intro.	Disc.	U.K. £	U.S. $	Can. $
Brown	Gloss	1952	1989	65.00	115.00	165.00
Charcoal grey	Gloss	1952	1984	95.00	165.00	225.00
Chestnut	Gloss	1958	1967	325.00	550.00	800.00
Grey	Gloss	1961	1989	85.00	150.00	215.00
Opaque	Gloss	1961	1973	150.00	250.00	350.00
Painted white	Gloss	1961	1967	225.00	375.00	500.00
Palomino	Gloss	1961	1989	80.00	150.00	200.00
Rocking horse grey	Gloss	c.1953	1962	350.00	600.00	900.00
White	Matt	1961	1984	85.00	150.00	200.00

SERIES: Connoisseur Horses

Height: 7 ¼", 18.4 cm

Colourway	Finish	Intro.	Disc.	U.K. £	U.S. $	Can. $
Dark brown	Matt	1970	1989	100.00	175.00	250.00

Model No. 1359

SUFFOLK PUNCH
CHAMPION HASSE DAINTY

Designer: Mr. Orwell
Height: 8", 20.3 cm

Colourway	Finish	Intro.	Disc.	U.K. £	U.S. $	Can. $
Light chestnut	Gloss	1954	Unknown	250.00	450.00	700.00
Dark chestnut	Gloss	Unknown	1971	225.00	400.00	625.00
Grey	Gloss	1965	1965	425.00	725.00	1,000.00
Palomino	Gloss	Unknown	Unknown	425.00	725.00	1,000.00

COLOURWAY DESCRIPTIONS

Light Chestnut: Light chestnut horse with much lighter chestnut hooves. Blended thin stripe down the front of the head. Mane and tail are cream with yellow ribbon braided through the mane ending with cream and maroon. Two maroon bows on the tail.

Dark Chestnut: Much darker chestnut horse with dark chestnut mane and tail. Definite white blaze extending over muzzle, and four short white socks. The mane ribbon is lemon with pink at the end and the tail bows are lemon and pink and indistinct.

Model No. 1361

HACKNEY

The black colourway is the authentic colouring of "Black Magic of Nork" and has white patches on the flanks.

Designer: Mr. Orwell
Height: 7 ¾", 19.7 cm

Colourway	Finish	Intro.	Disc.	U.K. £	U.S. $	Can. $
Black	Gloss	1955	1983	175.00	300.00	400.00
Black	Matt	1980	1983	150.00	250.00	350.00
Brown	Gloss	1955	1982	100.00	200.00	375.00
Chestnut	Gloss	1958	1967	400.00	675.00	1,000.00
Grey	Gloss	*1961*	1975	350.00	600.00	800.00
Opaque	Gloss	*1961*	1973	200.00	350.00	500.00
Painted white	Gloss	*1961*	1967	350.00	600.00	800.00
Palomino	Gloss	*1961*	1970	275.00	450.00	625.00
Rocking horse grey	Gloss	*c.1956*	1962	425.00	750.00	1,100.00
White	Matt	1970	1982	100.00	200.00	325.00

Model No. 1373   **PINTO PONY**

First Version: Tail attached to hind leg from hock down   Second Version: Tail hangs loose

Designer: Arthur Gredington
Height: 6 ½", 16.5 cm

FIRST VERSION: Tail is attached to the hind leg from the hock down.

Colourway	Finish	Intro.	Disc.	U.K. £	U.S. $	Can. $
Chestnut	Gloss	1958	1967	325.00	550.00	750.00
Grey	Gloss	1962	1970	325.00	550.00	750.00
Palomino	Gloss	*1961*	1970	300.00	500.00	700.00
Piebald (black and white)	Gloss	1972	Unknown	95.00	200.00	300.00
Skewbald (brown and white)	Gloss	1955	Unknown	95.00	200.00	300.00

SECOND VERSION: Tail hangs loose.

Colourway	Finish	DA #	Intro.	Disc.	U.K. £	U.S. $	Can. $
Piebald (black and white)	Gloss	67	Unknown	1989	85.00	175.00	250.00
Piebald (black and white)	Matt	67	Unknown	1989	75.00	175.00	250.00
Skewbald (brown and white)	Gloss	67	Unknown	1989	75.00	175.00	250.00
Skewbald (brown and white)	Matt	67	Unknown	1989	70.00	175.00	250.00

Model No. 1374   **GALLOPING HORSE**

Model no. 1374 was the horse used for no. 1377 Canadian Mounted Cowboy. However no. 1374 has only three hooves attached to the base compared to four hooves attached in the ridden variety.

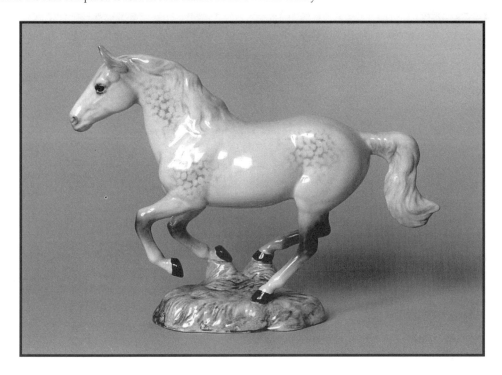

Designer: Mr. Orwell
Height: 7 ½", 19.1 cm

Colourway	Finish	Intro.	Disc.	U.K. £	U.S. $	Can. $
Brown	Gloss	1955	1975	175.00	325.00	500.00
Chestnut	Gloss	1958	1967	400.00	700.00	1,000.00
Grey	Gloss	1962	1973	225.00	400.00	600.00
Palomino	Gloss	*1961*	1973	175.00	350.00	500.00

Model No. 1375   **CANADIAN MOUNTIE**

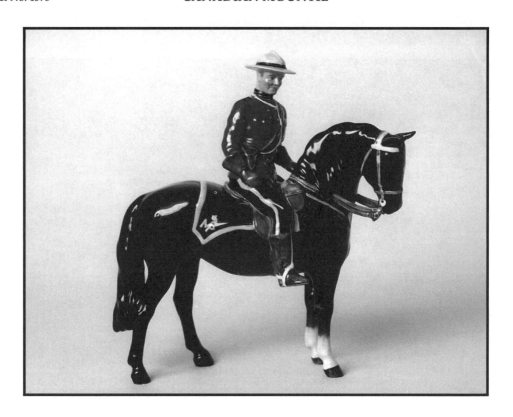

Designer: Arthur Gredington
Height: 8 ¼", 21.0 cm

Colourway	Finish	Intro.	Disc.	U.K. £	U.S. $	Can. $
Black	Gloss	1955	1976	375.00	650.00	1,000.00

Model No. 1377   **CANADIAN MOUNTED COWBOY**

The horse used for model 1377 was also that used for model 1374.

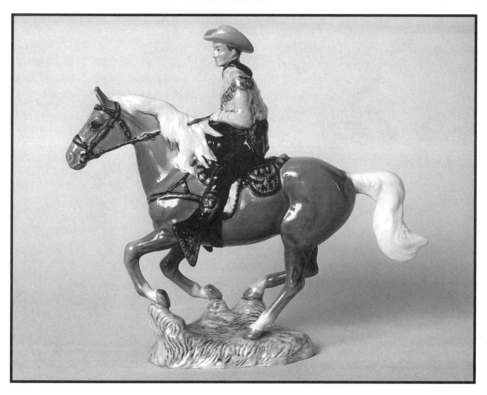

Designer: Mr. Orwell
Height: 8 ¾", 22.2 cm

Colourway	Finish	Intro.	Disc.	U.K. £	U.S. $	Can. $
Palomino	Gloss	1955	1973	400.00	700.00	1,000.00

Model No. 1391   MOUNTED INDIAN

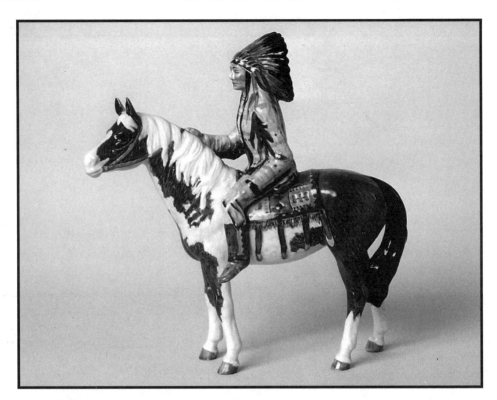

Designer: Mr. Orwell
Height: 8 ½", 21.6 cm

Colourway	Finish	Intro.	Disc.	U.K. £	U.S. $	Can. $
Skewbald	Gloss	1955	1990	275.00	450.00	650.00

GREY MATT
1182 Swish tail, 1st version; 2703 Spirit of Youth
2914 Spirit of Earth; 1549 Head tucked, 2nd version

ROCKING HORSE GREY
855 Stocky Jogging Mare, 3rd version; 975 Shire
1483 Girl's Pony; 951 Shire foal; 915 Lying foal
836 Foal, 1st version

BROWN MATT
2186 Quarter Horse; 1772 Connoisseur Thoroughbred
818 Shire; 1812 Mare; 1261 Palomino
2875 Sunlight Foal; 1407 Arab Foal

PALOMINO MATT
2688 Spirit of the Wind; 2703 Spirit of Youth
2689 Spirit of Freedom; 2916 Spirit of Peace

EARLY BROWN GLOSS
855 Stocky Jogging Mare, 2nd version
763 Foal, 1st version; 701 "Bois Roussel," 1st version

BROWN GLOSS
1182 Swish tail, 1st version; 2703 Spirit of Youth
1265 Arab "Xayal;" 728 Comical Foal
946 Grazing Foal, 1st version; 1793 Welsh Cob, 1st version

CHESTNUT GLOSS
1772 Thoroughbred; 976 Mare
1265 Arab "Xayal;" 836 Foal, 1st version
1085 Foal; 763 Foal, 1st version

PALOMINO GLOSS
1516 Walking Pony; 1771 Arab "Bahram"
1197 Head-up Pony; 1817 Foal; 1053 Shire Foal,
763 Foal, 3rd version; 1373 Pinto Pony, 1st version

1516 Spotted Walking Pony; 1772A Appaloosa
later colour version, earlier colour version
1483 Girl's Pony, Skewbald
1373 Pinto, Skewbald 1st version, Piebald 2nd version

OPAQUE GLOSS
1484 Hunter; 1050 Grazing Shire
1516 Walking Pony; 815 Foal; 1084 Foal; 1992 Horse

MISCELLANEOUS MODELS
2282 Norwegian Fjord; 1644 Highland Pony
2460 Lying Shire Foal; 2459 Lying Shire Mare

ARAB HORSES
2275 Bedouin Arab
2242 Arab Horse (authentic)
2269 Arab Stallion with Saddle (authentic)

PAINTED WHITE GLOSS
1564 Large Racehorse
1501 Huntsman; 996 Foal; 701 "Bois Roussel", 2nd version
868 Rearing Huntsman, 2nd Version

GREY GLOSS
1501 Huntsman; 1730 Huntswoman
1812 Mare; 1085 Foal; 1862 Racehorse and Jockey
997 Head-up Pony

MOUNTED MODELS
1877 Canadian Mounted Cowboy; 1145 Knight in Armour
1391 Mounted Indian; 1499 Girl on Pony
1375 Canadian Mountie; 1500 Boy on Pony

WHITE MATT
1501 Huntsman; 868 Rearing Huntsman, 2nd version
1033 Shetland Mare; 1034 Shetland Foal; 1730 Huntswoman

Model No. 1407   **ARAB FOAL**

Designer: Arthur Gredington
Height: 4 ½", 11.9 cm

Colourway	Finish	DA #	Intro.	Disc.	U.K. £	U.S. $	Can. $
Brown	Gloss	80	1956	1989	25.00	45.00	65.00
Brown	Matt	80	1979	1989	25.00	45.00	65.00
Chestnut	Gloss	—	1958	1967	250.00	425.00	575.00
Grey	Gloss	80	1961	1989	40.00	75.00	95.00
Opaque	Gloss	—	1961	1973	80.00	125.00	195.00
Painted white	Gloss	—	1961	1967	225.00	375.00	500.00
Palomino	Gloss	80	1961	1989	30.00	65.00	95.00
Rocking horse grey	Gloss	—	c.1957	1962	300.00	525.00	700.00
White	Matt	—	1970	1982	45.00	90.00	150.00

Model No. 1480

PONY
(Boy's Pony)

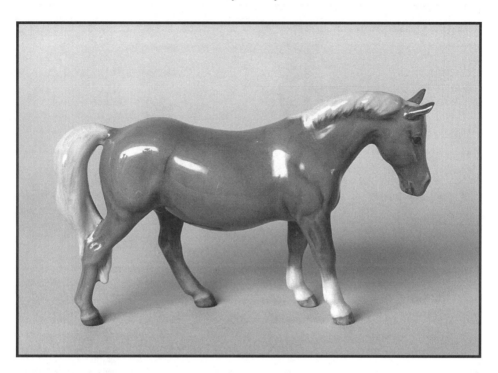

Designer: Arthur Gredington
Height: 3 ¾", 9.5 cm

Colourway	Finish	Intro.	Disc.	U.K. £	U.S. $	Can. $
Brown	Gloss	1957	1967	100.00	175.00	250.00
Chestnut	Gloss	1958	1967	350.00	600.00	800.00
Grey	Gloss	1957	1967	225.00	375.00	500.00
Opaque	Gloss	1957	1967	150.00	250.00	350.00
Painted white	Gloss	1957	1967	300.00	500.00	675.00
Palomino	Gloss	1957	1967	100.00	175.00	250.00
Rocking horse grey	Gloss	1957	1962	375.00	625.00	850.00

Model No. 1483

PONY
(Girl's Pony)

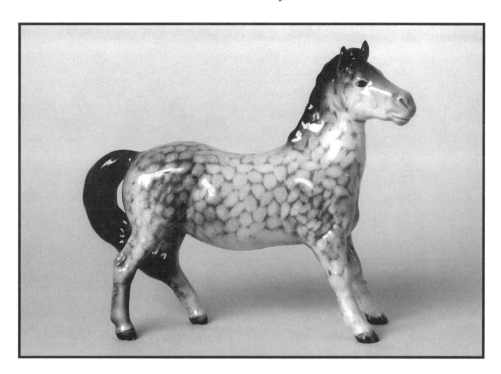

Designer: Arthur Gredington
Height: 5", 12.7 cm

Colourway	Finish	Intro.	Disc.	U.K. £	U.S. $	Can. $
Brown	Gloss	1957	1967	125.00	225.00	325.00
Chestnut	Gloss	1958	1967	450.00	750.00	1,000.00
Grey	Gloss	1957	1967	225.00	375.00	500.00
Opaque	Gloss	1957	1967	150.00	250.00	350.00
Painted white	Gloss	1957	1967	300.00	500.00	675.00
Palomino	Gloss	1957	1967	200.00	350.00	475.00
Rocking horse grey	Gloss	1957	1962	450.00	750.00	1,000.00
Skewbald (brown and white)	Gloss	1957	1967	150.00	250.00	350.00

Model No. 1484   HUNTSMAN'S HORSE

This model was used as the horse in model no. 1501 "The Huntsman."

Designer: Arthur Gredington
Height: 6 ¾", 17.2 cm

Colourway	Finish	Intro.	Disc.	U.K. £	U.S. $	Can. $
Brown	Gloss	1957	1982	65.00	125.00	175.00
Chestnut	Gloss	1958	1967	300.00	500.00	700.00
Grey	Gloss	1957	1982	85.00	150.00	200.00
Opaque	Gloss	1957	1973	160.00	275.00	375.00
Painted white	Gloss	1957	1967	275.00	475.00	650.00
Palomino	Gloss	1957	1982	75.00	150.00	225.00
Rocking horse grey	Gloss	1957	1962	375.00	650.00	875.00
White	Matt	1970	1982	70.00	150.00	200.00

Model No. 1499   **GIRL ON PONY**

    The pony used for model no. 1499 was also available separately as model no. 1483 "Girl's Pony." The Girl on Pony is available in two variations, one with the girl looking straight ahead and the other has the girl looking down at the pony's neck. There is no price difference between the two variations.

Designer: Arthur Gredington
Height: 5 ½", 14.0 cm

Colourway	Finish	Intro.	Disc.	U.K. £	U.S. $	Can. $
Brown	Gloss	1957	1965	325.00	550.00	750.00
Light dapple grey	Gloss	c.1961	1965	400.00	675.00	900.00
Rocking horse grey	Gloss	c.1961	1962	475.00	800.00	1,250.00
Skewbald	Gloss	1957	1965	125.00	275.00	375.00

Model No. 1500   **BOY ON PONY**

The pony used for model number 1500 was also available separately as model number 1480 "Boy's Pony. "

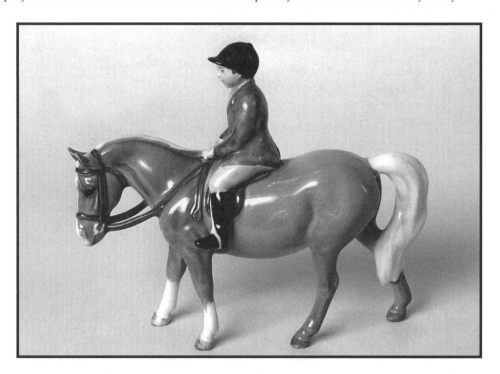

Designer: Arthur Gredington
Height: 5 ½", 14.0 cm

Colourway	Finish	Intro.	Disc.	U.K. £	U.S. $	Can. $
Brown	Gloss	c.1961	1976	325.00	550.00	750.00
Light dapple grey	Gloss	c.1961	1976	400.00	675.00	900.00
Palomino	Gloss	1957	1976	150.00	300.00	425.00
Rocking horse grey	Gloss	c.1961	1962	475.00	800.00	1,250.00
Skewbald	Gloss	Unknown	Unknown	500.00	850.00	1,500.00

Model No. 1501   **HUNTSMAN**

STYLE TWO: Standing

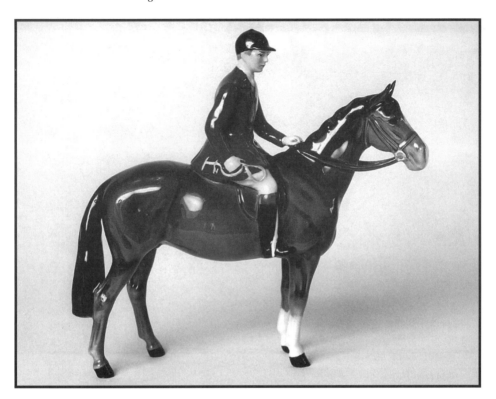

Designer: Arthur Gredington
Height: 8 ¼", 21.0 cm

Colourway	Finish	Intro.	Disc.	U.K. £	U.S. $	Can. $
Brown	Gloss	1957	1995	125.00	275.00	375.00
Chestnut	Gloss	1965	1967	500.00	850.00	1,250.00
Grey	Gloss	1962	1975	250.00	425.00	575.00
Opaque	Gloss	1971	1973	200.00	350.00	475.00
Painted white	Gloss	1958	1971	300.00	525.00	700.00
Palomino	Gloss	1965	1971	400.00	675.00	900.00
Rocking horse grey	Gloss	*c.1958*	1962	600.00	1,000.00	1,500.00
White	Matt	1971	1981	150.00	300.00	400.00

Model No. 1516

APPALOOSA
(Spotted Walking Pony)

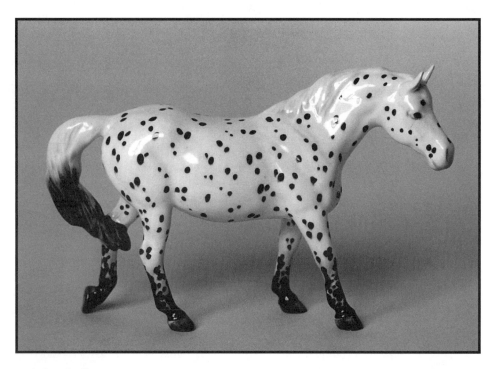

Designer: Arthur Gredington
Height: 5 ¼", 13.3 cm

Colourway	Finish	Intro.	Disc.	U.K. £	U.S. $	Can. $
Brown	Gloss	*1958*	*1967*	200.00	350.00	500.00
Chestnut	Gloss	*1958*	1967	475.00	800.00	1,000.00
Grey	Gloss	*1958*	1967	300.00	500.00	750.00
Opaque	Gloss	*1958*	1967	200.00	350.00	500.00
Painted white	Gloss	*1958*	1967	350.00	600.00	800.00
Palomino	Gloss	*1958*	1967	275.00	400.00	700.00
Rocking Horse Grey	Gloss	*1958*	1962	500.00	850.00	1,250.00
Spotted (British)	Gloss	1957	1966	350.00	600.00	900.00

Model No. 1546

H.M. QUEEN ELIZABETH II
ON IMPERIAL

The horse "Imperial" was also available separately as model number 1557.

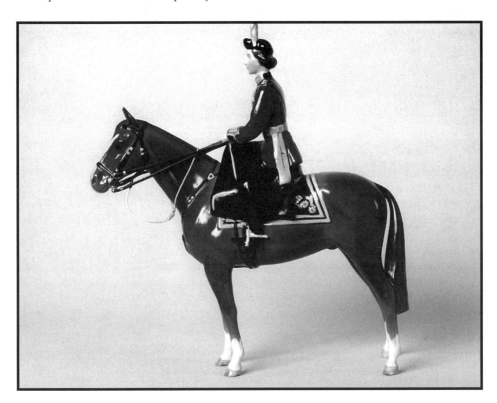

Designer: Mr. Folkard
Height: 10 ½", 26.7 cm

Colourway	Finish	Intro.	Disc.	U.K. £	U.S. $	Can. $
Chestnut	Gloss	1958	1981	250.00	450.00	625.00

Model No. 1549

HORSE
(Head Tucked, Leg Up)

There are two version of model no. 1549, the first has the tail angled towards the off-hind hock, the second has the tail straight down . At the present time the dates cannot be determined as to when the mould was changed.

Model 1549 - First Version | First Version - Tail angled toward off-hind hock | Second Version - Tail straight down

Designer: Pal Zalmen
Height: 7 ½", 19.1 cm

FIRST VERSION: Tail angled towards the off-hind hock

Colourway	Finish	Intro.	Disc.	U.K. £	U.S. $	Can. $
Brown	Gloss	1958	Unknown	65.00	125.00	150.00
Chestnut	Gloss	1958	1967	300.00	500.00	675.00
Grey	Gloss	*1961*	Unknown	85.00	150.00	200.00
Grey	Matt	1981	Unknown	75.00	150.00	200.00
Opaque	Gloss	1964	1973	175.00	300.00	400.00
Painted white	Gloss	*1961*	1967	275.00	475.00	625.00
Palomino	Gloss	*1961*	Unknown	75.00	150.00	200.00
Palomino	Matt	1981	Unknown	65.00	150.00	200.00
Rocking horse grey	Gloss	*c.1959*	*1962*	375.00	625.00	850.00
White	Matt	1970	Unknown	95.00	175.00	250.00

SECOND VERSION: Tail is straight down

Colourway	Finish	DA #	Intro.	Disc.	U.K. £	U.S. $	Can. $
Brown	Gloss	51	Unknown	1989	45.00	100.00	125.00
Grey	Gloss	—	Unknown	1989	65.00	115.00	150.00
Grey	Matt	—	Unknown	1989	55.00	115.00	150.00
Palomino	Gloss	—	Unknown	1989	55.00	100.00	125.00
Palomino	Matt	—	Unknown	1989	45.00	100.00	125.00
White	Matt	—	Unknown	1982	75.00	125.00	175.00

Model No. 1557   "IMPERIAL"

This horse was used in model no. 1546 with Queen Elizabeth as rider.

Designer: Albert Hallam and James Hayward
Height: 8 ¼", 21.0 cm

Colourway	Finish	Intro.	Disc.	U.K. £	U.S. $	Can. $
Brown	Gloss	1958	1982	65.00	125.00	175.00
Chestnut	Gloss	1958	1967	225.00	400.00	600.00
Grey	Gloss	1958	1982	85.00	150.00	225.00
Opaque	Gloss	1958	1973	175.00	300.00	400.00
Painted white	Gloss	1958	1967	275.00	475.00	625.00
Palomino	Gloss	1958	1982	75.00	175.00	225.00
Rocking horse grey	Gloss	1958	1962	375.00	625.00	850.00
White	Matt	1970	1982	95.00	175.00	225.00

Model No. 1564   **LARGE RACEHORSE**

This is the underlying model for the Connoisseur horse 1564 and the Harnessed version 1564.

Designer: Arthur Gredington
Height: 11 ¼", 28.5 cm

Colourway	Finish	Intro.	Disc.	U.K. £	U.S. $	Can. $
Brown	Gloss	1959	1982	100.00	175.00	250.00
Chestnut	Gloss	1959	1967	350.00	600.00	950.00
Grey	Gloss	1959	1982	150.00	275.00	400.00
Opaque	Gloss	1959	1973	200.00	350.00	500.00
Painted white	Gloss	1959	1967	425.00	725.00	975.00
Palomino	Gloss	1959	1982	125.00	275.00	400.00
Rocking horse grey	Gloss	1959	1962	600.00	1,000.00	1,500.00
White	Matt	1970	1982	100.00	325.00	500.00

SERIES: Connoisseur Horse

Designer: Arthur Gredington
Height: 12 ¼", 31.1 cm

Colourway	Finish	Intro.	Disc.	U.K. £	U.S. $	Can. $
Brown	Matt	1970	1981	150.00	300.00	450.00

SERIES: Harnessed Horses

Height: 11 ¼", 28.5 cm

Colourway	Finish	Intro.	Disc.	U.K. £	U.S. $	Can. $
Brown	Gloss	1974	By 1981	150.00	400.00	600.00

Model No. 1588   **H.R.H. DUKE OF EDINBURGH
ON ALAMEIN**

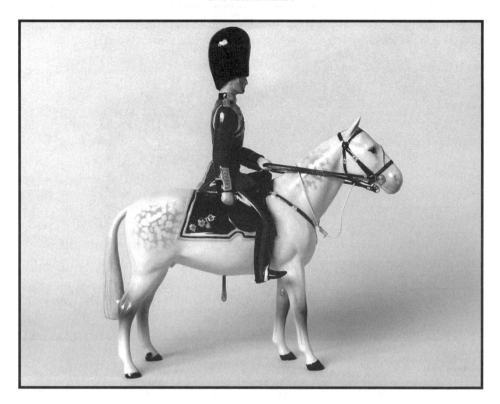

Designer: Mr. Folkard
Height: 10 ½", 26.7 cm

Colourway	Finish	Intro.	Disc.	U.K. £	U.S. $	Can. $
Light dapple grey	Gloss	1958	1981	275.00	450.00	600.00

Model No. 1624   **LIFEGUARD**

STYLE ONE: With trumpet

Designer: Arthur Gredington
Height: 9 ½" 24.0 cm

Colourway	Finish	DA #	Intro.	Disc.	U.K. £	U.S. $	Can. $
Light dapple grey	Gloss	22	1959	1977	400.00	750.00	1,000.00

Model No. 1641

CONNEMARA PONY
"TERESE OF LEAM"

SERIES: Mountain and Moorland Ponies

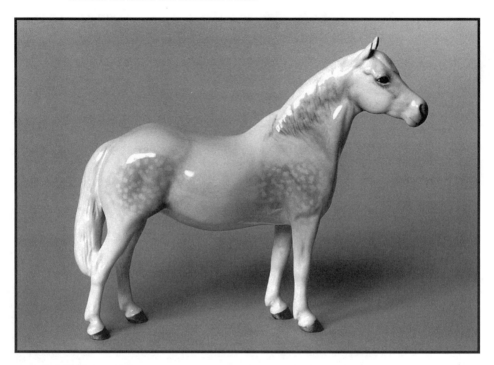

Designer:	Arthur Gredington
Height:	7", 17.8 cm

Colourway	Finish	Intro.	Disc.	U.K. £	U.S. $	Can. $
Grey	Gloss	1961	1984	135.00	225.00	300.00

Model No. 1642

DARTMOOR PONY
"JENTYL / WARLORD"

Warlord was commissioned, in a limited edition of 1,500, by P. R. Middleweek & Co. as the first in a series of Dartmoor Ponies.

SERIES: Mountain and Moorland Ponies

Designer: Arthur Gredington
Height: 6 ¼", 15.9 cm

Name	Colourway/Finish	Intro.	Disc.	U.K. £	U.S. $	Can. $
"Jentyl"	Brown/Gloss	1961	1984	110.00	200.00	250.00
"Warlord"	Bay/Gloss	1996	1996	50.00	100.00	125.00

Model No. 1643

WELSH MOUNTAIN PONY
"COED COCH MADOG"

SERIES: Mountain and Moorland Ponies

First Version: Tail is attached to off-side hind leg

Second Version: Tail hangs loose

Designer: Arthur Gredington
Height: 6 ¼", 15.9 cm

FIRST VERSION: Tail is attached to off-side hind leg.

Colourway	Finish	Intro.	Disc.	U.K. £	U.S. $	Can. $
Grey	Gloss	1961	Unknown	145.00	250.00	400.00

SECOND VERSION: Tail hangs loose.

Colourway	Finish	Intro.	Disc.	U.K. £	U.S. $	Can. $
Grey	Gloss	Unknown	1989	125.00	225.00	350.00

Model No. 1644

HIGHLAND PONY
"MACKIONNEACH"

SERIES: Mountain and Moorland Ponies

Designer: Arthur Gredington
Height: 7 ¼", 18.4 cm

Colourway	Finish	Intro.	Disc.	U.K. £	U.S. $	Can. $
Dun	Gloss	1961	1989	125.00	200.00	350.00
Opaque	Gloss	Unknown	Unknown	Extremely Rare		

Model No. 1645

EXMOOR PONY
"HEATHERMAN"

SERIES: Mountain and Moorland Ponies

Designer: Arthur Gredington
Height: 6 ½", 16.5 cm

Colourway	Finish	Intro.	Disc.	U.K. £	U.S. $	Can. $
Bay	Gloss	1961	1983	125.00	250.00	350.00

Model No. 1646

NEW FOREST PONY
"JONATHEN 3ᴿᴰ"

SERIES: Mountain and Moorland Ponies

First Version: Tail is attached to the near-side hock   Second Version: Tail hangs loose

Designer: Arthur Gredington
Height: 7", 17.8 cm

FIRST VERSION: Tail is attached to the near-side hock.

Colourway	Finish	Intro.	Disc.	U.K. £	U.S. $	Can. $
Bay	Gloss	1961	Unknown	135.00	225.00	350.00

SECOND VERSION: Tail hangs loose.

Colourway	Finish	Intro.	Disc.	U.K. £	U.S. $	Can. $
Bay	Gloss	Unknown	1984	115.00	200.00	300.00

Model No. 1647

FELL PONY
"DENE DAUNTLESS"

SERIES: Mountain and Moorland Ponies

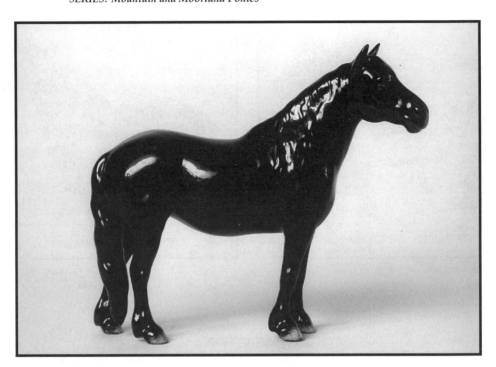

Designer: Arthur Gredington
Height: 6 ¾", 17.2 cm

Colourway	Finish	Intro.	Disc.	U.K. £	U.S. $	Can. $
Black	Gloss	1961	1982	110.00	200.00	300.00

Model No. 1648

SHETLAND PONY
"ESCHONCHAN RONAY"

SERIES: Mountain and Moorland Ponies

Designer: Arthur Gredington
Height: 4 ¾", 12.1 cm

Colourway	Finish	Intro.	Disc.	U.K. £	U.S. $	Can. $
Brown	Gloss	1961	1989	75.00	150.00	225.00

Model No. 1671

DALES PONY
"MAISIE"

SERIES: Mountain and Moorland Ponies

Designer:	Arthur Gredington
Height:	6 ½", 16.5 cm

Colourway	Finish	Intro.	Disc.	U.K. £	U.S. $	Can. $
Black	Gloss	1961	1982	110.00	200.00	300.00

Model No. 1730   **HUNTSWOMAN**

STYLE TWO: Rider and horse stood still

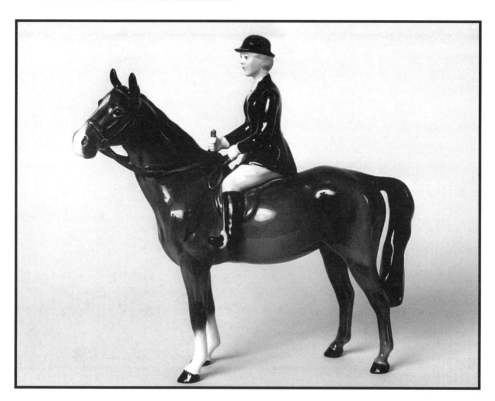

Designer: Arthur Gredington
Height: 8 ¼", 21.0 cm

Colourway	Finish	Intro.	Disc.	U.K. £	U.S. $	Can. $
Brown	Gloss	1960	1975	225.00	375.00	600.00
Grey	Gloss	1960	1995	125.00	225.00	400.00
Opaque	Gloss	1971	1973	200.00	450.00	650.00
Painted white	Gloss	1960	1971	375.00	625.00	850.00
Rocking horse grey	Gloss	1960	1962	600.00	1,000.00	1,250.00
White	Matt	1971	1981	150.00	325.00	500.00

Model No. 1734   LARGE HUNTER

FIRST VERSION: The head looks slightly overlarge and the body too much on the thin size.
The tail hangs straight down.

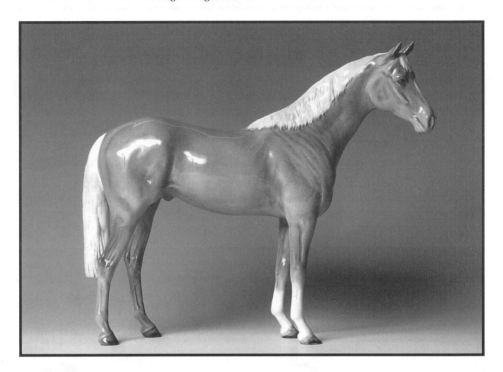

Designer: Arthur Gredington
Height: 11 ¼", 28.5 cm

Colourway	Finish	Intro.	Disc.	U.K. £	U.S. $	Can. $
Brown	Gloss	1961	1963	300.00	500.00	675.00
Chestnut	Gloss	1961	1963	550.00	925.00	1,250.00
Grey	Gloss	1961	1963	475.00	800.00	1,000.00
Opaque	Gloss	1961	1963	300.00	500.00	750.00
Painted white	Gloss	1961	1963	500.00	850.00	1,150.00
Palomino	Gloss	1961	1963	450.00	750.00	1,100.00
Rocking horse grey	Gloss	1961	1962	600.00	1,000.00	1,350.00

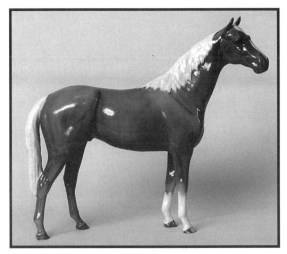

Second Version: Head and body in proportion

Large Hunter - Connoisseur Horse

SECOND VERSION: Head and body in proportion. The tail is slightly arched away from the body

Height: 11 ¾", 29.8 cm

Colourway	Finish	Intro.	Disc.	U.K. £	U.S. $	Can. $
Brown	Gloss	1963	1984	100.00	250.00	400.00
Chestnut	Gloss	1963	1967	450.00	750.00	1,000.00
Grey	Gloss	1963	1984	150.00	250.00	400.00
Opaque	Gloss	1963	1973	200.00	400.00	575.00
Painted white	Gloss	1963	1967	425.00	725.00	1,000.00
Palomino	Gloss	1963	1983	125.00	250.00	400.00
White	Matt	1970	1982	100.00	275.00	400.00

SERIES: Connoisseur Horses

Height: 12 ¼", 31.1 cm

Colourway	Finish	Intro.	Disc.	U.K. £	U.S. $	Can. $
Grey	Matt	1970	1982	150.00	300.00	450.00

Model No. 1771   ARAB "BAHRAM"

Arab "Bahram"   Arab "Bahram" Connoisseur Horse

Designer: Arthur Gredington
Height: 7 ½", 19.1 cm

Colourway	Finish	DA #	Intro.	Disc.	U.K. £	U.S. $	Can. $
Brown	Gloss	52	1961	1989	60.00	100.00	150.00
Brown	Matt	52	1980	1989	55.00	100.00	150.00
Chestnut	Gloss	—	1961	1967	225.00	400.00	525.00
Grey	Gloss	—	1961	1989	85.00	150.00	225.00
Grey	Matt	—	1980	1989	85.00	150.00	225.00
Opaque	Gloss	—	1961	1973	175.00	300.00	425.00
Painted white	Gloss	—	1961	1967	300.00	525.00	675.00
Palomino	Gloss	—	1961	1989	75.00	130.00	175.00
Palomino	Matt	—	1980	1989	65.00	130.00	175.00
Rocking horse grey	Gloss	—	1961	1962	Extremely Rare		
White	Matt	—	1970	1982	60.00	130.00	175.00

SERIES: Connoisseur Horses

Height: 8 ¼", 21.0 cm

Colourway	Finish	Intro.	Disc.	U.K. £	U.S. $	Can. $
Grey	Matt	1970	1989	125.00	200.00	300.00

Model No. 1772   **THOROUGHBRED STALLION**
(Large)

Thoroughbred Stallion

Thoroughbred Stallion - Connoisseur Horse

Designer: Arthur Gredington
Height: 8", 20.3 cm

Colourway	Finish	DA #	Intro.	Disc.	U.K. £	U.S. $	Can. $
Brown	Gloss	53	1961	1989	60.00	100.00	135.00
Chestnut	Gloss	—	1961	1967	325.00	550.00	750.00
Grey	Gloss	53	1961	1989	85.00	150.00	200.00
Opaque	Gloss	—	1961	1973	175.00	300.00	425.00
Painted white	Gloss	—	1961	1967	300.00	500.00	675.00
Palomino	Gloss	—	1961	1983	95.00	175.00	250.00
Rocking horse grey	Gloss	—	1961	1962	Extremely Rare		
White	Matt	—	1970	1982	60.00	150.00	225.00

SERIES: Connoisseur Horses

Height: 8 ¾", 22.2 cm

Colourway	Finish	Intro.	Disc.	U.K. £	U.S. $	Can. $
Bay	Matt	1970	1989	100.00	175.00	325.00

Model No. 1772A   **APPALOOSA STALLION**

Colourway No. 1, More detailed paintwork, striped hooves   Colourway No. 2, Less distinct roan areas, cream hooves

Designer: Arthur Gredington
Height: 8", 20.3 cm

COLOURWAY No. 1. More detailed paintwork with the head and neck in particular more "mottled."
Striped hooves.

Colourway	Finish	Intro.	Disc.	U.K. £	U.S. $	Can. $
Black and white	Gloss	1975	Unknown	125.00	225.00	325.00

COLOURWAY No. 2. Less distinct roan areas of black on head and neck and brown on lower body quarters.
Cream hooves.

Colourway	Finish	Intro.	Disc.	U.K. £	U.S. $	Can. $
Black and white	Gloss	Unknown	1989	100.00	175.00	325.00

Model No. 1793

WELSH COB
(Standing)

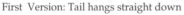

First Version: Tail hangs straight down

Second Version - Top part of tail arched away from body

Designer: Arthur Gredington
Height: 7 ½", 19.1 cm

FIRST VERSION: Tail hangs straight down.

Colourway	Finish	Intro.	Disc.	U.K. £	U.S. $	Can. $
Brown	Gloss	1962	c.1975/76	95.00	175.00	250.00
Chestnut	Gloss	1962	c.1975/76	375.00	625.00	850.00
Grey	Gloss	1962	c.1975/76	175.00	300.00	400.00
Opaque	Gloss	1962	c.1975/76	200.00	350.00	450.00
Painted white	Gloss	1962	c.1975/76	350.00	600.00	800.00
Palomino	Gloss	1962	1970	300.00	500.00	675.00
Piebald	Gloss	Unknown	Unknown		Very Rare	
White	Matt	1970	c.1975/76	95.00	200.00	300.00

SECOND VERSION: The tail was altered so that the top part (dock) arched away from the body.

Colourway	Finish	Intro.	Disc.	U.K. £	U.S. $	Can. $
Brown	Gloss	c.1975/76	1982	80.00	150.00	200.00
Grey	Gloss	c.1975/76	1982	150.00	250.00	350.00
White	Matt	c.1975/76	1982	80.00	175.00	275.00

Model No. 1811   MARE AND FOAL

The mare and foal are available separately as model nos. 1812 mare and 1813 foal.

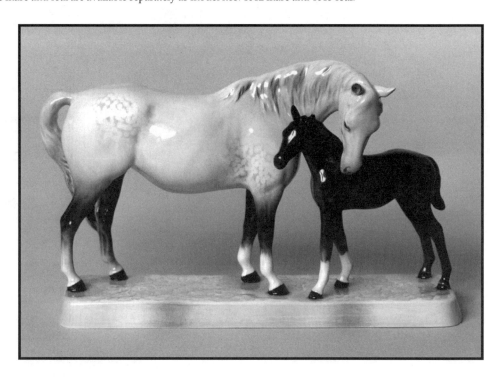

Designer: Arthur Gredington
Height: 6", 15.0 cm

Colourway	Finish	Intro.	Disc.	U.K. £	U.S. $	Can. $
Brown mare and chestnut foal	Gloss	1962	1975	200.00	350.00	500.00
Grey mare and black foal	Gloss	1962	1975	175.00	325.00	450.00

Model No. 1812

MARE
(Facing Right, Head Down)

Model no. 1811 was paired with foal model no. 1813 to make model no. 1811 "Mare and Foal."

Designer: Arthur Gredington
Height: 5 ¾", 14.6 cm

Colourway	Finish	DA #	Intro.	Disc.	U.K. £	U.S. $	Can. $
Brown	Gloss	54	1962	1989	45.00	100.00	125.00
Brown	Matt	—	1970	1989	40.00	100.00	125.00
Chestnut	Gloss	—	1962	1967	375.00	625.00	850.00
Grey	Gloss	—	1962	1989	65.00	125.00	200.00
Grey	Matt	—	1970	1989	55.00	125.00	200.00
Opaque	Gloss	—	1962	1973	150.00	275.00	400.00
Painted white	Gloss	—	1962	1967	275.00	450.00	700.00
Palomino	Gloss	—	1962	1989	55.00	125.00	200.00
Palomino	Matt	—	1970	1983	50.00	125.00	200.00
"Treacle"	Gloss	—	1992	1992	80.00	175.00	250.00
"Treacle"	Matt	—	1992	1992	80.00	175.00	250.00
White	Matt	—	1970	1982	65.00	150.00	250.00

Model No. 1813

FOAL
(Larger Thoroughbred Type)

First Version - Fine head and legs

Second Version - Plain head, thicker, less shapely legs

Designer: Arthur Gredington
Height: 4 ½", 11.9 cm

FIRST VERSION: Fine head and legs, off fore leg is placed well behind the near fore leg.

Colourway	Finish	Intro.	Disc.	U.K. £	U.S. $	Can. $
Brown	Gloss	1962	1982	30.00	50.00	75.00
Brown	Matt	1979	1982	30.00	50.00	75.00
Chestnut	Gloss	1962	1967	250.00	425.00	625.00
Grey	Gloss	1962	1982	45.00	100.00	150.00
Opaque	Gloss	1962	1973	90.00	150.00	225.00
Painted white	Gloss	1963	1967	200.00	350.00	500.00
Palomino	Gloss	1962	1982	35.00	100.00	150.00
White	Matt	1970	c.1982	55.00	100.00	130.00

SECOND VERSION: Plain head, thicker legs with less shape, off fore leg almost parallel to near fore leg.

Colourway	Finish	DA #	Intro.	Disc.	U.K. £	U.S. $	Can. $
Brown	Gloss	81	1982	1982	25.00	50.00	75.00
Brown	Matt	81	1982	1989	25.00	50.00	75.00
Grey	Gloss	—	1982	1989	30.00	60.00	100.00
Palomino	Gloss	—	1982	1989	25.00	60.00	100.00
Orange bay	Gloss	—	1982	c.1984	55.00	125.00	200.00
White	Matt	—	c.1982	1982	40.00	75.00	100.00

Model No. 1816

FOAL
(Smaller Thoroughbred Type, Facing Left)

First Version: Fine head, thin delicate legs

Second Version: Head and legs thicker

Designer: Arthur Gredington
Height: 3 ½", 8.9 cm

FIRST VERSION: Fine head and very thin delicate legs.

Colourway	Finish	Intro.	Disc.	U.K. £	U.S. $	Can. $
Brown	Gloss	1963	1975	30.00	50.00	70.00
Chestnut	Gloss	1963	1967	200.00	350.00	550.00
Grey	Gloss	1963	1975	45.00	80.00	115.00
Opaque	Gloss	1963	1973	75.00	150.00	200.00
Painted white	Gloss	1963	1967	175.00	300.00	450.00
Palomino	Gloss	1963	1975	40.00	80.00	115.00
White	Matt	1970	1975	40.00	80.00	115.00

SECOND VERSION: Head and legs made thicker and less shape to the legs.

Colourway	Finish	Intro.	Disc.	U.K. £	U.S. $	Can. $
Brown	Gloss	1975	1989	20.00	30.00	45.00
Brown	Matt	1979	1989	20.00	30.00	45.00
Grey	Gloss	1975	1983	30.00	60.00	90.00
Palomino	Gloss	1975	1989	30.00	60.00	90.00
White	Matt	1975	1989	30.00	60.00	90.00

Model No. 1817

FOAL
(Smaller Thoroughbred Type, Facing Right)

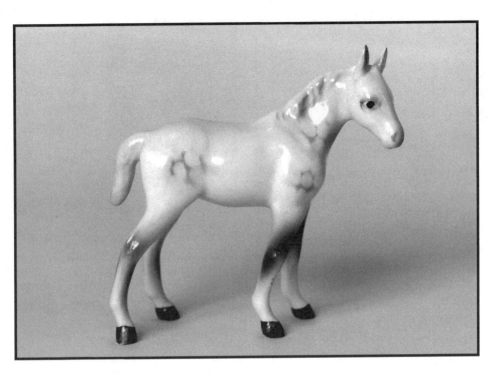

Designer: Arthur Gredington
Height: 3 ¼", 8.3 cm

Colourway	Finish	Intro.	Disc.	U.K. £	U.S. $	Can. $
Brown	Gloss	1963	1975	45.00	75.00	100.00
Chestnut	Gloss	1963	1967	225.00	375.00	550.00
Grey	Gloss	1963	1975	60.00	100.00	150.00
Opaque	Gloss	1963	1973	80.00	150.00	200.00
Painted white	Gloss	1963	1967	200.00	350.00	500.00
Palomino	Gloss	1963	1975	55.00	100.00	150.00
White	Matt	1970	1975	45.00	100.00	150.00

Model No. 1862   **HORSE AND JOCKEY**

STYLE TWO: Standing horse and jockey

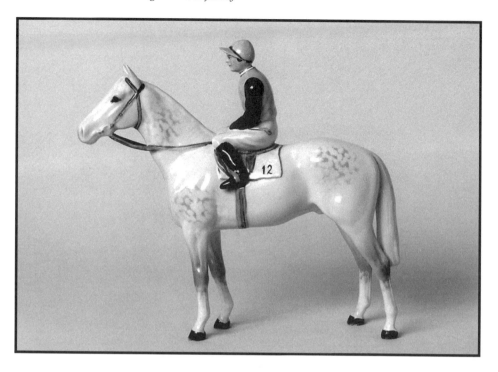

Designer: Arthur Gredington
Height: 8", 20.3 cm

Colourway	Finish	Intro.	Disc.	U.K. £	U.S. $	Can. $
Brown	Gloss	1963	1984	200.00	350.00	650.00
Light dapple grey	Gloss	1963	1983	250.00	450.00	750.00
Painted white	Gloss	Unknown	Unknown		Extremely Rare	

Model No. 1991

MARE
(Facing Right, Head Up)

FIRST VERSION: The end only of the tail is attached to the hock.

Designer: Arthur Gredington
Height: 5 ½", 14.0 cm

Colourway	Finish	DA #	Intro.	Disc.	U.K. £	U.S. $	Can. $
Brown	Gloss	55	1965	Unknown	45.00	85.00	110.00
Brown	Matt	55	1970	Unknown	40.00	85.00	110.00
Chestnut	Gloss	—	1965	Unknown	250.00	425.00	575.00
Grey	Gloss	55	1965	Unknown	65.00	175.00	250.00
Grey	Matt	—	1970	Unknown	55.00	175.00	250.00
Opaque	Gloss	—	1965	Unknown	100.00	250.00	400.00
Painted white	Gloss	—	1965	Unknown	250.00	425.00	575.00
Palomino	Gloss	55	1965	Unknown	50.00	175.00	250.00
Palomino	Matt	—	1970	Unknown	45.00	175.00	250.00
White	Matt	—	1970	Unknown	60.00	150.00	200.00

SECOND VERSION: The tail is attached to the quarters and the hock.

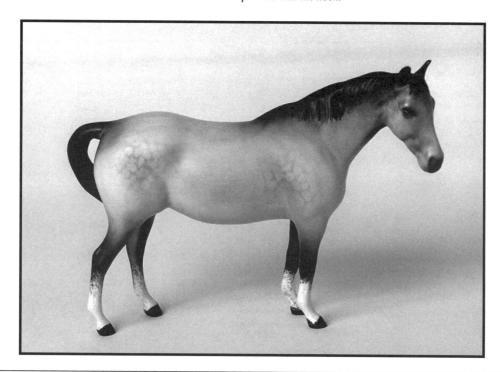

Colourway	Finish	DA #	Intro.	Disc.	U.K. £	U.S. $	Can. $
Brown	Gloss	55	Unknown	1989	35.00	75.00	100.00
Brown	Matt	55	Unknown	1989	35.00	75.00	100.00
Grey	Gloss	55	Unknown	1989	45.00	90.00	125.00
Grey	Matt	—	Unknown	1989	45.00	90.00	125.00
Palomino	Gloss	55	Unknown	1989	40.00	90.00	125.00
Palomino	Matt	—	Unknown	1989	35.00	90.00	125.00
White	Matt	—	Unknown	1982	45.00	100.00	150.00

Model No. 1992

THOROUGHBRED STALLION
(Small)

Designer: Arthur Gredington
Height: 5 ½", 14.0.cm

Colourway	Finish	DA #	Intro.	Disc.	U.K. £	U.S. $	Can. $
Brown	Gloss	56	1965	1989	35.00	75.00	100.00
Brown	Matt	56	1970	1989	35.00	75.00	100.00
Chestnut	Gloss	—	1965	1967	250.00	500.00	750.00
Grey	Gloss	56	1965	1989	45.00	125.00	175.00
Grey	Matt	—	1970	1989	45.00	125.00	175.00
Opaque	Gloss	—	1965	1973	90.00	225.00	400.00
Painted white	Gloss	—	1965	1967	250.00	450.00	600.00
Palomino	Gloss	—	1965	1989	50.00	125.00	175.00
Palomino	Matt	—	1970	1989	40.00	125.00	175.00
White	Matt	—	1970	1982	55.00	125.00	175.00

Model No. 2065   **ARKLE**

SERIES: *Connoisseur Horses*

Designer: Arthur Gredington
Height: 11 7/8", 30.1 cm

Colourway	Finish	DA #	Intro.	Disc.	U.K. £	U.S. $	Can. $
Bay	Matt	15	1970	1989	165.00	350.00	475.00

Model No. 2084

ARKLE
PAT TAAFFE UP

SERIES: Connoisseur Horses

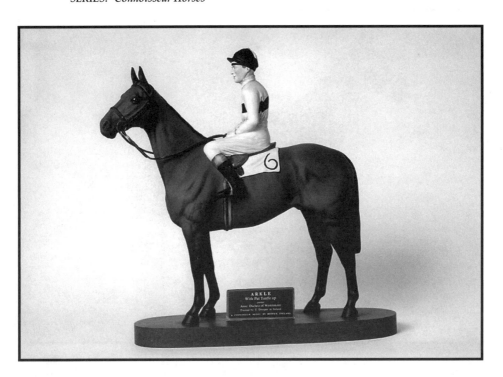

| Designer: | Arthur Gredington |
| Height: | 12 ½", 21.7 cm |

Colourway	Finish	Intro.	Disc.	U.K. £	U.S. $	Can. $
Bay	Matt	1970	1982	350.00	600.00	800.00

Model No. 2186   **QUARTER HORSE**

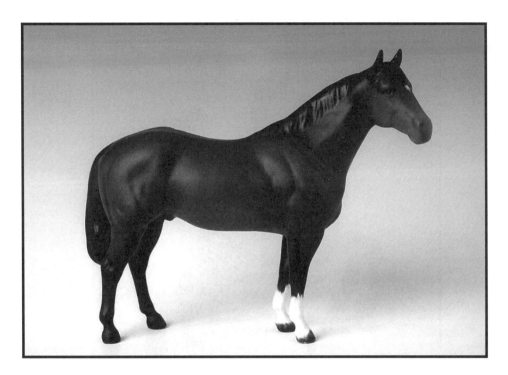

Designer: Arthur Gredington
Height: 8 ¼", 21.0 cm

Colourway	Finish	Intro.	Disc.		U.K. £	U.S. $	Can. $
Brown	Gloss	1969	1982	.	125.00	250.00	375.00
Brown	Matt	1970	1982		100.00	250.00	375.00
White	Matt	1973	1982		90.00	200.00	300.00

Model No. 2210   **HIGHWAYMAN**

SERIES: Connoisseur Horses

Designer: Albert Hallam
Height: 13 ¾", 34.9 cm

Colourway	Finish	Intro.	Disc.	U.K. £	U.S. $	Can. $
Bay	Matt	1970	1975	700.00	1,200.00	1,600.00

Model No. 2242   **ARAB STALLION**

This is an authentic rendition of an Arab horse. It is on a pottery (base) stand.

Designer: Albert Hallam
Height: 8 ½", 21.6 cm

Colourway	Finish	Intro.	Disc.	U.K. £	U.S. $	Can. $
Brown	Gloss	1970	1975	350.00	750.00	1,000.00

Model No. 2269   **ARAB STALLION WITH SADDLE**

SERIES: Connoisseur Horses

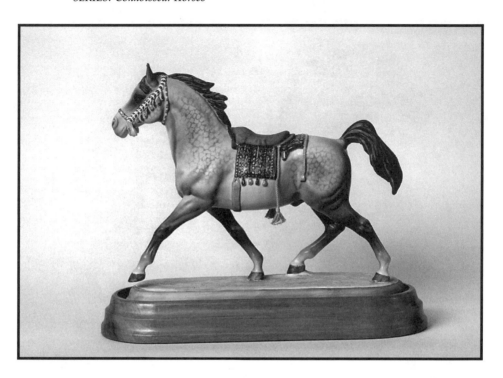

Designer: Albert Hallam
Height: 9 ½", 24.0 cm

Colourway	Finish	Intro.	Disc.	U.K. £	U.S. $	Can.
Dappled grey	Matt	1970	1975	875.00	1,400.00	1,750.00

Model No. 2275   **BEDOUIN ARAB**

SERIES: Connoisseur Horses

Designer: Albert Hallam
Height: 11 ½", 29.2 cm

Colourway	Finish	Intro.	Disc.	U.K. £	U.S. $	Can. $
Chestnut	Matt	1970	1975	850.00	1,400.00	2,250.00

Model No. 2282   **NORWEGIAN FJORD HORSE**

Designer: Albert Hallam
Height: 6 ½", 16.5 cm

Colourway	Finish	Intro.	Disc.	U.K. £	U.S. $	Can. $
Dun	Gloss	1970	1975	425.00	725.00	975.00

Model No. 2309   **BURNHAM BEAUTY**

Designer: Albert Hallam
Height: 10 ¾", 27.8 cm

Colourway	Finish	Intro.	Disc.	U.K. £	U.S. $	Can. $
Brown	Gloss	1972	1982	100.00	275.00	350.00
White	Matt	1974	1982	100.00	275.00	350.00

SERIES: Connoisseur Horses

Height: 11 ¼", 28.5 cm

Colourway	Finish	Intro.	Disc.	U.K. £	U.S. $	Can. $
Bay	Matt	1971	1982	150.00	350.00	450.00

SERIES: Harnessed Horses

Height: 10 ¾", 27.8 cm

Colourway	Finish	Intro.	Disc.	U.K. £	U.S. $	Can. $
Brown	Matt	1979	1984	175.00	375.00	500.00

Model No. 2340

CARDIGAN BAY

Two versions of model no. 2340 exist. The first version has only two hooves attached to the base making it unstable and prone to breakage. The base was remodelled to better support the model and has three hooves attached to it.

> *SERIES: Connoisseur Horses*

> *FIRST VERSION: Two legs attached to the base - off hind leg is not attached to the base.*

Designer:	Albert Hallam
Height:	9 ¼", 23.5 cm

Colourway	Finish	Intro.	Disc.	U.K. £	U.S. $	Can. $
Brown	Matt	1971	c.1972	550.00	950.00	1,350.00

SECOND VERSION: Three legs attached to the base - off hind leg is attached to the base.

Colourway	Finish	Intro.	Disc.	U.K. £	U.S. $	Can. $
Brown	Matt	c.1972	1976	400.00	750.00	1,000.00

Model No. 2345

NIJINSKY

SERIES: *Connoisseur Horses*

Designer: Albert Hallam
Height: 11 ¼", 28.5 cm

Colourway	Finsh	DA #	Intro.	Disc.	U.K. £	U.S. $	Can. $
Bay	Matt	16	1971	1989	165.00	325.00	450.00

Model No. 2352

NIJINSKY
LESTER PIGGOTT UP

SERIES: Connoisseur Horses

Designer: Albert Hallam
Height: 12 ½", 31.7 cm

Colourway	Finish	Intro.	Disc.	U.K. £	U.S. $	Can. $
Bay	Matt	1971	1982	375.00	650.00	875.00

Model No. 2421   THE WINNER

Designer: Albert Hallam
Height: 9 ½", 24.0 cm

Colourway	Finish	Intro.	Disc.	U.K. £	U.S. $	Can. $
Brown	Gloss	1973	1982	100.00	225.00	400.00
Brown	Matt	1973	1982	90.00	200.00	350.00
White	Matt	1973	1982	90.00	200.00	350.00

Model No. 2422   **MILL REEF**

The mahogany bay (gloss) variety was sold through Lawleys, Royal Doulton's retail shops, in the mid 1980s. When Mill Reef was withdrawn from the range at the end of 1989 a white matt variety was sold at the Beswick factory shop.

Designer: Albert Hallam
Height: 9", 22.9 cm

Colourway	Finish	Intro.	Disc.	U.K. £	U.S. $	Can. $
Mahogany bay	Gloss	1985	1988	135.00	275.00	375.00
White	Matt	1989	Unknown	100.00	275.00	400.00

SERIES: Connoisseur Horses

Colourway	Finish	Intro.	Disc.	U.K. £	U.S. $	Can. $
Brown/wooden plinth	Matt	1973	1989	110.00	250.00	350.00

Model No. 2431   **MOUNTIE STALLION**

SERIES: Connoisseur Horses

Designer: Graham Tongue
Height: 10", 25.4 cm

Colourway	Finish	Intro.	Disc.	U.K. £	U.S. $	Can. $
Black	Gloss	1973	1975	450.00	800.00	1,200.00

Model No. 2459   **SHIRE MARE**
(Lying)

Designer: Unknown
Height: 5", 12.7 cm

Colourways	Finish	Intro.	Disc.	U.K. £	U.S. $	Can. $
Brown	Gloss	1973	Unknown	275.00	475.00	625.00
Grey	Gloss	1973	1976	225.00	375.00	525.00

Model No. 2460

SHIRE FOAL
(Lying)

| Designer: | Unknown |
| Height: | 3 ½", 8.9 cm |

Colourway	Finish	Intro.	Disc.	U.K. £	U.S. $	Can. $
Dark brown	Gloss	1973	1976	150.00	275.00	350.00

Model No. 2464   **PERCHERON**

SERIES: Harnessed Horses

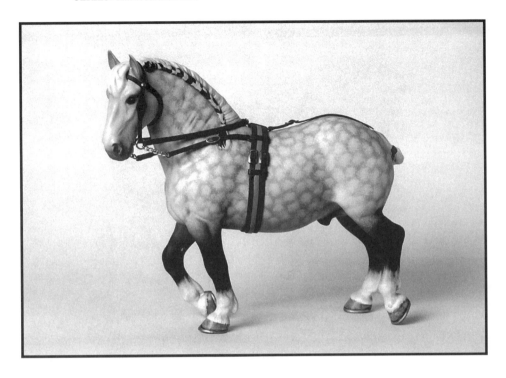

Designer: Unknown
Height: 9 ¾", 24.7 cm

Colourway	Finish	Intro.	Disc.	U.K. £	U.S. $	Can. $
Dappled grey	Matt	1974	1982	325.00	575.00	775.00

Model No. 2465

CLYDESDALE

SERIES: Harnessed Horses

First Version - Working Harness

Designer: Unknown
Height: 10 ¾", 27.8 cm

FIRST VERSION: Working Harness

Colourway	Finish	Intro.	Disc.	U.K. £	U.S. $	Can. $
Chocolate Brown	Matt	1974	1982	250.00	450.00	575.00

SECOND VERSION: Show Harness

Colourway	Finish	Intro.	Disc.	U.K. £	U.S. $	Can. $
Chocolate Brown	Matt	1974	1982	275.00	475.00	625.00

Model No. 2466

BLACK BEAUTY

This model was used in model no. 2466/2536 Black Beauty and Foal.

Designer: Graham Tongue
Height: 7 ¼", 18.4 cm

Colourway	Finish	DA #	Intro.	Disc.	U.K. £	U.S. $	Can. $
Black	Matt	65	1974	1989	45.00	95.00	125.00

Model No. 2467

LIPIZZANER WITH RIDER

SERIES: Connoisseur Horses

First Version - Hind legs attached to a circular base   Second Version - Tail and rear legs attached to oval base

Designer: Graham Tongue
Height: 10", 25.4 cm

FIRST VERSION: Hind legs attached to a circular base.

Colourway	Finish	Intro.	Disc.	U.K. £	U.S. $	Can. $
White	Gloss	1974	Unknown	475.00	800.00	1,100.00

SECOND VERSON: Tail and rear legs attached to an oval base.

Colourway	Finish	Intro.	Disc.	U.K. £	U.S. $	Can. $
White	Gloss	Unknown	1981	350.00	625.00	850.00

Model No. 2505   **STEEPLECHASER**

Designer: Graham Tongue
Height: 8 ¾", 22.2 cm

Colourway	Finish	Intro.	Disc.	U.K. £	U.S. $	Can. $
Dark brown	Gloss	1975	1981	425.00	725.00	1,000.00

Model No. 2510   **RED RUM**

SERIES: *Connoisseur Horses*

Designer: Graham Tongue
Height: 12", 30.5 cm

Colourway	Finish	DA #	Intro.	Disc.	U.K. £	U.S. $	Can. $
Bay	Matt	18	1975	1989	165.00	375.00	500.00

Model No. 2511

RED RUM
BRIAN FLETCHER UP

SERIES: Connoisseur Horses

Designer: Graham Tongue
Height: 12 ¼", 31.1 cm

Colourway	Finish	Intro.	Disc.	U.K. £	U.S. $	Can. $
Bay	Matt	1975	1982	395.00	750.00	1,000.00

Model No. 2535

PSALM
ANN MOORE UP

SERIES: Connoisseur Horses

Designer:	Graham Tongue
Height:	12 ¾", 32.4 cm

Colourway	Finish	Intro.	Disc.	U.K. £	U.S. $	Can. $
Brown	Matt	1975	1982	275.00	500.00	700.00

Model No. 2536   **BLACK BEAUTY FOAL**

Designer: Graham Tongue
Height: 3 ½", 8.9 cm

Colourway	Finish	DA #	Intro.	Disc.	U.K. £	U.S. $	Can. $
Black	Matt	66	1976	1989	30.00	50.00	70.00
Brown	Matt	—	1984	Unknown	30.00	50.00	70.00
Chocolate brown	Matt	—	1984	Unknown	30.00	50.00	70.00
Palomino	Matt	—	1984	Unknown	35.00	65.00	90.00
White	Matt	—	1984	Unknown	30.00	50.00	70.00

Model No. 2540   PSALM

SERIES: Connoisseur Horses

Designer: Graham Tongue
Height: 11 ½", 29.2 cm

Colourway	Finish	Intro.	Disc.	U.K. £	U.S. $	Can. $
Brown	Matt	1975	1982	225.00	400.00	550.00

Model No. 2541A

WELSH MOUNTAIN STALLION
"GREDINGTON SIMWNT"

This model of Gredington Simwnt was greatly adapted to produce "The Spirit of Whitfield."

SERIES: *Connoisseur Horses*

Designer: Graham Tongue
Height: 9", 22.9 cm

Colourway	Finish	Intro.	Disc.	U.K. £	U.S. $	Can. $
Light grey	Matt	1976	1989	225.00	400.00	600.00

Model No. 2558   GRUNDY

SERIES: *Connoisseur Horses*

Designer: Graham Tongue
Height: 11 ¼", 28.5 cm

Colourway	Finish	DA #	Intro.	Disc.	U.K. £	U.S. $	Can. $
Chestnut	Matt	20	1977	1989	165.00	375.00	525.00

Model No. 2562   **LIFEGUARD**

STYLE TWO: With sword

SERIES: Connoisseur Horses

Designer:	Graham Tongue
Height:	14 ½", 36.8 cm

Colourway	Finish	DA #	Intro.	Disc.	U.K. £	U.S. $	Can. $
Black	Gloss	22	1977	1989	375.00	625.00	875.00

Model No. 2578

SHIRE HORSE
(Large action shire)

Designer: Alan Maslankowski
Height: 8 ¼", 21.0 cm

Colourway	Finish	DA #	Intro.	Disc.	U.K. £	U.S. $	Can. $
Brown	Gloss	—	1980	1982	200.00	350.00	525.00
Brown	Matt	62	1978	1989	125.00	250.00	375.00
Grey	Gloss	—	1975	1982	250.00	450.00	600.00
Grey	Matt	—	1980	1983	225.00	375.00	575.00

SERIES: Harnessed Horses

Colourway	Finish	Intro.	Disc.	U.K. £	U.S. $	Can. $
Brown	Matt	1978	1982	150.00	275.00	425.00
Grey	Matt	1978	1982	225.00	400.00	575.00

Model No. 2582   **BLUES AND ROYALS**

SERIES: Connoisseur Horses

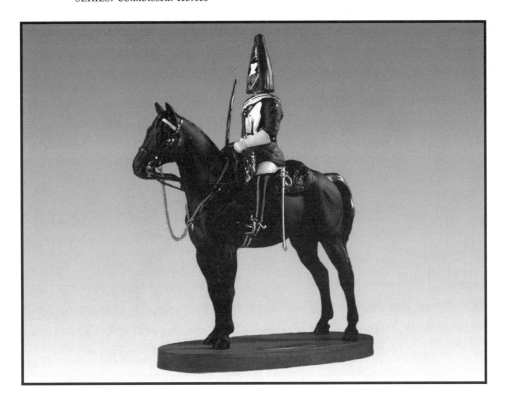

Designer: Graham Tongue
Height: 14 ½", 36.8 cm

Colourway	Finish	DA #	Intro.	Disc.	U.K. £	U.S. $	Can. $
Black	Matt	25	1987	1989	400.00	675.00	1,000.00

Model No. 2605

MORGAN STALLION
" TARRYALL MAESTRO "

SERIES: Connoisseur Horses

Designer: Graham Tongue
Height: 11 ½", 29.2 cm

Colourway	Finish	DA #	Intro.	Disc.	U.K. £	U.S. $	Can. $
Black	Matt	28	1979	1989	150.00	325.00	450.00

Model No. 2608   **THE MINSTREL**

SERIES: Connoisseur Horses

Designer: Graham Tongue
Height: 13 ¼", 33.6 cm

Colourway	Finish	DA #	Intro.	Disc.	U.K. £	U.S. $	Can. $
Chestnut	Matt	31	1980	1989	175.00	350.00	475.00

Model No. 2671   MOONLIGHT

SERIES: *Connoisseur Horses*

Designer: Graham Tongue
Height: 11 ¼", 28.5 cm

Colourway	Finish	DA #	Intro.	Disc.	U.K. £	U.S. $	Can. $
"Moonlight" - Grey	Matt	35	1986	1989	135.00	300.00	400.00
"Nightshade" - Black	Matt	—	1986	1989	175.00	300.00	400.00
"Sunburst" - Palomino	Matt	36	1986	1989	175.00	300.00	400.00

Model No. 2674   **TROY**

SERIES: Connoisseur Horses

Designer: Graham Tongue
Height: 11 ¾", 29.8 cm

Colourway	Finish	DA #	Intro.	Disc.	U.K. £	U.S. $	Can. $
Bay	Matt	37	1981	1989	165.00	350.00	450.00

Model No. 2688

SPIRIT OF THE WIND

Designer: Graham Tongue
Height: 8", 20.3 cm

Colourway	Finish	DA #	Intro.	Disc.	U.K. £	U.S. $	Can. $
Brown	Gloss	57	1982	1989	60.00	100.00	135.00
Brown	Matt	57	1982	1989	55.00	100.00	135.00
Grey	Gloss	—	1982	1989	80.00	150.00	200.00
Grey	Matt	—	1982	1989	80.00	150.00	200.00
Palomino	Gloss	—	1982	1989	70.00	150.00	200.00
Palomino	Matt	—	1982	1989	70.00	150.00	200.00

SERIES: On Wooden Plinth

Colourway	Finish	DA #	Intro.	Disc.	U.K. £	U.S. $	Can. $
Black	Matt	57	1986	1989	60.00	100.00	135.00
Brown	Matt	57	1986	1989	75.00	130.00	175.00
White	Matt	57	1982	1989	50.00	100.00	135.00

SERIES: On Ceramic Plinth

Colourway	Finish	Intro.	Disc.	U.K. £	U.S. $	Can. $
Brown	Gloss	c.1987	c.1987	75.00	130.00	175.00

SERIES: Britannia Collection

Colourway	Finish	Intro.	Disc.	U.K. £	U.S. $	Can. $
Bronze	Gloss	1989	1993	75.00	130.00	175.00

Model No. 2689

SPIRIT OF FREEDOM

Model number 2689 was used together with model number 2353 to become the Spirit of Affection.

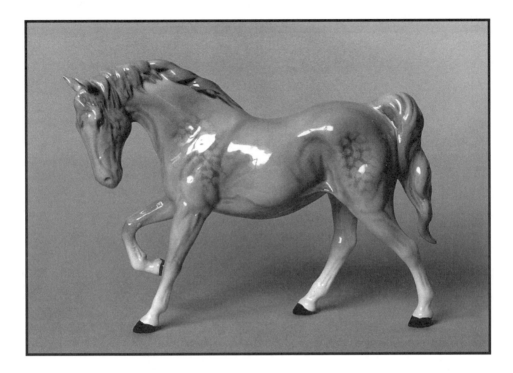

Designer: Graham Tongue
Height: 7", 17.8 cm

Colourway	Finish	DA #	Intro.	Disc.	U.K. £	U.S. $	Can. $
Brown	Gloss	58	1982	1989	60.00	100.00	135.00
Brown	Matt	58	1982	1989	55.00	100.00	135.00
Grey	Gloss	—	1982	1989	80.00	150.00	200.00
Grey	Matt	—	1982	1989	80.00	150.00	200.00
Palomino	Gloss	—	1982	1989	75.00	130.00	175.00
Palomino	Matt	—	1982	1989	75.00	130.00	175.00

SERIES: On Wooden Plinth

The black and brown versions were mounted on brown wooden plinths and the white version was issued on a black wooden plinth.

Colourway	Finish	DA #	Intro.	Disc.	U.K. £	U.S. $	Can. $
Black	Matt	58	1987	1989	55.00	100.00	125.00
Brown	Matt	58	1986	1989	70.00	125.00	175.00
White	Matt	58	1982	1989	50.00	100.00	125.00

SERIES: On Ceramic Plinth

Colourway	Finish	Intro.	Disc.	U.K. £	U.S. $	Can. $
Brown	Gloss	c.1987	c.1987	75.00	130.00	175.00

Model No. 2689/2536   # SPIRIT OF AFFECTION

The Spirit of Affection is the Spirit of Freedom with the Black Beauty Foal. In all versions but one, the mare and the foal are the same colour. The brown, grey and palomino versions were mounted on a brown wooden plinth and the white version was mounted on a black wooden plinth.

SERIES: On Wooden Plinth

Designer:	Graham Tongue
Height:	8", 20.3 cm

Colourway	Finish	DA #	Intro.	Disc.	U.K. £	U.S. $	Can. $
Brown	Matt	64	1984	1989	100.00	175.00	300.00
Grey mare, chocolate brown foal	Matt	—	1984	1989	125.00	250.00	375.00
Palomino	Matt	—	1984	1989	135.00	250.00	375.00
White	Matt	64	1984	1989	95.00	175.00	250.00

Model No. 2703 **SPIRIT OF YOUTH**

The Spirit of Youth is the same model as 2466 "Black Beauty."

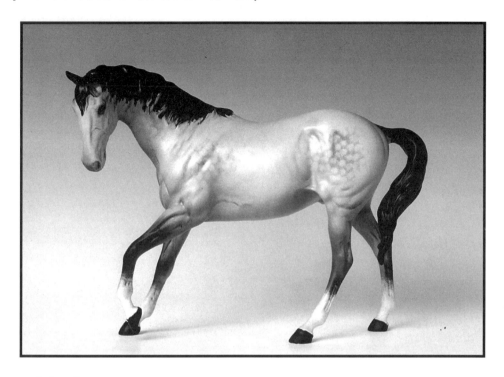

Designer: Graham Tongue
Height: 7", 17.8 cm

Colourway	Finish	DA #	Intro.	Disc.	U.K. £	U.S. $	Can. $
Brown	Gloss	59	1982	1989	60.00	100.00	125.00
Brown	Matt	59	1982	1989	55.00	100.00	125.00
Grey	Gloss	—	1982	1989	80.00	135.00	175.00
Grey	Matt	—	1982	1989	80.00	135.00	175.00
Palomino	Gloss	—	1982	1989	70.00	125.00	150.00
Palomino	Matt	—	1982	1989	70.00	125.00	150.00

SERIES: On Wooden Plinth.

The black and brown models were issued on a brown wooden plinth and the white model was issued on a black wooden plinth.

Colourway	Finish	DA #	Intro.	Disc.	U.K. £	U.S. $	Can. $
Black	Matt	59	1987	1989	55.00	100.00	125.00
Brown	Matt	59	1986	1989	70.00	125.00	150.00
White	Matt	59	1982	1989	50.00	100.00	125.00

SERIES: On Ceramic Plinth

Colourway	Finish	Intro.	Disc.	U.K. £	U.S. $	Can. $
Brown	Gloss	c.1987	c.1987	70.00	150.00	175.00

Model No. 2829   **SPIRIT OF FIRE**

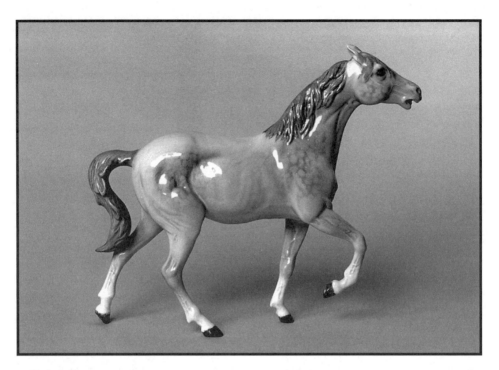

Designer: Graham Tongue
Height: 8", 20.3 cm

Colourway	Finish	DA #	Intro.	Disc.	U.K. £	U.S. $	Can. $
Brown	Gloss	60	1984	1989	60.00	100.00	125.00
Brown	Matt	60	1984	1989	55.00	100.00	125.00
Grey	Gloss	—	1984	1989	80.00	135.00	175.00
Grey	Matt	—	1984	1989	80.00	135.00	175.00
Palomino	Gloss	—	1984	1989	70.00	125.00	150.00
Palomino	Matt	—	1984	1989	70.00	125.00	150.00

SERIES: On Wooden Plinth

The black and brown versions were issued on a brown wooden plinth and the white version was issued on a black wooden plinth.

Colourway	Finish	DA #	Intro.	Disc.	U.K. £	U.S. $	Can. $
Black	Matt	60	1986	1989	55.00	100.00	125.00
Brown	Matt	60	1986	1989	70.00	125.00	150.00
White	Matt	60	1984	1989	50.00	100.00	125.00

SERIES: On Ceramic Plinth

Colourway	Finish	Intro.	Disc.	U.K. £	U.S. $	Can. $
Brown	Gloss	c.1987	c.1987	70.00	150.00	175.00

Model No. 2837   **SPRINGTIME**

SERIES: Spirited Foals

Designer: Graham Tongue
Height: 4 ½", 11.9 cm

VARIATION No. 1 Free Standing

Colourway	Finish	DA #	Intro.	Disc.	U.K. £	U.S. $	Can. $
Brown	Gloss	69	1984	1989	25.00	45.00	60.00

VARIATION No. 2 On Wooden Plinth

Colourway	Finish	DA #	Intro.	Disc.	U.K. £	U.S. $	Can. $
Black (wooden plinth)	Matt	—	1987	1989	30.00	50.00	65.00
Brown (wooden plinth	Matt	69	1986	1989	30.00	50.00	65.00
White (black plinth)	Matt	69	1984	1989	25.00	50.00	65.00

Model No. 2839   # YOUNG SPIRIT

Young Spirit was originally illustrated in a catalogue with his ears sticking out slightly. The model was changed to have the ears flat against the foals head, probably due to the potential problem of breakage in shipping. No date has been established for the mould change but it is probably either in the early stages of production, i.e. prototype or shortly after issue.

SERIES: Spirited Foals

Designer: Graham Tongue
Height: 4 ½", 11.9 cm

VARIATION No. 1 Free Standing

Colourway	Finish	DA #	Intro.	Disc.	U.K. £	U.S. $	Can. $
Brown	Gloss	70	1984	1989	25.00	45.00	60.00

VARIATION No. 2 On Wooden Plinth

Colourway	Finish	DA #	Intro.	Disc.	U.K. £	U.S. $	Can. $
Black (wooden plinth)	Matt	70	1987	1989	25.00	50.00	65.00
Brown (wooden plinth)	Matt	70	1986	1989	30.00	50.00	65.00
White (black plinth)	Matt	70	1984	1989	25.00	50.00	65.00

Model No. 2875   **SUNLIGHT**

SERIES: Spirited Foals

Designer: Graham Tongue
Height: 4 ½", 11.9 cm

VARIATION No. 1 Free Standing

Colourway	Finish	DA #	Intro.	Disc.	U.K. £	U.S. $	Can. $
Brown	Gloss	71	1987	1989	25.00	45.00	60.00

VARIATION No. 2 On Wooden Plinth

Colourway	Finish	DA #	Intro.	Disc.	U.K. £	U.S. $	Can. $
Black (wooden plinth)	Matt	71	1987	1989	25.00	50.00	65.00
Brown (woooden plinth)	Matt	71	1987	1989	30.00	50.00	65.00
White (black plinth)	Matt	71	1985	1989	25.00	50.00	65.00

Model No. 2876   ADVENTURE

SERIES: *Spirited Foals*

Designer: Graham Tongue
Height: 4 ½", 11.9 cm

VARIATION No. 1 *Free Standing*

Colourway	Finish	DA #	Intro.	Disc.	U.K. £	U.S. $	Can. $
Brown	Gloss	72	1987	1989	25.00	45.00	60.00

VARIATION No. 2 *On Wooden Plinth*

Colourway	Finish	DA #	Intro.	Disc.	U.K. £	U.S. $	Can. $
Black	Matt	—	1987	1989	30.00	50.00	65.00
Brown	Matt	72	1987	1989	30.00	50.00	65.00
White	Matt	72	1985	1989	25.00	50.00	65.00

Model No. 2914   **SPIRIT OF EARTH**

Designer: Graham Tongue
Height: 7 ½", 19.1 cm

Colourway	Finish	DA #	Intro.	Disc.	U.K. £	U.S. $	Can. $
Brown	Gloss	61	1987	1989	70.00	125.00	165.00
Brown	Matt	61	1987	1989	65.00	125.00	165.00
Grey	Gloss	—	1987	1989	95.00	160.00	200.00
Grey	Matt	—	1987	1989	85.00	150.00	200.00

SERIES: On Wooden Plinth

The black and brown versions were issued on a brown wooden plinth and the white version was issued on a black wooden plinth.

Colourway	Finish	Intro.	Disc.	U.K. £	U.S. $	Can. $
Black	Matt	1987	1989	65.00	125.00	165.00
Brown	Matt	1987	1989	70.00	125.00	165.00
White	Matt	1986	1989	55.00	100.00	135.00

SERIES: On Ceramic Plinth

Colourway	Finish	Intro.	Disc.	U.K. £	U.S. $	Can. $
Brown	Gloss	c.1987	c.1987	75.00	130.00	175.00

SERIES: Britannia Collection

Colourway	Finish	Intro.	Disc.	U.K. £	U.S. $	Can. $
Brown	Gloss	1989	1993	80.00	130.00	175.00

Model No. 2916   SPIRIT OF PEACE

Designer: Graham Tongue
Height: 4 ¾", 12.1 cm

Colourway	Finish	DA #	Intro.	Disc.	U.K. £	U.S. $	Can. $
Brown	Gloss	—	1987	1989	65.00	110.00	150.00
Brown	Matt	63	1987	1989	55.00	100.00	125.00
Grey	Gloss	—	1987	1989	80.00	150.00	200.00
Grey	Matt	—	1987	1989	80.00	125.00	175.00
Palomino	Gloss	—	1987	1989	90.00	150.00	200.00
Palomino	Matt	—	1987	1989	75.00	125.00	175.00

SERIES: On Wooden Plinth

The black and brown versions were issued on a brown wooden plinth and the white version was issued on a black wooden plinth.

Colourway	Finish	DA #	Intro.	Disc.	U.K. £	U.S. $	Can. $
Black	Matt	—	1987	1989	60.00	100.00	135.00
Brown	Matt	63	1987	1989	70.00	125.00	175.00
White	Matt	63	1986	1989	50.00	100.00	125.00

SERIES: On Ceramic Plinth

Colourway	Finish	Intro.	Disc.	U.K. £	U.S. $	Can. $
Brown	Gloss	c.1987	c.1987	85.00	150.00	200.00

Model No. 2935   **SPIRIT OF NATURE**

Designer: Graham Tongue
Height: 5 ½", 14.0 cm

Colourway	Finish	Intro.	Disc.	U.K. £	U.S. $	Can. $
Brown	Gloss	1987	1989	60.00	110.00	150.00
Brown	Matt	1987	1989	55.00	100.00	125.00
Grey	Gloss	1987	1989	80.00	150.00	200.00
Grey	Matt	1987	1989	80.00	125.00	175.00
Palomino	Gloss	1987	1989	70.00	150.00	200.00
Palomino	Matt	1987	1989	70.00	125.00	175.00

SERIES: On Wooden Plinth

The black and brown versions were mounted on brown wooden plinths and the white version was mounted on a black wooden plinth.

Colourway	Finish	DA #	Intro.	Disc.	U.K. £	U.S. $	Can. $
Black	Matt	—	1987	1989	65.00	125.00	175.00
Brown	Matt	73	1987	1989	70.00	125.00	175.00
White	Matt	—	1987	1989	55.00	100.00	150.00

SERIES: On Ceramic Plinth

Colourway	Finish	Intro.	Disc.	U.K. £	U.S. $	Can. $
Brown	Gloss	c.1987	c.1987	70.00	125.00	175.00

Model No. 3426   **CANCARA**

Modelled from "Downland Cancara" graded Trakehner stallion famous for advertising Lloyds Bank. Backstamp - "1994 Special Beswick Centenary."

SERIES: *On wooden plinth*

Designer: Graham Tongue
Height: 16 ½", 41.9 cm

Colourway	Finish	DA #	Intro.	Disc.	U.K. £	U.S. $	Can. $
Black	Matt	234	1994	1994	375.00	650.00	1,000.00

Model No. 3464   **TALLY HO**

This model was made exclusively for the mail order company Grattans. The horse and rider, from the model "Rearing Huntsman," with three hounds are on a natural effect base (all gloss). This model stands on a wooden plinth which is topped with green baise and has a brass plaque on the front. Backstamp - "Beswick Ware Made in England Tally Ho! Beswick Centenary 1894-1994 © 1994 Royal Doulton."

Designer: Unknown
Height: 11" x 14", 27.9 x 35.5 cm

Colourway	Finish	Intro.	Disc.	U.K. £	U.S. $	Can. $
Brown	Gloss	1994	1994	300.00	500.00	750.00

HOLLYDELL DIXIE
(Shetland Pony)

This Shetland Pony was the 1995 Beswick Collectors Circle "Special." It was decorated to represent Shetland Mare, Supreme Champion "Hollydell Dixie," and was issued in a limited edition of 553 in August 1995. Both the Beswick and BCC backstamps appear on this model..

Designer: Amanda Hughes-Lubeck
Height: 5 ¼", 13.3 cm

Colourway	Finish	DA #	Intro.	Disc.	U.K. £	U.S. $	Can. $
Skewbald (BCC95)	Gloss	185	1995	1995	200.00	350.00	500.00

SPIRIT OF WHITFIELD

This model of "Kruger" was commissioned by the Chatterley Whitfield Minig Museum. Only four models exist.

Designer: Graham Tongue
Height: 9", 22.9 cm

Colourway	Finish	Intro.	Disc.	U.K. £	U.S. $	Can. $
Brown	Matt	1987	1987		Auction Sale 1994, £2,750.00	

WARLORDS MARE
"ANOTHER BUNCH"

Another Bunch, issued in a special edition of 1,500, was the second in a series of specially commissioned models for P. R. Middleweeks & Co. from The John Beswick Studios. This photograph is of the original clay model.

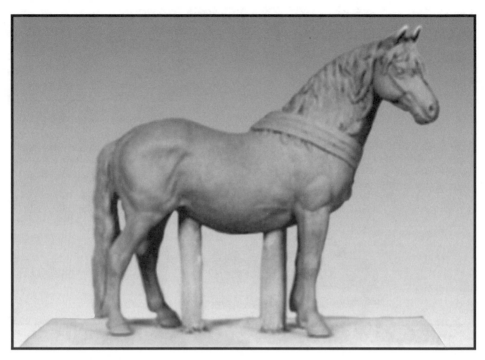

Designer: Graham Tongue
Height: 6", 15.1 cm

Colourway	Finish	Intro.	Disc.	U.K. £	U.S. $	Can. $
Bay/brown with red, white and blue sash	Gloss	1997	1997	60.00	—	—

WALL ORNAMENTS
- HORSES

Photograph not
available at press time

Photograph not
available at press time

Model No. 686
HORSE'S HEAD LOOKING LEFT THROUGH A HORSESHOE
First Version - Flat back

Designer:	Mr. Owen
Height:	7 ¼″ x 6″, 18.4 x 15.0 cm
Colour:	1. Brown - gloss
	2. Dark chestnut - gloss
Issued:	1938-1939
Varieties:	807

Description	U.K. £	U.S. $	Can. $
1. Brown	90.00	200.00	300.00
2. Dark chestnut	110.00	225.00	350.00

Model No. 687
HORSE'S HEAD LOOKING RIGHT THROUGH A HORSESHOE
First Version - Flat back

Designer:	Mr. Owen
Height:	7 ¼″ x 6″, 18.4 x 15.0 cm
Colour:	1. Brown - gloss
	2. Dark chestnut - gloss
Issued:	1939-1939
Varieties:	806

Description	U.K. £	U.S. $	Can. $
1. Brown	90.00	200.00	300.00
2. Dark chestnut	110.00	225.00	350.00

Model No. 806
HORSE'S HEAD LOOKING RIGHT THROUGH A HORSESHOE
Second Version - Raised back

Designer:	Mr. Owen
Height:	7 ¼″ x 6″, 18.4 x 15.0 cm
Colour:	Brown - gloss
Issued:	1939-1968
Varieties:	687

Description	U.K. £	U.S. $	Can. $
Gloss	75.00	150.00	225.00

Model No. 807
HORSE'S HEAD LOOKING LEFT THROUGH A HORSESHOE
Second Version - Raised back

Designer:	Mr. Owen
Height:	7 ¼″ x 6″, 18.4 x 15.0 cm
Colour:	Brown - gloss
Issued:	1938-1968
Varieties:	686

Description	U.K. £	U.S. $	Can. $
Gloss	75.00	150.00	225.00

Model No. 1382
HUNTER HEAD

Designer: Arthur Gredington
Height: 4″ x 4″, 10.1 x 10.1 cm
Colour: Brown - gloss
Issued: 1955-1969

Description	U.K. £	U.S. $	Can. $
Gloss	55.00	125.00	150.00

Model No. 1384
PALOMINO HEAD

Designer: Arthur Gredington
Height: 4″x 4″, 10.1 x 10.1 cm
Colour: Palomino - gloss
Issued: 1955-1969

Description	U.K. £	U.S. $	Can. $
Gloss	70.00	125.00	150.00

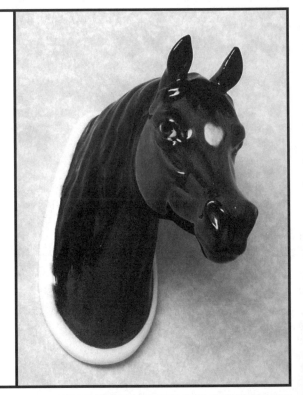

Model No. 1385
ARAB HEAD

Designer: Arthur Gredington
Height: 4″ x 4″, 10.1 x 10.1 cm
Colour: Dark brown - gloss
Issued: 1955-1969

Description	U.K. £	U.S. $	Can. $
Gloss	65.00	125.00	150.00

Model No. 1505
HUNTSMAN

Designer: Albert Hallam and James Hayward
Height: 8 ½″, 21.6 cm
Colour: 1.   Brown - gloss
              2.   Copper lustre
Issued: 1958-1962

Description	U.K. £	U.S. $	Can. $
1. Brown	175.00	300.00	400.00
2. Copper lustre	125.00	225.00	275.00

Model No. 1513
"TAKING OFF"

Designer: Colin Melbourne
Height: 9", 22.9 cm
Colour: 1.   Brown - gloss
              2.   Copper lustre
Issued: 1958-1962

Description	U.K. £	U.S. $	Can. $
1. Brown	175.00	300.00	400.00
2. Copper lustre	125.00	225.00	275.00

Model No. 1514
"LANDING"

Designer: Colin Melbourne
Height: 7 ¾", 19.7 cm
Colour: 1.   Brown - gloss
              2.   Copper lustre
Issued: 1958-1962

Description	U.K. £	U.S. $	Can. $
1. Brown	175.00	300.00	400.00
2. Copper lustre	125.00	225.00	275.00

Model No. 1515
"GOING OVER"

Designer: Colin Melbourne
Height: 7 ½", 19.1 cm
Colour: 1.   Brown - gloss
              2.   Copper lustre
Issued: 1958-1962

Description	U.K. £	U.S. $	Can. $
1. Brown	175.00	300.00	400.00
2. Copper lustre	125.00	225.00	275.00

Model No. 2699
TROY

Designer:	Unknown
Height:	6", 15.0 cm
Colour:	Brown - matt
Issued:	1984-1989
Series:	Champions All

Description	U.K. £	U.S. $	Can. $
Matt	50.00	100.00	125.00

Model No. 2700
ARKLE

Designer:	Unknown
Height:	6", 15.0 cm
Colour:	Bay - matt
Issued:	1984-1989
Series:	Champions All

Description	U.K. £	U.S. $	Can. $
Matt	50.00	100.00	125.00

Model No. 2701
THE MINSTREL

Designer: Unknown
Height: 6", 15.0 cm
Colour: Chestnut - matt
Issued: 1984-1989
Series: Champions All

Description	U.K. £	U.S. $	Can. $
Matt	50.00	100.00	125.00

Model No. 2702
RED RUM

Designer: Unknown
Height: 6", 15.0 cm
Colour: Bay - matt
Issued: 1984-1989
Series: Champions All

Description	U.K. £	U.S. $	Can. $
Matt	50.00	100.00	125.00

MISCELLANEOUS

Model No. 2093
OLD STAFFORDSHIRE LION

Designer:	Graham Tongue	
Height:	5 ¾", 14.6 cm	
Colour:	Grey, cream, green - gloss	
Issued:	1967-1971	

Description	U.K. £	U.S. $	Can. $
Gloss		Extremely Rare	

Model No. 2094
OLD STAFFORDSHIRE UNICORN

Designer:	Graham Tongue	
Height:	6", 15.0 cm	
Colour:	Grey, cream, green - gloss	
Issued:	1967-1971	

Description	U.K. £	U.S. $	Can. $
Gloss		Extremely Rare	

Model No. 2137
T'ANG HORSE - Small

Designer:	Graham Tongue	
Height:	8", 20.3 cm	
Colour:	Green/bronze - gloss	
Issued:	1967-1972	

Description	U.K. £	U.S. $	Can. $
Gloss	300.00	525.00	750.00

Photograph not
available at press time

Model No. 2182
HERALDIC UNICORN ON BASE

Designer:	Graham Tongue	
Height:	8 ½", 21.6 cm	
Colour.	Unknown	
Issued:	Unknown	

Description	U.K. £	U.S. $	Can. $
	350.00	600.00	800.00

Model No. 2205
T'ANG HORSE- Large

Designer:	Graham Tongue
Height:	13", 33.0 cm
Colour:	Green/bronze - gloss
Issued:	1968-1972

Description	U.K. £	U.S. $	Can. $
Gloss	375.00	650.00	875.00

Model No. 2222
LION (CAERNARVON 1969)

Designer:	Mrs. Elliot
Height:	4", 10.1 cm
Colour:	Cream, red lettering - matt
Issued:	1968-1969
Series:	Pair with 2223

Description	U.K.£	U.S.$	Can.$
Matt	Only known example in the Beswick Museum		

Note: Issued to commemorate the investiture of Prince of Wales, Caernarvon, 1969.

Model No. 2223
UNICORN (PRINCE OF WALES)

Designer:	Mrs. Elliott
Height:	4", 10.1 cm
Colour.	Cream, red lettering - matt
Issued:	1968-1969
Series:	Pair with 2222

Description	U.K. £	U.S. $	Can. $
Matt	Only known example in the Beswick Museum		

Note: Issued to commemorate the Investiture of the Prince of Wales, Caernarvon, 1969.

Model No. 2514
"WHITE HORSE WHISKY"

Designer:	Alan Maslankowski
Height:	6 ¾", 17.2 cm
Colour:	White - gloss
Issued:	1974
Series:	Advertising

Description	U.K. £	U.S. $	Can. $
Gloss	525.00	900.00	1,200.00

Model No. 3021   UNICORN

Designer: Graham Tongue
Height: 9", 2.9 cm
Series: Britannia Collection

Colourway	Finish	Intro	Disc.	U.K. £	U.S. $	Can. $
Cream	Matt	1989	Unknown	250.00	400.00	550.00
Dark bronze	Gloss	1989	1992	150.00	250.00	325.00

Chapter Eight
WILD ANIMALS

The wild animals in this group have been produced by John Beswick for more than fifty years. Many are authentic and true to life in shape and colour, others are comical.

Beswick wild animals are very popular with collectors. They are less of a minefield for the inexperienced than some of the other series, as the animals are familiar and can be easily identified, since most carry the Beswick backstamp.

As you can see, Beswick produced these animals in a random order. It was not until the late 1930s that realism was created by the use of natural colours, instead of the very popular blue gloss used in earlier days. Around this time, the models were also refined to represent real animals.

The variety of animals is enormous and most animals are represented, ranging from the smallest mouse to the very large African elephant. The powerful bison, the gentle springbok and the elegant giraffe are just some of these superb pieces.

At the time of the introduction of the Connoisseur Series in 1967, most of the items were horses, and it was not until 1973 that three wild animals were absorbed into the series. These were the already existing versions of two elephants, numbers 998 and 1770, both free standing, and a puma on a rock, number 1702. As the name suggests, the Connoisseur Series comprises prestige models, and consequently were and are more expensive than the rest of the animals.

It is interesting to note that Mr. Gredington was the modeller responsible for the majority of the wild animals. Some collectors collect models from one particular designer or modeller, and these would make an excellent choice.

Many of the wild animals are avidly sought after. The search is a challenge, but well worth the effort if you can find your treasured piece.

Model No. 315
SQUIRREL - on pottery base

Designer:	Miss Greaves
Height:	8 ¾″, 22.2 cm
Colour:	See below
Issued:	1935-by 1954

Description	U.K. £	U.S. $	Can. $
1. Blue - gloss	150.00	300.00	400.00
2. Blue/brown - satin	110.00	200.00	300.00
3. Cream - satin matt	110.00	200.00	300.00
4. Natural - satin	150.00	300.00	400.00

Model No. 368
FROG - on pottery base

Designer:	Miss Greaves
Height:	6 ¾″, 16.5 cm
Colour:	See below
Issued:	1936-by 1954

Description	U.K. £	U.S. $	Can. $
1. Blue - gloss	150.00	275.00	375.00
2. Blue/brown - satin	110.00	200.00	300.00
3. Cream - satin matt	110.00	200.00	300.00
4. Green - satin matt	110.00	200.00	300.00
5. Natural - satin	150.00	275.00	375.00

Model No. 316
RABBIT - on pottery base

Designer:	Miss Greaves	
Height:	6 ¾″, 17.2 cm	
Colour:	1.	Blue - gloss
	2.	Blue/brown - satin
	3.	Cream - satin matt
	4.	Natural - satin
Issued:	1935-by 1954	

Description	U.K. £	U.S. $	Can. $
1. Blue	150.00	300.00	400.00
2. Blue/brown	110.00	200.00	300.00
3. Cream	110.00	200.00	300.00
4. Natural	150.00	300.00	400.00

Model No. 383
SEAL - on pottery base

Designer: Mr. Owen
Height: 10", 25.4 cm
Colour: 1. Blue - gloss
              2. Blue/brown - satin
              3. Cream - satin matt
              4. Natural - satin
Issued: 1936-by 1954

Description	U.K. £	U.S. $	Can. $
1. Blue	150.00	250.00	350.00
2. Blue/brown	100.00	200.00	300.00
3. Cream	100.00	200.00	300.00
4. Natural	150.00	275.00	400.00

Model No. 397
MONKEY - on pottery base

Designer: Mr. Owen
Height: 7", 17.8 cm
Colour: 1. Blue - gloss
              2. Blue/brown - satin
              3. Cream - satin matt
              4. Natural - satin
Issued: 1936-by 1954

Description	U.K. £	U.S. $	Can. $
1. Blue	135.00	250.00	375.00
2. Blue/brown	110.00	200.00	300.00
3. Cream	110.00	175.00	250.00
4. Natural	135.00	275.00	400.00

Model No. 417
POLAR BEAR - on pottery base

Designer: Mr. Owen
Height: 7", 17.8 cm
Colour: 1. Blue - gloss
    2. Cream - satin matt
    3. Natural - satin
Issued: 1936-by 1954

Description	U.K. £	U.S. $	Can. $
1. Blue	150.00	350.00	475.00
2. Cream	110.00	200.00	300.00
3. Natural	150.00	325.00	450.00

Model No. 455
RABBIT BOOKEND

Designer: James Hayward
Height: 6 ¾", 17.2 cm
Colour: 1. Various - satin matt
    2. Blue - gloss
    3. White - matt
Issued: 1937-by 1954

Description	U.K. £	U.S. $	Can. $
1. Various	75.00	125.00	175.00
2. Blue	100.00	200.00	275.00
3. White	75.00	125.00	175.00

Note: Prices given are for single bookends.

Model No. 568/569
CHARACTER ELEPHANT

Designer: Mr. Owen
Height: 1. Large - 9", 22.9 cm
    2. Small - 4 ¾", 12.1 cm
Colour: 1. Blue - gloss
    2. Cream - satin matt
Issued: 1938-by 1954

Description	U.K. £	U.S. $	Can. $
1. Blue, large	400.00	650.00	925.00
2. Cream, large	400.00	650.00	925.00
3. Blue, small	250.00	400.00	575.00
4. Cream, small	250.00	400.00	575.00

Model No. 663
ELEPHANT TOOTHBRUSH HOLDER

Designer: Miss Catford
Height: 4 ½", 11.9 cm
Colour: 1. Various - satin matt
    2. Blue - gloss
    3. White - matt
Issued: 1938 -by 1954

Description	U.K. £	U.S. $	Can. $
1. Various	175.00	325.00	425.00
2. Blue	175.00	325.00	425.00
3. White	175.00	325.00	425.00

Model No. 664
FOX TOOTHBRUSH HOLDER

Designer:	Miss Catford
Height:	4 ¾", 12.1 cm
Colour:	1. Various - satin matt
	2. Blue - gloss
	3. White - matt
Issued:	1938-by 1954

Description	U.K. £	U.S. $	Can. $
1. Various	175.00	325.00	425.00
2. Blue	175.00	325.00	425.00
3. White	175.00	325.00	425.00

Model No. 665
RABBIT TOOTHBRUSH HOLDER

Designer:	Miss Catford
Height:	4 ¾", 12.1 cm
Colour:	1. Various - satin matt
	2. Blue - gloss
	3. White - matt
Issued:	1938-by 1954

Description	U.K. £	U.S. $	Can. $
1. Various	175.00	325.00	425.00
2. Blue	175.00	325.00	425.00
3. White	175.00	325.00	425.00

Model No. 692
ELEPHANT WITH HOWDAH

Designer:	Unknown
Height:	4 ¼", 10.8 cm
Colour:	Blue - gloss
Issued:	1939-by 1954

Description	U.K. £	U.S. $	Can. $
Blue	175.00	300.00	500.00

Model No. 696
DEER ON ROCK

Designer:	Arthur Gredington
Height:	8", 20.3 cm
Colour:	See below
Issued:	1939-1954
Set:	721

Description	U.K. £	U.S. $	Can. $
1. Blue - gloss	100.00	125.00	150.00
2. Brown- gloss	85.00	100.00	125.00
3. Cream - satin	75.00	100.00	125.00
4. Flambé - gloss	200.00	335.00	450.00

Model No. 697
HIPPOPOTAMUS

Designer:	Mr. Watkin
Height:	2 ¼", 5.7 cm
Colour:	1. Blue - gloss
	2. Cream - satin matt
Issued:	1939-by 1954
Series:	Fun Models

Description	U.K. £	U.S. $	Can. $
1. Blue	100.00	175.00	225.00
2. Cream	100.00	175.00	225.00

Model No. 698
GIRAFFE

Designer:	Mr. Watkin
Height:	1. Large - Unknown
	2. Small - 4", 10.1 cm
Colour:	1. Blue - gloss 2. Cream - satin matt
Issued:	1939-by 1954
Series:	Fun Models

Description	U.K. £	U.S. $	Can. $
1. Blue, large	150.00	275.00	400.00
2. Cream, large	150.00	275.00	400.00
3. Blue, small	100.00	200.00	300.00
4. Cream, small	100.00	200.00	300.00

Photograph not
available at press time

Model No. 709
BEAVER

Designer:	Mr. Watkin
Height:	Unknown
Colour:	Unknown
Issued:	1939-Unknown

Description	U.K. £	U.S. $	Can. $
		Extremely Rare	

Note: Possibly not put into production.

Model No. 711
PANDA

Designer:	Mr. Watkin
Height:	4 ½", 11.9 cm
Colour:	1. Black and white - gloss
	2. Blue - gloss
	3. Cream - satin matt
Issued:	1939-by 1954

Description	U.K. £	U.S. $	Can. $
1. Black/white	85.00	175.00	225.00
2. Blue	135.00	250.00	300.00
3. Cream	85.00	150.00	200.00

Model No. 720
PANDA CUB

Designer: James Haywood
Height: 3 ¾", 9.5 cm
Colour: 1.   Black and white - gloss
             2.   Blue - gloss
             3.   Cream - satin matt
Issued: 1939-by 1954

Description	U.K. £	U.S. $	Can. $
1. Black/white	95.00	175.00	225.00
2. Blue	110.00	250.00	300.00
3. Cream	95.00	150.00	200.00

Model No. 721
DEER ON BASE

Designer: Arthur Gredington
Height: 4 ½", 11.9 cm
Colour: See below
Issued: 1939-by 1954
Set: 696

Description	U.K. £	U.S. $	Can. $
1. Blue - gloss	100.00	165.00	200.00
2. Brown - gloss	85.00	135.00	175.00
3. Green - matt	100.00	125.00	150.00
4. White - matt	100.00	125.00	150.00

Model No. 738
PANDA WITH BALL

Designer: Mr. Watkin
Height: 4 ½", 11.9 cm
Colour: 1.   Black and white - gloss
             2.   Blue - gloss
             3.   Cream - satin matt
Issued: 1939-by 1954

Description	U.K. £	U.S. $	Can. $
1. Black/white	95.00	175.00	225.00
2. Blue	135.00	250.00	325.00
3. Cream	95.00	150.00	200.00

Model No. 823
RABBIT - On haunches

Designer: Arthur Gredington
Height: 3", 7.6 cm
Colour: 1.   Blue - gloss
             2.   Brown - gloss
Issued: 1940-1971
Set: 824, 825, 826

Description	U.K. £	U.S. $	Can. $
1. Blue	45.00	90.00	125.00
2. Brown	20.00	40.00	60.00

Model No. 824
RABBIT - Scratching ear

Designer: Arthur Gredington
Height: 2 ¼", 5.7 cm
Colour: 1.   Blue - gloss
            2.   Brown - gloss
Issued: 1940-1971
Set: 823, 825, 826

Description	U.K. £	U.S. $	Can. $
1. Blue	45.00	90.00	125.00
2. Brown	20.00	30.00	40.00

Model No. 825
RABBIT - Crouching

Designer: Arthur Gredington
Height: 1 ½", 3.8 cm
Colour: 1.   Blue - gloss
            2.   Brown - gloss
Issued: 1940-1971
Set: 823, 824, 826

Description	U.K. £	U.S. $	Can. $
1. Blue	15.00	20.00	30.00
2. Brown	35.00	75.00	100.00

Model No. 826
RABBIT - Seated

Designer: Arthur Gredington
Height: 2", 5.0 cm
Colour: 1.   Blue - gloss
            2.   Brown - gloss
Issued: 1940-1971
Set: 823, 824, 825

Description	U.K. £	U.S. $	Can. $
1. Blue	15.00	20.00	30.00
2. Brown	35.00	75.00	100.00

Model No. 828
ELEPHANT

Designer: Mr. Owen
Colour: 1. Blue - gloss
         2. Cream - satin matt
         3. Pale grey - gloss
Issued: 1940-by 1954

Description	Colour	Height	U.K. £	Price U.S. $	Can. $
Large	Blue	6", 15.0 cm	150.00	250.00	350.00
Large	Cream	6", 15.0 cm	125.00	200.00	275.00
Large	Pale grey	6", 15.0 cm	135.00	225.00	300.00
Medium	Blue	4 ½", 11.9 cm	125.00	200.00	275.00
Medium	Cream	4 ½", 11.9 cm	110.00	180.00	240.00
Medium	Pale grey	4 ½", 11.9 cm	115.00	190.00	250.00
Small	Blue	3", 7.6 cm	100.00	170.00	235.00
Small	Cream	3", 7.6 cm	70.00	110.00	170.00
Small	Pale grey	3", 7.6 cm	85.00	140.00	200.00

Model No. 830
LIZARD

Designer: Miss Joachim
Height: Unknown
Colour: Green - gloss
Issued: 1940-Unknown

Description	U.K. £	U.S. $	Can. $
Green		Extremely Rare	

Model No. 841
LEOPARD - Seated

Designer: Arthur Gredington
Height: 6 ¼", 15.9 cm
Colour: Tan brown, black spots - gloss
Issued: 1940-by 1954

Description	U.K. £	U.S. $	Can. $
Tan brown/black	375.00	625.00	800.00

Model No. 845A
ZEBRA
First Version - Tan with black stripes

Designer: Arthur Gredington
Height: 7 ¼", 18.4 cm
Colour: Tan with black stripes - gloss
Issued: 1940-Unknown

Description	U.K. £	U.S. $	Can. $
Tan/black	275.00	475.00	675.00

Model No. 845B
ZEBRA
Second Version - White with black stripes

Designer: Arthur Gredington
Height: 7 ¼", 18.4 cm
Colour: White with black stripes - gloss
Issued: Unknown-1969

Description	U.K. £	U.S. $	Can. $
White/black	125.00	275.00	400.00

Model No. 853
GIRAFFE - Small

Designer:	Arthur Gredington
Height:	7 ¼″, 18.4 cm
Colour:	1. Natural - gloss
	2. Stone - satin finish
	3. White - gloss
Issued:	1940-1975

Description	U.K. £	U.S. $	Can. $
1. Natural	110.00	225.00	300.00
2. Stone	75.00	125.00	175.00
3. White	85.00	150.00	200.00

Model No. 954
STAG - Lying

Designer:	Arthur Gredington
Height:	5 ½″, 14.0 cm
Colour:	Light brown - gloss
Issued:	1941-1975

Description	U.K. £	U.S. $	Can. $
Light brown	50.00	100.00	175.00

Model No. 974
ELEPHANT - Trunk stretching - small

Designer:	Arthur Gredington
Height:	4 ¾″, 12.1 cm
Colour:	Grey - gloss or matt
Issued:	1. Gloss - 1943 -1996
	2. Matt - 1985-1988

Description	U.K. £	U.S. $	Can. $
1. Gloss	30.00	50.00	70.00
2. Matt	35.00	80.00	100.00

Model No. 981
STAG - Standing

Designer:	Arthur Gredington
Height:	8", 20.3 cm
Colour:	1. Light brown - gloss or matt
	2. Bronze with black shading - satin
Issued:	1a. Gloss - 1942-1997
	1b. Matt - 1985-1988
	2. Satin - 1989-1992
Series:	2. Britannia Collection

Description	U.K. £	U.S. $	Can. $
1a. Gloss	25.00	40.00	80.00
1b. Matt	40.00	70.00	100.00
2. Satin	45.00	80.00	110.00

Model No. 998
ELEPHANT - Trunk stretching - large

Designer:	Arthur Gredington
Height:	10 ¼", 26.0 cm
Colour:	Natural - gloss or satin matt
Issued:	1. Gloss - 1943-1975
	2. Satin matt - 1970-1973
Series:	Model in satin matt finish was transferred to Connoisseur Series in 1973.

Description	U.K. £	U.S. $	Can. $
1. Gloss	225.00	375.00	550.00
2. Satin matt	250.00	425.00	550.00

Model No. 999A
DOE

Designer:	Arthur Gredington
Height:	6", 15.0 cm
Colour:	1. Light brown - gloss
	2. Light and dark brown - matt
Issued:	1. Gloss - 1943-1997
	2. Matt - 1985-1988

Description	U.K. £	U.S. $	Can. $
1. Gloss	20.00	35.00	50.00
2. Matt	25.00	45.00	65.00

Model No. 999B
DOE AND FAWN - on wooden plinth

Designer:	Arthur Gredington
Height:	7", 17.8 cm
Colour:	Light brown - gloss
Issued:	1993-1996

Description	U.K. £	U.S. $	Can. $
Gloss	40.00	75.00	100.00

Note: Doe is no. 999, Fawn is no. 1000.

Model No. 1000A
FAWN
First Version - tail up

Designer:	Arthur Gredington
Height:	3 ½", 8.9 cm
Colour:	Light brown - gloss
Issued:	1943-1955

Description	U.K. £	U.S. $	Can. $
Gloss	55.00	100.00	150.00

Model No. 1000B
FAWN
Second Version - tail down

Designer:	Arthur Gredington
Remodelled:	Mr. Orwell
Height:	3 ½", 8.9 cm
Colour:	Light brown - gloss or matt
Issued:	1. Gloss - 1955-1997
	2. Matt - 1985-1988

Description	U.K. £	U.S. $	Can. $
1. Gloss	14.00	25.00	35.00
2. Matt	20.00	35.00	45.00

Model No. 1003
FAWNIE

Designer:	Arthur Gredington
Height:	5 ¼", 13.3 cm
Colour:	Grey-brown - gloss
Issued:	1944-1967
Series:	Fun Models

Description	U.K. £	U.S. $	Can. $
Gloss	90.00	175.00	250.00

Model No. 1005
KANGARINE

Designer:	Arthur Gredington
Height:	5", 12.7 cm
Colour:	1. Blue with white markings - gloss
	2. Brown - gloss
Issued:	1944-1966
Series:	Fun Models

Description	U.K. £	U.S. $	Can. $
1. Blue	135.00	250.00	400.00
2. Brown	120.00	225.00	350.00

Model No. 1007
SQUIRREL - Standing

Designer:	Arthur Gredington
Height:	2 ¼", 5.7 cm
Colour:	Tan - gloss
Issued:	1944-c.1963
Set:	1008, 1009
Series:	Fun Models

Description	U.K. £	U.S. $	Can. $
Gloss	45.00	85.00	130.00

Model No. 1008
SQUIRREL - Lying

Designer:	Arthur Gredington
Height:	1 ¾", 4.5 cm
Colour:	Tan - gloss
Issued:	1944-c.1963
Set:	1007, 1009
Series:	Fun Models

Description	U.K. £	U.S. $	Can. $
Gloss	45.00	85.00	130.00

Model No. 1009
SQUIRREL - With Nut Cracker

Designer:	Arthur Gredington
Height:	4 ½", 11.9 cm
Colour:	Tan - gloss
Issued:	1944-c.1963
Set:	1007, 1008
Series:	Fun Models

Description	U.K. £	U.S. $	Can. $
Gloss	70.00	150.00	200.00

Model No. 1016A
FOX - Standing

Designer: Arthur Gredington
Height: 5 ½", 14.0 cm
Colour: Red-brown and white - gloss or matt
Issued: 1. Gloss - 1945-1997
             2. Matt - 1985-1988
Varieties: 1016B

Description	.U.K. £	U.S. $	Can. $
1. Gloss	25.00	45.00	60.00
2. Matt	30.00	50.00	75.00

Model No. 1016B
FOX - Standing - on wooden plinth

Designer: Arthur Gredington
Height: 6 ¾", 17.2 cm
Colour: Natural - gloss
Issued: 1993-1996
Varieties: 1016A

Description	U.K. £	U.S. $	Can. $
Gloss	30.00	50.00	75.00

Model No. 1017
FOX - Curled

Designer: Arthur Gredington
Height: 1 ¾", 3.2 cm
Colour: Red brown - gloss or matt
Issued: 1. Gloss - 1945 -1996
             2. Matt - 1985-1988

Description	U.K. £	U.S. $	Can. $
1. Gloss	15.00	25.00	50.00
2. Matt	30.00	50.00	75.00

Model No. 1019
BISON

Designer: Arthur Gredington
Height: 5 ¾", 14.6 cm
Colour: Dark brown - gloss
Issued: 1945-1973

Description	U.K. £	U.S. $	Can. $
Gloss	125.00	225.00	275.00

Model No. 1021
STOAT

Designer:	Arthur Gredington
Height:	5 ½", 14.0 cm
Colour:	1. Tan (summer coat) - gloss
	2. White (winter coat) - gloss
Issued:	1945-1963

Description	U.K. £	U.S. $	Can. $
1. Tan	190.00	350.00	500.00
2. White	180.00	300.00	400.00

Model No. 1024
HARE - Running

Designer:	Arthur Gredington
Height:	5 ¼", 12.7 cm
Colour:	Tan - gloss
Issued:	1945-1963

Description	U.K. £	U.S. $	Can. $
Gloss	275.00	450.00	600.00

Model No. 1025
HARE - Seated

Designer:	Arthur Gredington
Height:	7", 17.8 cm
Colour:	Tan - gloss
Issued:	1945-1963

Description	U.K. £	U.S. $	Can. $
Gloss	250.00	425.00	575.00

Model No. 1038
KOALA BEAR

Designer:	Arthur Gredington
Height:	3 ½", 8.9 cm
Colour:	Grey - gloss
Issued:	1945-1971
Set:	1039, 1040

Description	U.K. £	U.S. $	Can. $
Gloss	40.00	70.00	90.00

Model No. 1039
KOALA BEAR - On branch

Designer:	Arthur Gredington
Height:	2 ¼", 5.7 cm
Colour:	Grey - gloss
Issued:	1945-1973
Set:	1038, 1040

Description	U.K. £	U.S. $	Can. $
Gloss	25.00	50.00	65.00

Model No. 1040
KOALA BEAR

Designer:	Arthur Gredington
Height:	2 ¼", 5.7 cm
Colour:	Grey - gloss
Issued:	1945-1973
Set:	1038, 1039

Description	U.K. £	U.S. $	Can. $
Gloss	25.00	50.00	65.00

Model No. 1043
CAMEL FOAL

Designer:	Arthur Gredington
Height:	5", 12.7 cm
Colour:	Light and dark brown - gloss
Issued:	1946-1971
Set:	1044

Description	U.K. £	U.S. $	Can. $
Gloss	65.00	120.00	175.00

Model No. 1044
CAMEL

Designer:	Arthur Gredington
Height:	7", 17.8 cm
Colour:	Light and dark brown - gloss
Issued:	1946-1973
Set:	1043

Description	U.K. £	U.S. $	Can. $
Gloss	110.00	195.00	275.00

Model No. 1048
SPRINGBOK

Designer:	Arthur Gredington
Height:	7 ¼", 18.4 cm
Colour:	Tan and white - gloss
Issued:	1946-1963

Description	U.K. £	U.S. $	Can. $
Gloss	275.00	500.00	700.00

Model No. 1049
CHIMPANZEE WITH PIPE

Designer:	Arthur Gredington
Height:	4 ¾", 12.1 cm
Colour:	Brown - gloss
Issued:	1946-1969

Description	U.K. £	U.S. $	Can. $
Gloss	110.00	200.00	300.00

Model No. 1082
LEOPARD

Designer:	Arthur Gredington
Height:	4 ¾", 12.1 cm
Colour:	1. Golden brown with black markings - gloss
	2. Black - satin
Issued:	1946-1975

Description	U.K. £	U.S. $	Can. $
1. Gloss	110.00	200.00	300.00
2. Satin	95.00	175.00	225.00

Model No. 1089
KOALA BEAR - With fruit

Designer:	Miss Jones
Height:	3 ½", 8.9 cm
Colour:	Grey - gloss
Issued:	1947-1971

Description	U.K. £	U.S. $	Can. $
Gloss	40.00	70.00	90.00

Model No. 1160
KANGAROO

Designer:	Arthur Gredington
Height:	5 ¾", 14.6 cm
Colour:	Brown - gloss
Issued:	1949-1966

Description	U.K. £	U.S. $	Can. $
Gloss	115.00	200.00	275.00

Model No. 1255
MONKEY WITH DRUM

Designer:	Miss Granoska
Height:	2 ½", 6.4 cm
Colour:	Brown and green - gloss
Issued:	1952-1963
Set:	1256, 1257, 1258, 1259, 1260

Description	U.K. £	U.S. $	Can. $
Gloss	150.00	250.00	350.00

Model No. 1256
MONKEY WITH TUBA

Designer:	Miss Granoska
Height:	2 ½″, 6.4 cm
Colour:	Brown and green - gloss
Issued:	1952-1963
Set:	1255, 1257, 1258, 1259, 1260

Description	U.K. £	U.S. $	Can. $
Gloss	150.00	250.00	350.00

Model No. 1257
MONKEY WITH FIDDLE

Designer:	Miss Granoska
Height:	2 ½″, 6.4 cm
Colour:	Brown and green - gloss
Issued:	1952-1963
Set:	1255, 1256, 1258, 1259, 1260

Description	U.K. £	U.S. $	Can. $
Gloss	150.00	250.00	350.00

Model No. 1258
MONKEY WITH SAXOPHONE

Designer:	Miss Granoska
Height:	2 ½″, 6.4 cm
Colour:	Brown and green - gloss
Issued:	1952-1963
Set:	1255, 1256, 1257, 1259, 1260

Description	U.K. £	U.S. $	Can. $
Gloss	150.00	250.00	350.00

Model No. 1259
MONKEY WITH GUITAR

Designer:	Miss Granoska
Height:	2 ½″, 6.4 cm
Colour:	Brown and green - gloss
Issued:	1952-1963
Set:	1255, 1256, 1257, 1258, 1260

Description	U.K. £	U.S. $	Can. $
Gloss	150.00	250.00	350.00

Model No. 1260
MONKEY WITH BANJO

Designer:	Miss Granoska
Height:	2 ½", 6.4 cm
Colour:	Brown and green - gloss
Issued:	1952-1963
Set:	1255, 1256, 1257, 1258, 1259

Description	U.K. £	U.S. $	Can. $
Gloss	150.00	250.00	350.00

Model No. 1308
SKUNK

Designer:	Arthur Gredington
Height:	2 ¾", 7.0 cm
Colour:	Black and white - gloss
Issued:	1953-1963
Set:	1309, 1310

Description	U.K. £	U.S. $	Can. $
Gloss	85.00	150.00	200.00

Model No. 1309
SKUNK

Designer:	Arthur Gredington
Height:	1 ½", 3.8 cm
Colour:	Black and white - gloss
Issued:	1953-1963
Set:	1308, 1310

Description	U.K. £	U.S. $	Can. $
Gloss	50.00	95.00	125.00

Model No. 1310
SKUNK

Designer:	Arthur Gredington
Height:	2", 5.0 cm
Colour:	Black and white - gloss
Issued:	1953-1963
Set:	1307, 1309

Description	U.K. £	U.S. $	Can. $
Gloss	50.00	95.00	125.00

Model No. 1313
BEAR - Standing

Designer:	Arthur Gredington
Height:	2 ½", 6.4 cm
Colour:	Black or brown - gloss
Issued:	1953-1966
Set:	1314, 1315

Description	U.K. £	U.S. $	Can. $
1. Black	75.00	125.00	175.00
2. Brown	75.00	125.00	175.00

Model No. 1314
BEAR - On hind legs

Designer:	Arthur Gredington
Height:	4 ½", 11.9 cm
Colour:	Black or brown - gloss
Issued:	1953-1966
Set:	1313, 1315

Description	U.K. £	U.S. $	Can. $
1. Black	75.00	125.00	175.00
2. Brown	75.00	125.00	175.00

Model No. 1315
BEAR CUB - Seated

Designer:	Arthur Gredington
Height:	2 ¼", 5.7 cm
Colour:	Black or brown - gloss
Issued:	1953-1966
Set:	1313, 1314

Description	U.K. £	U.S. $	Can. $
1. Black	50.00	85.00	125.00
2. Brown	50.00	85.00	125.00

Model No. 1335
TORTOISE MOTHER WITH HAT

Designer:	Miss Granoska
Length:	2 ¾", 7.0 cm
Colour:	Brown - gloss
Issued:	1954-1973
Set:	1336, 1337

Description	U.K. £	U.S. $	Can. $
Gloss	65.00	125.00	175.00

Model No. 1336
TORTOISE GIRL WITH BONNET

Designer:	Miss Granoska
Length:	1 ¾", 4.5 cm
Colour:	Brown - gloss
Issued:	1954-1973
Set:	1335, 1337

Description	U.K. £	U.S. $	Can. $
Gloss	40.00	75.00	125.00

Model No. 1337
TORTOISE BOY WITH CAP

Designer:	Miss Granoska
Length:	1 ¾", 4.5 cm
Colour:	Brown - gloss
Issued:	1954-1973
Set:	1335, 1336

Description	U.K. £	U.S. $	Can. $
Gloss	40.00	75.00	125.00

Model No. 1379
BUSH BABY - With mirror

Designer:	Mr. Orwell
Height:	2", 5.0 cm
Colour:	Grey-brown - gloss
Issued:	1955-1966
Set:	1380, 1381

Description	U.K. £	U.S. $	Can. $
Gloss	60.00	100.00	150.00

Model No. 1380
BUSH BABY - With candlestick

Designer:	Mr. Orwell
Height:	2", 5.0 cm
Colour:	Grey-brown - gloss
Issued:	1955-1966
Set:	1379, 1381

Description	U.K. £	U.S. $	Can. $
Gloss	60.00	100.00	150.00

Model No. 1381
BUSH BABY - With book

Designer:	Mr. Orwell
Height:	1 ½", 3.8 cm
Colour:	Grey-brown - gloss
Issued:	1955-1966
Set:	1379, 1380

Description	U.K. £	U.S. $	Can. $
Gloss	60.00	100.00	150.00

Model No. 1440
FOX - Standing

Designer:	Arthur Gredington
Height:	2 ½", 6.4 cm
Colour:	Red-brown and white - gloss or matt
Issued:	1. Gloss - 1956-1997
	2. Matt - 1985-1988

Description	U.K. £	U.S. $	Can. $
1. Gloss	12.00	25.00	40.00
2. Matt	15.00	30.00	35.00

Model No. 1486
TIGERESS

Designer:	Colin Melbourne
Height:	4 ¼", 10.8 cm
Colour:	Tan with black stripes and markings - gloss
Issued:	1957-1975

Description	U.K. £	U.S. $	Can. $
Gloss	150.00	250.00	350.00

Model No. 1506
LION - Facing right

Designer:	Colin Melbourne
Height:	5 ¼", 13.3 cm
Colour:	Golden brown - gloss
Issued:	1957-1967
Set:	1507, 1508

Description	U.K. £	U.S. $	Can. $
Gloss	75.00	150.00	225.00

Model No. 1507
LIONESS - Facing left

Designer:	Colin Melbourne	
Height:	4 ¾", 12.1 cm	
Colour:	1. Golden brown - gloss	
	2. Black - satin	
Issued:	1957-1967	
Set:	1506, 1508	

Description	U.K. £	U.S. $	Can. $
1. Gloss	85.00	150.00	200.00
2. Satin	60.00	100.00	150.00

Model No. 1508
LION CUB - Facing right

Designer:	Colin Melbourne
Height:	4", 10.1 cm
Colour:	Golden brown - gloss
Issued:	1957-1967
Set:	1506, 1507

Description	U.K. £	U.S. $	Can. $
Gloss	50.00	100.00	150.00

Model No. 1532
HIPPOPOTAMUS

Designer:	Colin Melbourne
Height:	3 ½", 8.9 cm
Colour:	Dark grey with pink underneath - gloss
Issued:	1958-1966

Description	U.K. £	U.S. $	Can. $
Gloss	200.00	350.00	450.00

Model No. 1533
POLAR BEAR

Designer:	Arthur Gredington	
Height:	4 ¾", 12.1 cm	
Colour:	1. Blue - gloss	
	2. White - gloss	
Issued:	1958-1966	

Description	U.K. £	U.S. $	Can. $
1. Blue	150.00	300.00	400.00
2. White	135.00	250.00	350.00

Model No. 1534
SEAL

Designer: Arthur Gredington
Length: 5 ¾", 14.6 cm
Colour: Grey - gloss
Issued: 1958-1966

Description	U.K. £	U.S. $	Can. $
Gloss	125.00	275.00	400.00

Model No. 1551
CHAMOIS

Designer: Pal Zalmen
Height: 4", 10.1 cm
Colour: Fawn or grey - gloss
Issued: 1958-1971
Series: Fun Models

Description	U.K. £	U.S. $	Can. $
1. Fawn	60.00	100.00	135.00
2. Grey	60.00	100.00	135.00

Model No. 1597
GIRAFFE

Designer: J. Lawson
Height: 4 ¼", 10.8 cm
Colour: Tan with dark patches - gloss
Issued: 1959-1971
Series: Fun Models

Description	U.K. £	U.S. $	Can. $
Gloss	80.00	140.00	185.00

Model No. 1615A
BABYCHAM
First Version - Large eyes

Designer:	Albert Hallam
Height:	4″, 10.1 cm
Colour:	Yellow - gloss
Issued:	1960-1975
Series:	Fun Models

Description	U.K. £	U.S. $	Can. $
Gloss	60.00	100.00	140.00

Model 1615B
BABYCHAM
Second Version - Small eyes, name on ribbon

Designer:	Albert Hallam
Height:	4", 10.1 cm
Colour:	Yellow - gloss
Issued:	Unknown
Series:	Fun Models

Description	U.K. £	U.S. $	Can. $
Gloss	75.00	125.00	175.00

Model No. 1631
GIRAFFE - Large

Designer:	J. Lawson
Height:	12″, 30.5 cm
Colour:	Light brown with dark brown patches - gloss
Issued:	1959-1975

Description	U.K. £	U.S. $	Can. $
Gloss	200.00	400.00	575.00

Note: Pattern and colour varies.

Model No. 1678
MOUSE

Designer:	Albert Hallam		
Height:	2 ½", 6.4 cm		
Colour:	Grey - gloss		
Issued:	1960-1997		

Description	U.K. £	U.S. $	Can. $
Gloss	7.00	15.00	20.00

Model No. 1688
REINDEER

Designer:	J. Lawson		
Height:	3 ¾", 9.5 cm		
Colour:	Fawn or grey - gloss		
Issued:	1960-1971		
Series:	Fun Models		

Description	U.K. £	U.S. $	Can. $
1. Fawn	60.00	100.00	125.00
2. Grey	60.00	100.00	125.00

Model No. 1702
PUMA ON ROCK

Designer:	Arthur Gredington	
Height:	8 ½", 21.6 cm	
Colour:	1.	Black - gloss
	2.	Tawny - gloss or matt
Issued:	1.	Black
		a. Gloss - 1960-1973
Reissued:		b. Gloss - 1979-1983
Issued:	2.	Tawny
		a. Gloss - 1960-1975
		b. Matt - 1970-1973
		c. Satin matt - 1973-1989
Reissued:		d. Gloss - 1979-1983
Series:	2c.	Connoisseur Series

Description	U.K. £	U.S. $	Can. $
1. Black			
a. Gloss	165.00	275.00	375.00
b. Reissued	185.00	300.00	425.00
2. Tawny			
a. Gloss	140.00	225.00	325.00
b. Matt	125.00	200.00	275.00
c. Satin matt	150.00	250.00	350.00
d. Reissued	190.00	325.00	425.00

Model No. 1720
ELEPHANT AND TIGER

Designer:	Arthur Gredington
Height:	12", 30.5 cm
Colour:	Grey, tan with black stripes - gloss
Issued:	1960-1975

Description	U.K. £	U.S. $	Can. $
Gloss	750.00	1,250.00	1,500.00

Note: The elephant is the same model as used in 1770.

Model No. 1733
COMICAL FOX

Designer:	Harry Sales
Height:	3 ¼", 8.3 cm
Colour:	Red-brown and white - gloss
Issued:	1961-1968
Series:	Fun Models

Description	U.K. £	U.S. $	Can. $
Gloss	75.00	125.00	165.00

Model No. 1748
FOX - Seated

Designer:	Arthur Gredington
Height:	3", 7.6 cm
Colour:	Red-brown and white - gloss or matt
Issued:	1. Gloss - 1961-1997
	2. Matt - 1985-1988

Description	U.K. £	U.S. $	Can. $
1. Gloss	10.00	15.00	20.00
2. Matt	15.00	25.00	35.00

Model No. 1761
FOXY BANK

Designer:	Albert Hallam
Height:	8 ½", 21.6 cm
Colour:	Tan, brown and black on white - gloss
Issued:	1961-1967
Series:	Fun Models / Money bank

Description	U.K. £	U.S. $	Can. $
Gloss	80.00	135.00	175.00

Model No. 1770
ELEPHANT - Trunk in salute

Designer:	Arthur Gredington
Height:	12", 30.5 cm
Colour:	Grey - gloss or satin matt
Issued:	1. Gloss - 1961-1975
	2. Satin matt - 1970-1973

Description	U.K. £	U.S. $	Can. $
1. Gloss	200.00	375.00	500.00
2. Satin matt	250.00	450.00	575.00

Note: Satin matt transferred to Connoiseur Series in 1973. Elephant same model as used in 1720.

Model No. 1815
PANDA CUB

Designer:	Albert Hallam
Height:	2 ¼", 5.7 cm
Colour:	Black and white - gloss or matt
Issued:	1. Gloss - 1962-1997
	2. Matt - 1985-1988

Description	U.K. £	U.S. $	Can. $
1. Gloss	10.00	15.00	25.00
2. Matt	15.00	25.00	35.00

Model No. 1823
PUMA ON ROCK

Designer:	Arthur Gredington
Height:	6", 15.0 cm
Colour:	1. Black - gloss
	2. Tawny - gloss
Issued:	1. Black - 1962-1973
	2. Tawny - 1962-1975

Description	U.K. £	U.S. $	Can. $
1. Black	100.00	185.00	300.00
2. Tawny	120.00	250.00	325.00

Model No. 1943
BEAVER ON LOG - Facing left

Designer:	Albert Hallam
Height:	2 ½", 6.4 cm
Colour:	Tan - gloss
Issued:	1964-1967

Description	U.K. £	U.S. $	Can. $
Gloss	125.00	200.00	300.00

Model No. 2089
LION - Facing left

Designer:	Graham Tongue
Height:	5 ½″, 14.0 cm
Colour:	Golden brown - gloss
Issued:	1967-1984

Description	U.K. £	U.S. $	Can. $
Gloss	50.00	100.00	150.00

Model No. 2090
MOOSE

Designer:	Arthur Gredington
Height:	6 ¼″, 15.9 cm
Colour:	Dark brown - gloss or satin matt
Issued:	1967-1973

Description	U.K. £	U.S. $	Can. $
1. Gloss	350.00	575.00	750.00
2. Satin matt	350.00	575.00	750.00

Model No. 2096
TIGER

Designer:	Graham Tongue
Height:	7 ½″, 19.1 cm
Colour:	Tan with black stripes - gloss or matt
Issued:	1. Gloss - 1967-1990
	2. Matt - 1985-1988

Description	U.K. £	U.S. $	Can. $
1. Gloss	90.00	190.00	250.00
2. Matt	75.00	150.00	200.00

Note: Example known in black satin matt - very rare.

Model No. 2097
LIONESS - Facing right

Designer:	Graham Tongue
Height:	5 ¾″, 14.6 cm
Colour:	Golden brown - gloss
Issued:	1967-1984

Description	U.K. £	U.S. $	Can. $
Gloss	65.00	125.00	175.00

Model No. 2098
LION CUB - Facing left

Designer: Graham Tongue
Height: 4", 10.1 cm
Colour: Golden brown - gloss
Issued: 1967-1984

Description	U.K. £	U.S. $	Can. $
Gloss	35.00	75.00	125.00

Model No. 2131
RABBIT

Designer: Albert Hallam, Graham Tongue
Height: 3", 7.6 cm
Colour: Light brown and white - gloss
Issued: 1967-1973
Series: Fun Models

Description	U.K. £	U.S. $	Can. $
Gloss	85.00	150.00	200.00

Model No. 2132
RABBIT WITH BABY

Designer: Albert Hallam
Height: 3", 7.6 cm
Colour: Light brown and white - gloss
Issued: 1967-1971
Series: Fun Models

Description	U.K. £	U.S. $	Can. $
Gloss	85.00	150.00	200.00

Model No. 2194
RACOON ON LOG

Designer: Albert Hallam
Height: 4 ¼", 10.8 cm
Colour: Dark grey - gloss
Issued: 1968-1972

Description	U.K. £	U.S. $	Can. $
Gloss	175.00	300.00	425.00

Model No. 2195
BEAVER ON LOG - Facing right

Designer: Albert Hallam
Height: 4 ½", 11.9 cm
Colour: Brown - gloss
Issued: 1968-c.1973

Description	U.K. £	U.S. $	Can. $
Gloss	175.00	300.00	425.00

Model No. 2237
BABYCHAM WALL PLAQUE

Designer: Graham Tongue
Height: 3" x 6 ¼", 7.6 x 15.9 cm (Concave)
Colour: Unknown - gloss
Issued: c.1970-c.1975
Series: Wall Plaques

Description	U.K. £	U.S. $	Can. $
Gloss	100.00	175.00	225.00

Photograph not
available at press time

Photograph not
available at press time

Model No. 2253
HEDGEHOG

Designer: Harry Sales
Height: 3 ½" 8.9 cm
Colour: 1.   Blue - gloss
              2.   Brown - gloss
Issued: 1969-1971
Series: Moda Range

Description	U.K. £	U.S. $	Can. $
1. Blue	125.00	200.00	250.00
2. Brown	125.00	200.00	250.00

Model No. 2302
MOUSE

Designer: Albert Hallam
Height: 1 ¾", 8.9 cm
Colour: Unknown
Issued: 1969-Unknown

Description	U.K. £	U.S. $	Can. $
Possibly not put into production.			

Model No. 2312
KANGAROO

Designer:	Albert Hallam		
Height:	5″, 12.7 cm		
Colour:	Light and dark brown - gloss		
Issued:	1970-1973		

Description	U.K. £	U.S. $	Can. $
Gloss	150.00	275.00	375.00

Model No. 2348
FOX

Designer:	Graham Tongue		
Height:	12 ½″, 31.7 cm		
Colour:	Red-brown and white - gloss		
Issued:	1970-1984		
Series:	Fireside Model		

Description	U.K. £	U.S. $	Can. $
Gloss	200.00	325.00	475.00

Model No. 2554A
LION ON ROCK

Designer:	Graham Tongue		
Height:	8 ¼″, 21.0 cm		
Colour:	Golden brown - satin matt		
Issued:	1975-1984		
Varieties:	2554B (standing)		
Series:	Connoisseur		

Description	U.K. £	U.S. $	Can. $
Satin matt	175.00	350.00	450.00

Model No. 2554B
LION - Standing

Designer:	Graham Tongue		
Height:	6 ¾″, 17.2 cm		
Colour:	Golden brown - gloss		
Modelled:	1975		
Issued:	1987-1995		

Description	U.K. £	U.S. $	Can. $
Gloss	125.00	250.00	350.00

Model No. 2613
PANDA "CHI CHI"
First Version - With bamboo shoot

Designer:	Unknown
Height:	3 ¾", 9.5 cm
Colour:	Black and white - gloss
Issued:	1978-c.1980
Varieties:	2944

Description	U.K. £	U.S. $	Can. $
Gloss		Rare	

Note: This model was produced for the London Natural History Museum.

Model No. 2629
STAG

Designer:	Graham Tongue
Height:	13 ½", 34.3 cm
Colour:	1. Golden brown - satin matt
	2. Bronze with black shading - satin
Issued:	1. 1978-1989 2. 1989-1992
Series:	2. Connoisseur

Description	U.K. £	U.S. $	Can. $
1. Satin matt	175.00	300.00	400.00
2. Satin	150.00	250.00	350.00

Note: Transferred to (DA 32) 08/89, "Majestic Stag."

Model No. 2686
OTTER

Designer:	David Lyttleton
Height:	2 ¼", 5.7 cm
Colour:	Grey - matt
Issued:	1985-1985

Description	U.K. £	U.S. $	Can. $
Matt	35.00	50.00	75.00

Note: Part of a trial run in 1985 but never put into general production.

Model No. 2687
BADGER

Designer:	David Lyttleton
Height:	3", 7.6 cm
Colour:	Black - matt
Issued:	1985-1985

Description	U.K. £	U.S. $	Can. $
Matt	35.00	50.00	75.00

Note: Part of a trial run in 1985 but never put into general production.

Model No. 2693
SEAL

Designer:	Graham Tongue		
Height:	3 ½", 8.9 cm		
Colour:	Grey - matt		
Issued:	1985-1985		

Description	U.K. £	U.S. $	Can. $
Matt	35.00	50.00	75.00

Note: Part of a trial run in 1985 but never put into general production.

Model No. 2725
CHEETAH ON ROCK

Designer:	Graham Tongue		
Height:	6 ½", 16.5 cm		
Colour:	Pale brown with dark spots - satin finish		
Issued:	1981-1989		
Series:	Connoisseur		

Description	U.K. £	U.S. $	Can. $
Satin finish	150.00	250.00	350.00

Note: Transferred to R.D. backstamp (DA 39) 08/89 later called "The Watering Hole."

Model No. 2944
PANDA "CHI CHI"
Second Version - Without bamboo shoot

Designer:	Unknown		
Height:	3 ¾", 9.5 cm		
Colour:	Black and white - matt		
Issued:	1985-1985		
Varieties:	2613		

Description	U.K. £	U.S. $	Can. $
Matt	150.00	250.00	325.00

Note: Part of a trial run in 1985 but did not go into general production.

Model No. 3009
CHEETAH - Standing

Designer:	Graham Tongue		
Height:	5", 12.7 cm		
Colour:	Golden brown with dark spots - gloss		
Issued:	1986-1995		

Description	U.K. £	U.S. $	Can. $
Gloss	60.00	150.00	200.00

Model No. 3392
BADGER CUB

Designer:	Amanda Hughes-Lubeck
Height:	2″, 5.0 cm
Colour:	Black and white - gloss
Issued:	1992-1997
Set:	3393, 3394

Description	U.K. £	U.S. $	Can. $
Gloss	12.00	20.00	30.00

Model No. 3393
BADGER - Male

Designer:	Amanda Hughes-Lubeck
Height:	2″, 5.0 cm
Colour:	Black and white - gloss
Issued:	1992-1997
Set:	3392, 3394

Description	U.K. £	U.S. $	Can. $
Gloss	15.00	25.00	45.00

Model No. 3394
BADGER - Female

Designer:	Amanda Hughes-Lubeck
Height:	2″, 5.0 cm
Colour:	Black and white - gloss
Issued:	1992 -1997
Set:	3392, 3393

Description	U.K. £	U.S. $	Can. $
Gloss	15.00	25.00	45.00

Model No. 3397
HARVEST MOUSE

Designer:	Martyn Alcock
Height:	2 ¼″, 5.7 cm
Colour:	Brown - gloss
Issued:	1992-1997

Description	U.K. £	U.S. $	Can. $
Gloss	15.00	25.00	45.00

Model No. 3399
WOODMOUSE

Designer: Martyn Alcock
Height: 3 ¼", 8.3 cm
Colour: Brown - gloss
Issued: 1992-1997

Description	U.K. £	U.S. $	Can. $
Gloss	15.00	25.00	45.00

Model No. 3568
MEERKAT - Seated

Designer: Martyn Alcock
Height: 3", 7.6 cm
Colour: Grey/brown - gloss
Issued: 1996 in a limited edition of 1,250

Description	U.K. £	U.S. $	Can. $
Gloss	20.00	30.00	40.00

Model No. 3571
MEERKAT - Standing

Designer: Martyn Alcock
Height: 3 ½", 8.9 cm
Colour: Grey/brown - gloss
Issued: 1996 in a limited edition of 1,250

Description	U.K. £	U.S. $	Can. $
Gloss	20.00	30.00	40.00

WILD ANIMAL
WALL PLAQUES

Model No. 2933
LION'S HEAD

Designer: Graham Tongue
Height: 6", 15.0 cm
Colour: Golden brown - matt
Issued: 1985-1989

Description	U.K. £	U.S. $	Can. $
Matt	50.00	85.00	115.00

Model No. 2934
TIGER'S HEAD

Designer: Arthur Gredington
Height: 6", 15.0 cm
Colour: Tan - matt
Issued: 1985-1989

Description	U.K. £	U.S. $	Can. $
Matt	50.00	85.00	115.00

Model No. 2936
STAG'S HEAD

Designer: Graham Tongue
Height: 6", 15.0 cm
Colour: Light brown - matt
Issued: 1985-1989

Description	U.K. £	U.S. $	Can. $
Matt	50.00	85.00	115.00

A FLOW CHART FOR THE MAKING OF BESWICK ANIMALS

BALL CLAY
CHINA CLAY
FLINT
STONE

MODELLING   MOULDMAKING

The Clay Slip is poured into a mould and after a short time the surplus

slip is poured off leaving a thickness of clay adhering to the mould. after drying the model is removed from the mould.

Removing mould marks and making good any imperfections.

BLUNGER   SLIP PUMP   CLAY PRESS   CLAY-SLIP BLUNGER   CASTING   FETTLING AND SPONGING

Every piece is carefully inspected before firing.

The first fire converts the clay model to a hard slightly porous form called Biscuit.

The model is covered with liquid glaze.

The glaze is fired producing a surface of glass on the model.

INSPECTION   BISCUIT FIRE   GLAZING   GLOST FIRING

Artists applying colour

The colour is fired on to the glaze.

Final inspection before packing.

DECORATING   DECORATING FIRING   INSPECTION   PACKING   TRANSPORTATION

Chapter Nine

THE CM SERIES

This unique series of models, all created by Colin Melbourne, evokes great emotion amongst collectors; it is either loved or hated there are no half measures here. The models were called "contemporary" when they were in production during the late 1950s. They reflected the mood of the time, both in style and in decoration. None of the decorations are realistic, and all are stylized, some to a greater extent than others.

The decoration for the models in this section fall into two categories:

Series 1. Issued 1956-62

This series is sub-divided in three groups:

1. Colour combinations—charcoal grey/red/white gloss
2. Spotted colour combinations—yellow/shaded charcoal/black
3. Solid colours—grey/brown/green blue/white

Series 2. Issued 1962-66

This was called the chalk design. The background colour was white and the decorations in geometric shapes or floral designs appeared in a variety of colourways.

INDEX BY MODEL NUMBER

Model No. 1409
BISON - Large

Designer:	Colin Melbourne
Length:	7 ½″ x 10 ½″, 19.1 x 26.7 cm
Colour:	For colour combinations and varieties see page 393
Issued:	1956-by 1963

Description	U.K. £	U.S. $	Can. $
Series 1	150.00	250.00	325.00
Series 2	200.00	325.00	450.00

Model No. 1410
COW

Designer:	Colin Melbourne
Height:	5″, 12.7 cm
Colour:	For colour combinations and varieties see page 393
Issued:	1956-by 1963

Description	U.K. £	U.S. $	Can. $
Series 1	150.00	250.00	325.00

Model No. 1411
HORSE

Designer:	Colin Melbourne
Height:	8 ½″, 21.6 cm
Colour:	For colour combinations and varieties see page 393
Issued:	1956-by 1966

Description	U.K. £	U.S. $	Can. $
Series 1	150.00	225.00	325.00
Series 2	225.00	375.00	500.00

Model No. 1412
CAT - Large

Designer:	Colin Melbourne
Height:	9 ½″, 24.0 cm
Colour:	For colour combinations and varieties see page 393
Issued:	1956-by 1966

Description	U.K. £	U.S. $	Can. $
Series 1	175.00	300.00	400.00
Series 2	200.00	350.00	450.00

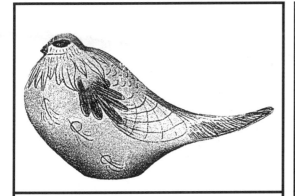

Model No. 1413
DOVE

Designer: Colin Melbourne
Height: 9", 22.9 cm
Colour: For colour combinations and varieties
see page 393
Issued: 1956-by 1965

Description	U.K. £	U.S. $	Can. $
Series 1	125.00	200.00	250.00
Series 2	150.00	250.00	325.00

Model No. 1414
BISON - Medium

Designer: Colin Melbourne
Length: 5 ½" x 8 ¾", 14.0 x 22.2 cm
Colour: For colour combinations and varieties
see page 393
Issued: 1956-by 1966

Description	U.K. £	U.S. $	Can. $
Series 1	150.00	250.00	325.00
Series 2	175.00	275.00	375.00

Model No. 1415
BIRD

Designer: Colin Melbourne
Height: 5 ¼", 13.3 cm
Colour: For colour combinations and varieties
see page 393
Issued: 1956-by 1965

Description	U.K. £	U.S. $	Can. $
Series 1	125.00	200.00	250.00
Series 2	150.00	250.00	325.00

Model No. 1416
COCK - Small

Designer: Colin Melbourne
Height: 5", 12.7 cm
Colour: For colour combinations and varieties
see page 393
Issued: 1956-by 1965

Description	U.K. £	U.S. $	Can. $
Series 1	150.00	250.00	325.00
Series 2	175.00	275.00	375.00

Model No. 1417
CAT

Designer:	Colin Melbourne
Height:	5 ½", 14.0 cm
Colour:	For colour combinations and varieties see page 393
Issued:	1956-by 1966

Description	U.K. £	U.S. $	Can. $
Series 1	80.00	125.00	150.00
Series 2	175.00	275.00	375.00

Model No. 1418
FOX - Small

Designer:	Colin Melbourne
Length:	2" x 8", 5.0 x 20.3 cm
Colour:	For colour combinations and varieties see page 393
Issued:	1956-by 1966

Description	U.K. £	U.S. $	Can. $
Series 1	100.00	175.00	225.00
Series 2	150.00	250.00	325.00

Photograph not
available at press time

Model No. 1419
LION

Designer:	Colin Melbourne
Height:	4 ¾", 12.1 cm
Colour:	For colour combinations and varieties see page 393
Issued:	1956-by 1963

Description	U.K. £	U.S. $	Can. $
Series 1	150.00	250.00	325.00

Model No. 1420
OWL - Small

Designer:	Colin Melbourne
Height:	4 ¾", 12.1 cm
Colour:	For colour combinations and varieties see page 393
Issued:	1956-by 1965

Description	U.K. £	U.S. $	Can. $
Series 1	125.00	225.00	275.00
Series 2	150.00	250.00	325.00

Model No. 1462
OWL - Large

Designer: Colin Melbourne
Height: 8 ¼", 21.0 cm
Colour: For colour combinations and varieties
see page 393
Issued: 1956-by 1965

Description	U.K. £	U.S. $	Can. $
Series 1	150.00	250.00	325.00
Series 2	175.00	300.00	400.00

Model No. 1463
BULLDOG

Designer: Colin Melbourne
Height: Unknown
Colour: For colour combinations and varieties
see page 393
Issued: 1956-1970

Description	U.K. £	U.S. $	Can. $
Series 1	125.00	200.00	275.00

Model No. 1465
ZEBRA

Designer: Colin Melbourne
Height: 6", 15.0 cm
Colour: For colour combinations and varieties
see page 393
Issued: 1956-by 1966

Description	U.K. £	U.S. $	Can. $
Series 1	200.00	350.00	450.00
Series 2	225.00	400.00	500.00

Model No. 1467
COCK - Large

Designer: Colin Melbourne
Height: 11 ¾", 29.8 cm
Colour: For colour combinations and varieties
see page 393
Issued: 1956-by 1963

Description	U.K. £	U.S. $	Can. $
Series 1	200.00	350.00	450.00
Series 2	250.00	425.00	550.00

Model No. 1468
BISON - Small

Designer:	Colin Melbourne
Height:	Unknown
Colour:	For colour combinations and varieties see page 393
Issued:	1956-by 1966

Description	U.K. £	U.S. $	Can. $
Series 1	150.00	250.00	325.00
Series 2	200.00	325.00	450.00

Model No. 1469
DACHSHUND

Designer:	Colin Melbourne
Length:	7", 17.8 cm
Colour:	For colour combinations and varieties see page 393
Issued:	1957-1970

Description	U.K. £	U.S. $	Can. $
Series 1	100.00	175.00	225.00
Series 2	150.00	250.00	325.00

Model No. 1470
CLOWN ON HORSE - Small

Designer:	Colin Melbourne
Height:	5 ¾", 14.6 cm
Colour:	For colour combinations and varieties see page 393
Issued:	1957-by 1966

Description	U.K. £	U.S. $	Can. $
Series 1	175.00	300.00	400.00
Series 2	225.00	375.00	500.00

Model No. 1471
GOOSE

Designer:	Colin Melbourne
Height:	3 ½", 8.9 cm
Colour:	For colour combinations and varieties see page 393
Issued:	1957-by 1962

Description	U.K. £	U.S. $	Can. $
Series 1	125.00	200.00	275.00

Model No. 1472
POODLE

Designer:	Colin Melbourne
Height:	5 ¾", 14.6 cm
Colour:	For colour combinations and varieties see page 393
Issued:	1957-1962

Description	U.K. £	U.S. $	Can. $
Series 1	175.00	300.00	400.00

Model No. 1473
PIG

Designer:	Colin Melbourne
Length:	2 ½" x 6", 6.4 x 15.0 cm
Colour:	For colour combinations and varieties see page 393
Issued:	1957-by 1965

Description	U.K. £	U.S. $	Can. $
Series 1	125.00	225.00	275.00
Series 2	150.00	250.00	325.00

Model No. 1474
CAT

Designer:	Colin Melbourne
Height:	5 ¼", 13.3 cm
Colour:	For colour combinations and varieties see page 393
Issued:	1957-by 1966

Description	U.K. £	U.S. $	Can. $
Series 1	150.00	250.00	350.00
Series 2	175.00	300.00	400.00

Model No. 1475
FOX - Large

Designer:	Colin Melbourne
Length:	10 ½", 26.7 cm
Colour:	For colour combinations and varieties see page 393
Issued:	1957-by 1966

Description	U.K. £	U.S. $	Can. $
Series 1	150.00	250.00	300.00
Series 2	175.00	275.00	375.00

Model No. 1476
CLOWN ON HORSE - Large

Designer: Colin Melbourne
Height: 8 ½", 21.6 cm
Colour: For colour combinations and varieties
              see page 393
Issued: 1957-by 1966

Description	U.K. £	U.S. $	Can. $
Series 1	275.00	425.00	600.00
Series 2	325.00	550.00	700.00

Model No. 1481
REINDEER

Designer: Colin Melbourne
Height: 5 ½", 14.0 cm
Colour: For colour combinations and varieties
              see page 393
Issued: 1957-by 1966

Description	U.K. £	U.S. $	Can. $
Series 1	175.00	300.00	400.00
Series 2	200.00	350.00	450.00

Model No. 1482
PEACOCK

Designer: Colin Melbourne
Height: 3 ½", 8.9 cm
Colour: For colour combinations and varieties
              see page 393
Issued: 1957-by 1965

Description	U.K. £	U.S. $	Can. $
Series 1	150.00	250.00	325.00
Series 2	175.00	300.00	400.00

Chapter Ten
LITTLE LIKABLES

INDEX BY MODEL NUMBER

LL1
FAMILY GATHERING™
(Hen and Two Chicks)

Designer:	Diane Griffiths
Height:	4 ½", 11.9 cm
Colour:	White hen and chicks with yellow beaks and gold comb on hen - gloss
Issued:	1985 - 1987

Description	U.S. $	Can. $	U.K. £
Gloss	70.00	95.00	40.00

LL2
WATCHING THE WORLD GO BY™
(Frog)

Designer:	Robert Tabbenor
Height:	3 ¾", 9.5 cm
Colour:	White frog, black and green eyes - gloss
Issued:	1985 - 1987

Description	U.S. $	Can. $	U.K. £
Gloss	110.00	155.00	65.00

LL3
HIDE AND SEEK™
(Pig and Two Piglets)

Designer:	Robert Tabbenor
Height:	3 ¼", 8.3 cm
Colour:	White pigs with pink noses, ears and tails - gloss
Issued:	1985 - 1987

Description	U.S. $	Can. $	U.K. £
Gloss	70.00	95.00	40.00

LL4
MY PONY™
(Pony)

Designer:	Diane Griffiths
Height:	7 ¼", 18.4 cm
Colour:	White pony with blue highlights in mane and tail - gloss
Issued:	1985 - 1987

Description	U.S. $	Can. $	U.K. £
Gloss	95.00	130.00	55.00

LL5
ON TOP OF THE WORLD™
(Elephant)

Designer:	Diane Griffiths
Height:	3 ¾", 9.5 cm
Colour:	White elephant with black eyes and gold nails - gloss
Issued:	1985 - 1987

Description	U.S. $	Can. $	U.K. £
Gloss	70.00	95.00	40.00

LL6
TREAT ME GENTLY™
(Fawn)

Designer:	Diane Griffiths
Height:	4 ½", 11.9 cm
Colour:	White fawn with black and brown eyes, black nose and gold hoof - gloss
Issued:	1985 - 1987

Description	U.S. $	Can. $	U.K. £
Gloss	70.00	95.00	40.00

LL7
OUT AT LAST™
(Duckling)

Designer:	Robert Tabbenor
Height:	3 ¼", 8.3 cm
Colour:	White duck with black and brown eyes and gold beak - gloss
Issued:	1985 - 1987

Description	U.S. $	Can. $	U.K. £
Gloss	70.00	95.00	40.00

LL8
CATS CHORUS™
(Cats)

Designer:	Robert Tabbenor
Height:	4 ¾", 12.1 cm
Colour:	Two white cats with black and green eyes, black nose, pink ears and mouth - gloss
Issued:	1985 - 1987

Description	U.S. $	Can. $	U.K. £
Gloss	70.00	95.00	40.00

Chapter Eleven
STUDIO SCULPTURES

The series of Studio Sculptures made a very brief appearance, most for a maximum of two years, and some for only six months, between 1984 and 1985. When the collection was launched, Harry Sales, Beswick's Design Manager, explained "The new bonded ceramic body gives us endless opportunities to capture every minute detail of the subject and bring the sculptures to life."

The models in this new medium formed four groups, of which two are relevant to this book. These are: the "Countryside Series" which consists of fourteen models and includes birds, a squirrel, dogs, and rabbits, and the "Young Friends Series" which contained four different models, two of which are in two colourways, of pet cats and dogs. None of the models were "free standing" for the model incorporated a base, and some had an additional wooden plinth.

The Studio Sculptures were completely different in style and detail because of the different medium used. They were also different in price! In 1985 their prices ranged from £13.95 to £59.00 and they were considerably more than models in earthenware. For example the Studio Sculpture Wren "Early Bird" retailed at £15.95 whilst the Beswick Wren (993) was £4.95 quite a difference. Therefore it was not too surprising to find that overall the series was not the expected commercial success and so it was not listed in the 1986 price list.

INDEX BY MODEL NUMBER

For other figurines in the Studio Sculpture Series see *The Charlton Standard Catalogue of Royal Doulton Beswick Storybook Figurines*.

Beatrix Potter Series- SS1, SS2, SS3, SS4, SS11, SS26, SS27

Thelwell Series - SS7, SS12; SS23-25 not allocated.

SS5
PUPPY LOVE (Two puppies)

Designer:	Unknown
Height:	4 ½", 11.9 cm
Colour:	1. One brown/white, one black/white - satin matt
	2. One black/white, one white with black patches - satin matt
Issued:	1984-1986
Series:	Young Friends

Description	U.K. £	U.S. $	Can. $
1. Brown/black	60.00	115.00	140.00
2. Black/white	60.00	115.00	140.00

SS6
I SPY
(Two kittens)

Designer:	Unknown
Height:	4 ½", 11.9 cm
Colour:	1. Two white cats - satin matt
	2. One tabby, one ginger - satin matt
Issued:	1984-1986
Series:	Young Friends

Description	U.K. £	U.S. $	Can. $
1. White	60.00	115.00	140.00
2. Tabby/ginger	60.00	115.00	140.00

SS8
CONTENTMENT
(Dutch Rabbits)

Designer:	Unknown
Length:	4 ¾", 12.1 cm
Colour:	1. Brown and white - satin matt
	2. Black and white - satin matt
Issued:	1984-1986
Series:	Countryside

Description	U.K. £	U.S. $	Can. $
1. Brown/white	40.00	75.00	100.00
2. Black/white	40.00	75.00	100.00

SS9
BRIGHT EYES
(Dutch Rabbit)

Designer:	Unknown
Length:	4 ½", 11.9 cm
Colour:	1. Brown and white - satin matt
	2. Black and white - satin matt
Issued:	1984-1986
Series:	Countryside

Description	U.K. £	U.S. $	Can. $
1. Brown/white	40.00	75.00	100.00
2. Black/white	40.00	75.00	100.00

SS10
MIND HOW YOU GO
(Goose and goslings)

Designer:	Unknown
Length:	5 ¼", 13.3 cm
Colour:	White goose and yellow goslings - satin matt
Issued:	1984-1986
Series:	Countryside

Description	U.K. £	U.S. $	Can. $
Satin matt	55.00	90.00	115.00

SS13
HAPPY LANDINGS
(Swan on wooden base)

Designer:	Unknown
Height:	5", 12.7 cm
Colour:	White - satin matt
Issued:	1984-1986
Series:	Countryside

Description	U.K. £	U.S. $	Can. $
Satin matt	55.00	90.00	115.00

SS14
THE CHASE
(Dogs on wooden base)

Designer:	Unknown
Height:	4", 10.1 cm
Colour:	Shaded brown and white - satin matt
Issued:	1984-1986
Series:	Countryside

Description	U.K. £	U.S. $	Can. $
Satin matt	75.00	125.00	170.00

SS15
HIDE AND SEEK
(Dogs on wooden base)

Designer:	Unknown
Height:	4 ½", 11.9 cm
Colour:	Shaded brown - satin matt
Issued:	1984-1986
Series:	Countryside

Description	U.K. £	U.S. $	Can. $
Satin matt	75.00	125.00	170.00

SS16
MENU FOR TODAY
(Spaniel puppy with kitten)

Designer:	Unknown
Height:	3 ½", 8.9 cm
Colour:	1. Brown puppy, white kitten - satin matt
	2. Brown puppy, tabby kitten - satin matt
Issued:	1984-1986
Series:	Young Friends

Description	U.K. £	U.S. $	Can. $
1. Brown/white	55.00	100.00	125.00
2. Brown/tabby	55.00	100.00	125.00

SS17
SHARING
(German Shepherd puppy with kitten)

Designer:	Unknown
Height:	3 ½", 8.9 cm
Colour:	Black and brown dog, white kitten - satin matt
Issued:	1984-1986
Series:	Young Friends

Description	U.K. £	U.S. $	Can. $
Satin matt	65.00	110.00	150.00

SS18
PLANNING AHEAD
(Squirrel)

Designer:	Unknown
Height:	3", 7.6 cm
Colour:	Red - satin matt
Issued:	1984-1986
Series:	Countryside

Description	U.K. £	U.S. $	Can. $
Satin matt	40.00	75.00	100.00

SS19
EARLY BIRD
(Wren)

Designer:	Unknown
Height:	2 ½", 6.4 cm
Colour:	Dark and light brown - satin matt
Issued:	1984-1986
Series:	Countryside

Description	U.K. £	U.S. $	Can. $
Satin matt	40.00	75.00	100.00

Photograph not
available at press time

SS20
GOLDEN RETRIEVER - on wooden base

Designer:	Unknown
Height:	5″, 12.7 cm
Colour:	Golden brown - satin matt
Issued:	1984-1986
Series:	Countryside

Description	U.K. £	U.S. $	Can. $
Satin matt	75.00	125.00	170.00

Photograph not
available at press time

SS21
POINTER - on wooden base

Designer:	Unknown
Height:	5″, 12.7 cm
Colour:	White and brown - satin matt
Issued:	1984-1986
Series:	Countryside

Description	U.K. £	U.S. $	Can. $
Satin matt	75.00	125.00	170.00

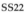

Photograph not
available at press time

SS22
ENGLISH SETTER - on wooden base

Designer:	Unknown
Height:	5″, 12.7 cm
Colour:	White and liver - satin matt
Issued:	1984-1986
Series:	Countryside

Description	U.K. £	U.S. $	Can. $
Satin matt	75.00	125.00	170.00

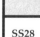

SS28
ROBIN

Designer:	Unknown
Height:	3″, 7.6 cm
Colour:	Brown and red - satin matt
Issued:	1985-1986
Series:	Countryside

Description	U.K. £	U.S. $	Can. $
Satin matt	40.00	75.00	100.00

SS29
BLUE TIT

Designer: Unknown
Height: 2 ½", 6.4 cm
Colour: Yellow, green and white - satin matt
Issued: 1985-1986
Series: Countryside

Description	U.K. £	U.S. $	Can. $
Satin matt	40.00	75.00	100.00

SS30
CHAFFINCH

Designer: Unknown
Height: 2 ¼", 5.7 cm
Colour: Brown, ochre, grey, black - satin matt
Issued: 1985-1986
Series: Countryside

Description	U.K. £	U.S. $	Can. $
Satin matt	40.00	75.00	100.00

Chapter Twelve

WHISKY FLASKS

INDEX BY MODEL NUMBER

Model No. 2051
LOCH NESS MONSTER (NESSIE)

Designer: Albert Hallam
Height: 3", 7.6 cm
Colour: Grey-green - gloss
Issued: 1965-1986

Description	U.K. £	U.S. $	Can. $
1. Head stopper	25.00	40.00	50.00
2. Base stopper	20.00	30.00	40.00

Model No. 2104
EAGLE

Designer: Graham Tongue
Height: 4", 10.1 cm
Colour: Brown - gloss
Issued: 1967-1986

Description	U.K. £	U.S. $	Can. $
Gloss	20.00	30.00	40.00

Model No. 2281
EAGLE

Designer: Graham Tongue
Height: 11", 27.9 cm
Colour: Brown - gloss
Issued: 1969-1984

Description	U.K. £	U.S. $	Can. $
Gloss	100.00	150.00	200.00

Note: Model no. 2281 was remodelled in 1980 with a removable head stopper.

Model No. 2350
HAGGIS BIRD

Designer: James Haywood
Remodelled: Albert Hallam
Height: 2 ½", 6.4 cm
Colour: Brown - gloss
Issued: 1971-1986

Description	U.K. £	U.S. $	Can. $
Gloss	15.00	25.00	30.00

Model No. 2561
GROUSE

Designer:	David Lyttleton	
Height:	9", 22.9 cm	
Colour:	Brown and red - gloss	
Issued:	1976-1984	

Description	U.K. £	U.S. $	Can. $
Gloss	110.00	190.00	240.00

Note: Model no. 2561 was remodelled with a removable head stopper.

Model No. 2583
OSPREY

Designer:	David Lyttleton	
Height:	7 ¾", 19.7 cm	
Colour:	Browns and white - gloss	
Issued:	1977-1986	

Description:	U.K. £	U.S. $	Can. $
Gloss	80.00	135.00	170.00

Model No. 2636
SQUIRREL

Designer:	David Lyttleton	
Height:	3 ½", 8.9 cm	
Colour:	Red-brown - gloss	
Issued:	1978-1986	

Description	U.K. £	U.S. $	Can. $
Gloss	15.00	30.00	40.00

Model No. 2639
KESTREL

Designer:	Graham Tongue	
Height:	6 ½", 16.5 cm	
Colour:	Dark grey and white - gloss	
Issued:	1979-1986	

Description	U.K. £	U.S. $	Can. $
Gloss	80.00	135.00	170.00

Model No. 2640
BUZZARD

Designer:	Graham Tongue
Height:	6 ½", 16.5 cm
Colour:	Dark brown and grey - gloss
Issued:	1979-1986

Description	U.K. £	U.S. $	Can. $
Gloss	80.00	135.00	170.00

Model No. 2641
MERLIN

Designer:	Graham Tongue
Height:	6 ½", 16.5 cm
Colour:	Dark grey and white - gloss
Issued:	1979-1986

Description	U.K. £	U.S. $	Can. $
Gloss	80.00	135.00	170.00

Model No. 2642
PEREGRINE FALCON

Designer:	Graham Tongue
Height:	6 ½", 16.5 cm
Colour:	Dark grey and white - gloss
Issued:	1979-1986

Description	U.K. £	U.S. $	Can. $
Gloss	80.00	135.00	170.00

Model No. 2678
EAGLE

Designer:	Graham Tongue
Height:	10 ½", 26.7 cm
Colour:	Light and dark brown - gloss
Issued:	1980- 1987

Description	U.K. £	U.S. $	Can. $
Gloss	110.00	185.00	230.00

Model No. 2686
OTTER

Designer:	David Lyttleton
Height:	2 ¼", 5.7 cm
Colour:	Grey and brown - gloss
Issued:	1981-1986

Description	U.K. £	U.S. $	Can. $
Gloss	15.00	25.00	30.00

Model No. 2687
BADGER

Designer:	David Lyttleton
Height:	3", 7.6 cm
Colour:	Black and white - gloss
Issued:	1981-1986

Description	U.K. £	U.S. $	Can. $
Gloss	15.00	25.00	30.00

Model No. 2693
SEAL

Designer:	Graham Tongue
Height:	3 ½", 8.9 cm
Colour:	Grey - gloss
Issued:	1980-1986

Description	U.K. £	U.S. $	Can. $
Gloss	15.00	25.00	30.00

Model No. 2781
TAWNY OWL

Designer:	Graham Tongue
Height:	6 ¼", 15.9 cm
Colour:	Brown - gloss
Issued:	1982-1987

Description	U.K. £	U.S. $	Can. $
Gloss	75.00	125.00	175.00

Model No. 2798
GROUSE

Designer:	David Lyttleton
Height:	9 ½", 24.0 cm
Colour:	Brown and red - matt
Issued:	1982-1987

Description	U.K. £	U.S. $	Can. $
Gloss	90.00	150.00	225.00

Model No. 2809
BARN OWL

Designer:	Graham Tongue
Height:	6 ¾", 17.2 cm
Colour:	Tan-brown and white - gloss
Issued:	1983-1987

Description	U.K. £	U.S . $	Can. $
Gloss	75.00	125.00	175.00

Model No. 2825
SHORT EARED OWL

Designer:	Graham Tongue
Height:	6 ¾", 17.2 cm
Colour:	Dark and light brown - gloss
Issued:	1983-1987

Description	U.K. £	U.S. $	Can. $
Gloss	75.00	125.00	175.00

Model No. 2826
SNOWY OWL

Designer:	Graham Tongue
Height:	1. 6 ½", 16.5 cm
	2. 5 ¾", 14.6 cm
Colour:	White - gloss
Issued:	1983-1987

Description	U.K. £	U.S . $	Can. $
1. Large	75.00	125.00	175.00
2. Small	60.00	110.00	140.00

Chapter Thirteen

COMMISSIONED

MODELS

During the early 1990s Beswick used some of its current freestanding models and now attached them to either a ceramic or wooden base.

Various companies, including British Coal, one of the major home shopping networks and a direct mail corporation, seem to be the largest commissioners of these items.

Little is known about these models, for they are not listed in the Beswick product line.

INDEX BY MODEL NUMBER

Model No. 818
"HORSES GREAT AND SMALL" - on ceramic base

Designer: Arthur Gredington
Height: 10", 25.4 cm
Colour: Dark brown and white - gloss
Issued: Unknown

Description	U.K. £	U.S. $	Can. $
Gloss	95.00	200.00	275.00

Model No. 967
COCKER SPANIEL "HORSESHOE PRIMULA"

Designer: Arthur Gredington
Height: 6 ¾", 17.1 cm
Colour: Golden brown - gloss
Issued: Unknown

Description	U.K. £	U.S. $	Can. $
Gloss	85.00	200.00	275.00

Model No. 1436/1460
"SHARING" - on ceramic base

Designer: Arthur Gredington and Colin Melbourne
Height: 4 ¾", 12.1 cm
Colour: Grey cat, brown dog - gloss
Issued: Unknown

Description	U.K. £	U.S. $	Can. $
Gloss	80.00	150.00	225.00

Model No. 1558/1678
"WATCH IT" - on ceramic base

Designer: Albert Hallam and Pal Zalmen
Height: 8 ¾", 22.2 cm
Colour: Chocolate point cat, grey mouse - gloss
Issued: Unknown

Description	U.K. £	U.S. $	Can. $
Gloss	80.00	175.00	250.00

Model No. 1886/3093
"PLAYTIME" - on ceramic base

Designer:	Albert Hallam
Height:	5", 12.7 cm
Colour:	White kitten with pink or lemon ball of wool - gloss
Issued:	Unknown

Description	U.K. £	U.S. $	Can. $
Gloss	55.00	120.00	175.00

Model No. 2221
ST. BERNARD "CORNA GARTH STROLLER"
- on ceramic base

Designer:	Albert Hallam
Height:	6 ¾", 17.1 cm
Colour:	Dark brown, tan and white - gloss
Issued:	Unknown

Description	U.K. £	U.S. $	Can. $
Gloss	95.00	200.00	275.00

Model No. 2590/1436
"GOOD FRIENDS" - on ceramic base

Designer:	Colin Melbourne
Height:	6", 15.2 cm
Colour:	White and tan dog, ginger kitten - gloss
Issued:	Unknown

Description	U.K. £	U.S. $	Can. $
Gloss	85.00	175.00	225.00

Model No. 4677
SOLID FRIENDSHIP - on wooden plinth

Designer:	Albert Hallam and Warren Platt
Height:	5 ½", 14.0 cm
Colour:	White mouse, black and white cat, and white dog with brown patches - gloss
Issued:	1993

Description	U.K. £	U.S. $	Can. $
Gloss	95.00	200.00	275.00

Note: This model was a special commission for British Coal.

INDEX OF MODEL NUMBERS

ALPHABETICAL INDEX

432

ROYAL DOULTON IS OUR SPECIALITY!

We Buy ✦ We Sell ✦ We Appraise

Colonial House Features the Largest Selection of Current and Discontinued Items in the Following Lines:

- ✦ OLD & NEW ROYAL DOULTON FIGURES & CHARACTER JUGS
- ✦ HUMMELS
- ✦ DAVID WINTER COTTAGES
- ✦ DEPT. 56 COTTAGES AND SNOWBABIES

- ✦ ROYAL WORCESTER
- ✦ WEE FOREST FOLK
- ✦ WALT DISNEY CLASSICS
- ✦ SWAROVSKI CRYSTAL
- ✦ LLADRO
- ✦ LILLIPUT LANE

Send for our latest product catalogue!

Colonial House Of Collectibles

We carry Current & Discontinued Beanie Babies!

WE DO MAIL ORDER

Monday to Saturday
10 am to 5 pm
or by appointment

182 Front Street, Berea, OH 44017
Tel: (440) 826-4169 or (800) 344-9299
Fax: (440) 826-0839
E-mail: yworrey@aol.com